KT-144-852

WYE COLLEGE
UNIVERSITY OF LONDON

Farm Management Pocketbook

by

JOHN NIX

with Paul Hill

TWENTY-FIFTH EDITION

(1995)

SEPTEMBER 1994

Copies of this book may be obtained from Publications, Department of
Agricultural Economics, Wye College, near Ashford, Kent, TN25 5AH.
(Tel. 01233-812401 ext. 285; Fax. 01233-813320)

PRICE £7.00
(12 to 49 copies: £6.50)
(50 to 199 copies: £6.25)
(200-499 copies: £6.00)
(Over 500 copies: £5.75)
ISBN 0 86266 182 X

FOREWORD TO THE FIRST EDITION

This booklet is intended for farmers, advisers, students and everyone else who, frequently or infrequently, find themselves hunting for data relating to farm management—whether it is for blunt pencil calculations on the back of an envelope or for feeding into a computer. The material contained is based upon the sort of information which the author finds himself frequently having to look up in his twin roles as adviser and teacher in farm management. There are several excellent handbooks already in existence, but this pocketbook endeavours to cover a wider field and thus to be substantially more comprehensive. It is intended that most of the data herein contained will have a national application, although there is inevitably some bias towards conditions in the south-eastern half of the country.

The development of farm planning techniques in recent years has outstripped the quality and quantity of data available. It is hoped that this booklet will go a little further in supplying the type of information required. It cannot, however, claim to be the ultimate in this respect. For example, there are many variations in labour requirements according to farm conditions and sizes and types of machine used and there are many more variations in sheep and beef systems than are dealt with here. More detailed data on these lines are gradually becoming available from various sources. It is hoped further to refine the material in this booklet and to keep it up to date in subsequent editions, as the information becomes available. As a help towards this end, any comments or criticisms will be gratefully received.

The author wishes to thank his many friends and colleagues who have given him so much time and help in compiling this information.

John Nix
October, 1966

First published October 1966
Twenty-fifth Edition   September 1994

FOREWORD TO TWENTY-FIFTH EDITION

This is the silver anniversary edition. It is in fact twenty eight, not twenty five, years since the first edition was published (1966), since it was not produced every year until 1976. A quarter of a million copies of the various editions have been sold since the first issue.

Things have changed a little over that period. For example, in 1966 wheat was £25 a tonne (actually 25 shillings a cwt.) and milk 3.3p a litre (3 shillings a gallon). However, a tonne of nitrogen fertilizer then cost £21, dairy nuts £35 and a new tractor could be had for £700.

Inflation would seem to have hit the price of this book even harder. The first edition cost six bob (i.e. 30p) compared with £7 for this edition, an increase of 23 fold. Clearly scandalous, especially since the retail price index rose only tenfold. However, the author has not spent most of his working life dealing in figures for nothing. The first edition contained 90 pages, the present one 220. Thus in real terms the cost *per page* has actually fallen . . .

The temptation with this edition was to mark the special occasion by introducing a range of new, exciting enterprises. This has been resisted. Ostriches are the present media favourites (it was llamas a few years ago) and the farming journals tell us every week of some new crop or variety that is about to transform every arable farmer's life and make him a fortune. However, only when a significant number of farmers begin to produce an enterprise will it be included—unless it is clearly a potential winner. Each additional enterprise adds to the weight and price of the book, apart from the time taken to produce it.

However, as ever, virtually all the data in this edition have been checked over and updated, with various amendments and small additions, e.g. industrial linseed and the return of flax.

The improvements made to the profitability of many of our main enterprises which began with the sterling devaluation of September 1992 continue, and look like doing so for at least the next couple of years. It is as well to remember, however, that this is not true for all producers and enterprises. One thinks, for example, of pigs, fruit and vegetables. We are constantly reminded, too, of what may be in store later in this decade because of further CAP reforms, GATT, etc. I will only say that I am by no means pessimistic on behalf of my many farming friends, though naturally having constantly to remind them to "take care". One never knows.

Most of the figures are predicted forward one year, *i.e.* to 1995. Thus the crops data relate to the 1995 harvest, *i.e.* the 1995/96 marketing year (N.B. not just, in the case of product prices, those prevailing at or just after harvest time). The livestock data relate either to the 1995 calendar year (*e.g.* for milk production) or to 1995/96 (*e.g.* for winter finished beef), as appropriate. The estimates were made during the first half of the summer of 1994. In a few cases current (*i.e.* mid-1994) figures are given, where it seemed particularly difficult to try to forecast ahead. The year to which the figures relate is normally stated.

The figures for yields and prices assume a "normal", or average, season, based on trends, *e.g.* for potatoes, looking 18-24 months ahead to 1995/96, no one can predict what the *actual* average yield and price for that particular year will be. Similarly with pig production: no attempt is made to predict the *actual* position of the pig cycle during 1995—only what the average trend figure is likely to be, in neither an "up" or "down" stage, given estimated changes in the relevant indices.

The data in this book should always be used with caution. *The figures should be adjusted as appropriate according to circumstances and price and cost differences.* As far as possible the assumptions in the tables are set out so as to enable this to be done fairly readily.

The authors wish to thank all those who assisted with this edition.

John Nix
July, 1994

CONTENTS

I. GROSS MARGIN DATA

1. GENERAL NOTES

Definition. The Gross Margin of an enterprise is its enterprise output less its variable costs. Enterprise output includes the market value of production retained on the farm. The variable costs must (a) be specific to the enterprise and (b) vary in proportion to the size of the enterprise, i.e. number of hectares or head of stock. The main items of variable costs are: Crops: fertilizer, seed, sprays, casual labour and contract work specific to the crop. Non-Grazing Livestock: concentrate feed, vet. and med., marketing expenses. Grazing Livestock: as for non-grazing livestock, plus forage crop variable costs.

Points to Note about the concept are as follows:

1. The gross margin is in no sense a profit figure. The so-called "fixed costs" (rent, labour, machinery, general overheads—see pages 132-137) have to be covered by the total farm gross margin before arriving at a profit.

2. The gross margin of an enterprise will differ from season to season, partly because of yield and price differences affecting output and partly because variable costs may vary, e.g. the number and type of sprays required. Different soils and other natural factors, as well as level of management, will also cause differences between farms.

3. Items of variable cost may vary from farm to farm, e.g. some farmers use casual labour (a variable cost) to plant and pick their potatoes, others use only regular labour (a fixed cost); some farmers employ a contractor to combine their cereals (a variable cost), others employ their own equipment (a fixed cost); some employ a contractor to cart their sugar beet to the factory (a variable cost), others have their own lorry (a fixed cost). These differences must be borne in mind in making inter-farm comparisons.

4. Provided points 2 and 3 are borne in mind, comparison of gross margins (particularly averages over several seasons) with standards can be a useful check on technical efficiency.

5. The other main usefulness of gross margins lies in farm planning. This is not simply a matter of substituting high gross margin enterprises for low gross margin enterprises. The gross margin is only one relevant feature of an enterprise, although an important one. It says nothing about the call the enterprise makes on the basic farm resources—labour at different times of the year, machinery, buildings, working capital requirements, etc. All these factors and more have to be taken into account in the planning process.

1

6. This is not to argue that these other costs should be allocated. Complete allocation of many farm expenses is only possible on an arbitrary basis, since they are shared by two or more, possibly all, farm enterprises. Allocation can therefore be completely misleading when making planning decisions. The same is true even when regular labour and machinery are employed specifically on certain enterprises, if such costs are calculated on a per hectare or per head basis. This is because when enterprises are substituted, expanded, contracted or deleted the variable costs for each enterprise will vary roughly in proportion to the size of that enterprise, but other costs will not, except possibly for fuel and some repair costs. Most "fixed" costs may stay the same, others will change—but not smoothly in small amounts at a time. Either the same regular labour force will cope with a revised plan or a smaller or larger number of men will be needed. The same is true of tractors, other machines and buildings. Such cost changes must of course be taken into account, but allocating these costs on a per hectare or per head basis will not aid, and may positively confuse, planning decisions. The only point of making such calculations is for efficiency comparisons, e.g. labour costs per cow.

7. Allocating fixed costs at a flat rate (e.g. per hectare) for all enterprises, deducting this from the gross margin and hence calculating a "net profit" from each enterprise can also be misleading. It ignores the whole problem of enterprise inter-relationships, differences between enterprises in total and seasonal requirements for labour, machinery and capital, and other factors such as different quality land on the same farm.

8. Changes in the scale of an enterprise may well affect its gross margin per unit, e.g. increasing the area of winter wheat from 30 per cent to 50 per cent on a farm will mean more wheat being taken after wheat, and a smaller proportion of the crop being drilled under the best conditions; hence yields will in all probability fall. Even if yields remain the same, variable costs (e.g. fertilizer use) will probably increase.

9. Gross margins used for planning future changes should also take account of possible changes in price, and the effect of changes in production techniques.

Low, Average and High Levels

The three performance and production levels given for most crop and livestock enterprises are meant for the most part to indicate differences in natural factors, soil productivity, and/or managerial skill, *given the level of variable cost inputs*. They refer, at each level, to *an average over several years* taking *trends* into account. The evidence on the effect of significantly higher levels of variable inputs on gross margins is conflicting and highly uncertain, depending on many factors, including soil type, and varying with season.

2. CASH CROPS

WINTER WHEAT

Production level	Low	Average	High
Yield: tonnes per ha (cwt. per acre)			
Feed	5·75 (46)	7·25 (57·5)	8·75 (70)
Milling	5·2 (41)	6·5 (51·75)	7·8 (62)
Price per tonne (Feed/Milling): £90/£104	£	£	£
Sale Value			
Feed	515 (209)	650 (263)	785 (318)
Milling	540 (219)	675 (273)	810 (328)
Area Payment ...	250 (101)	250 (101)	250 (101)
OUTPUT: Feed ...	765 (310)	900 (364)	1035 (419)
OUTPUT: Milling	790 (320)	925 (374)	1060 (429)

		Feed	Milling
Variable Costs:			
Seed		45 (18)	50 (20)
Fertilizer		70 (28·5)	80 (32·5)
Sprays		105 (42·5)	115 (46·5)
TOTAL VARIABLE COSTS		220 (89)	245 (99)

GROSS MARGIN per ha (acre)	545 (221)	680 (275)	815 (330)

Notes

1. *Prices/Area Payments.* The area payments *for the 1995 harvest crop* will depend on the Green £ rate (value of the ECU) on 1st July, 1995. The ECU value for the 1994 crop was 93.2453p; *the same value for the 1995 crop is assumed.* The area payments for cereals then are as follows, to the nearest £/ha (£0.5/acre in brackets):

Harvest Year	England	Scotland (non LFA)	Scotland (LFA)	Wales (non LFA)	Wales (LFA)	N. Ireland
1994	194 (78·5)	182 (73·5)	157 (63·5)	169 (68·5)	108 (44)	154 (62)
1995 (est.)*	249 (100·5)	234 (94·5)	202 (81·5)	217 (88)	139 (56·5)	198 (80)

   * *(Assuming regional base areas are not exceeded, other than in Scotland non LFA)*

Intervention prices vary with the value of the Green £. In late July 1994 (ECU value 94·865p) the November 1994 intervention price for eligible cereals was approximately £102/tonne, rising to approximately £109 in May 1995. The 1995/6 figures were approximately £94·50 and £101·50 respectively.

Feed wheat prices for the *1993* harvest crop stayed below £100/tonne until March, when they rose, to £120 by late June. In midsummer 1994 the feed wheat price for the *1994* harvest crop, averaged over the whole 1994/95 marketing year, looks like being around £105 a tonne, £10 or more above earlier expectations.

The table above relates to the *1995* harvest. The average prices are assumed at £90/tonne for feed and approximately £104 for milling, and the rounded compensatory (area) payment £250/ha (£101/acre). These prices are averages for the whole of the (1995/6) marketing year: prices are typically £5/tonne less at harvest time and £10 above by the end of the season. For any wheat going into intervention the net price would be substantially less.

Feed v. Milling. It is assumed that the yield of milling wheat *averages* 10·35 % below that of feed wheat (the difference could be greater on high-yielding land and less on moderate quality land and also tends to be greater on second than on first wheats). The combined, weighted average is just over 7·0 tonnes/ha. The assumed milling premium of approximately £14/tonne (16%) is that needed to give the same gross margin for both, given the difference in yield and variable costs. Obviously different relative yields and premiums will give different gross margins: these can be readily calculated. The actual premium in any one season varies according to quality and scarcity: it was very high in 1992/93 but very much lower in 1993/94. The best breadmaking wheat achieves substantially higher premiums.

2. *First v. Second Wheats.* The evidence concerning the effect of different types and lengths of rotational breaks on subsequent cereal yields is variable. The table below (for *feed* wheat only, 1995 harvest) assumes a yield reduction of approximately 12·5% for second wheats compared with first and higher fertilizer and seed costs as shown; (the later the sowing date the less the yield gap tends to be). The same price and area payment is assumed as in the initial table. Only average and high levels are shown. Third wheats could yield 10-15% below second wheats; variable costs are likely to be similar.

Production level	Average		High	
Year (after break)	First	Second	First	Second
Yield: tonnes per ha (cwt per acre)	7·75 (61·5)	6·75 (53·5)	9·25 (73·5)	8·0 (63·5)
	£	£	£	£
OUTPUT	945 (382)	855 (346)	1080 (437)	970 (393)
VARIABLE COSTS	210 (85)	230 (93)	210 (85)	230 (93)
GROSS MARGIN per ha (acre) ...	735 (297)	625 (253)	870 (352)	740 (300)

4. *Straw* is not included above. Average yield is approx. 3·5 tonnes per hectare; value £10 to £30 per tonne according to region and season; variable costs (string) approx. £1·25 per tonne. In 1993, 51% of the area of wheat straw in England and Wales was baled and 49% ploughed in or cultivated. Burning is no longer permitted in England and Wales.

5. *Sprays.* Amounts variable according to season and system.

6. If a *Contractor* is employed, extra variable costs (£ per hectare) will be approximately as follows:

Spraying:	£11 (material included above)
Drilling:	£18
Combining:	£80 (excluding carting)
	£96 (including carting)
Drying:	£60 to £120 (according to yield and moisture content; transport one way is included; *this assumes that ⅔ of the crop needs to be dried in an average season*).
Baling Straw:	£42·50 (including string).

7. *Fuel and Repairs* (per hectare): grain £75, straw £27.

8. *Specialized Equipment Prices:* see pages 115-117.

9. *Labour:* see page 96.

N.B.—Approximately 80% of spot sales of home-grown wheat are for feed and 20% for milling, primarily breadmaking. About 15% of the crop is retained on the farm. Only 20 to 25% of the UK wheat area is sown with milling varieties.

SPRING WHEAT

Production level					Low	Average	High
Yield: tonnes per hectare (cwt. per acre)			...		4·00 (32)	5·25 (42)	6·25 (50)
					£	£	£
Price per tonne: £100							
Sale Value	...	...	...	...	400 (162)	525 (212)	625 (253)
Area Payment	...	...	...	...	250 (101)	250 (101)	250 (101)
OUTPUT	...	...	...	...	650 (263)	725 (293)	875 (354)
Variable Costs:							
Seed	...	...	...	...		57·5 (23·5)	
Fertilizer	...	...	...	...		65·0 (26·5)	
Sprays	...	...	...	...		72·5 (29)	
TOTAL VARIABLE COSTS	...	...	...			195 (79)	
GROSS MARGIN per ha (acre)		...	...		455 (184)	530 (214)	680 (275)

Notes

1. *Price:* In general, see Winter Wheat. A higher proportion of spring wheat is sold for milling compared with winter wheat. The average price taken above, for the 1995 harvest, (£100/tonne), assumes three-quarters sold for milling, one-quarter for feed.

2. *Straw.* See Winter Wheat, page 4.

3. If a *Contractor* is employed, extra variable costs (£ per hectare) will be as shown for Winter Wheat above.

4. *Fuel and Repairs* (per hectare): grain £70, straw £25.

5. *Specialized Equipment Prices:* see pages 115-117.

6. *Labour:* see page 98.

N.B.—Normally only 3 or 4% of the UK wheat area is spring sown and the percentage is only significantly higher following a particularly wet autumn. However, the new CAP Reform support system (in which the flat rate area payments per hectare mean a higher payment *per tonne* for lower yielding crops) and movements towards greater emphasis on breadmaking quality wheats both encourage more spring sowing.

For the 1995/96 area payments in ECU/ha see page 46.

WINTER BARLEY

Production level	Low	Average	High
Yield: tonnes per ha (cwt. per acre)			
Feed	4·75 (38)	6·00 (48)	7·25 (57·5)
Malting	4·00 (32)	5·00 (40)	6·05 (48)
Price per tonne (Feed/Malting): £87/£104	£	£	£
Sale Value (Feed and Malting)	415 (168)	520 (211)	630 (255)
Area Payment	250 (101)	250 (101)	250 (101)
OUTPUT (Feed and Malting)	665 (269)	770 (312)	880 (356)

Variable Costs:	Feed	Malting
Seed	47·5 (19)	52·5 (21)
Fertilizer	65·0 (26·5)	52·5 (21)
Sprays	87·5 (35·5)	95·0 (39)
TOTAL VARIABLE COSTS	200 (81)	200 (81)

GROSS MARGIN per ha (acre)	465 (188)	570 (231)	680 (275)

1. *Prices.* See Winter Wheat for CAP Reform details, but note intervention is available for feed barley. Prices are the assumed averages for the whole 1995/6 marketing year; prices are typically £5/tonne less at harvest time and £10 above by the end of the season. The feed price (£87/tonne) is taken as £3/tonne below feed wheat. The malting premium assumed, £17/ tonne, is that required to equate the output and hence the gross margin for feed barley, the total variable costs being the same (though not their composition). The *actual* premium obtained over feed barley will vary according to season and quality: for the best malting barleys the premium is usually at least £25 and prices can exceed £160 a tonne. These higher prices for quality are normally available even at harvest time (when the differential over feed normally exceeds £20).

2. *Straw* not included. Average yield is approx. 2·75 tonnes per hectare; value £10 to £30 per tonne according to region and season; variable cost (string) approx. £1·05 per tonne. In 1993, 88% of the area of barley straw in England and Wales was baled and 12% ploughed in or cultivated. Burning is no longer permitted in England and Wales.

3. *Fertilizer.* Costs on continuous barley will be approximately £15 higher.

4. If *Contractor* employed, extra variable costs as shown for Winter Wheat (p. 4, note 6).

5. *Fuel and Repairs* (per hectare): grain £75. straw £25.

6. *Specialized Equipment Prices:* see pages 115-117.

7. *Labour:* see pages 97-98.

SPRING BARLEY

Production level	Low	Average	High
Yield: tonnes per ha (cwt. per acre)			
Feed	4·00 (32)	5·00 (40)	6·00 (47·5)
Malting	3·35 (26·5)	4·15 (33)	5·00 (40)
Price per tonne (Feed/Malting): £87/£104	£	£	£
Sale Value (Feed and Malting)	350 (141)	435 (176)	520 (210)
Area Payment	250 (101)	250 (101)	250 (101)
OUTPUT (Feed and Malting)	600 (242)	685 (277)	770 (311)

Variable Costs:	Feed	Malting
Seed	50 (20)	55 (22)
Fertilizer	52·5 (21)	42·5 (17)
Sprays	47·5 (19)	52·5 (21)
TOTAL VARIABLE COSTS	150 (60)	150 (60)

GROSS MARGIN per ha (acre)	450 (182)	535 (217)	620 (251)

Notes: As for Winter Barley above.

The UK percentage of winter barley in the 1992, 1993 and (est.) 1994 harvests was 60%, 56% and 58% respectively. For England and Wales the percentages in the same three years were, respectively, 76, 70 and 73. Naturally the proportion of spring barley increases following a wet autumn. In Scotland and Northern Ireland the percentage of winter barley is only between 15 and 20%. The relative profitability of spring versus winter crops is improved under the new support system in that the flat rate area payments per hectare mean a higher payment *per tonne* for lower yielding crops.

N.B. About two-thirds of spot sales of barley are sold for feed and one-third for malting. Just over a third of the crop is retained on the farm. *On average only about 10% of winter barley is sold for malting, compared with just over 30% of the spring crop.*

WINTER OATS

Production level					Low	Average	High
Yield: tonnes per ha (cwt. per acre)				...	4·75 (38)	6·00 (48)	7·25 (57·5)

Price per tonne (Feed/Milling): £92·50/£100

					£	£	£
Sale Value							
Feed	...	...	...	...	440 (178)	555 (225)	670 (271)
Milling	...	...	...	...	475 (192)	600 (243)	725 (294)
Area Payment	...	...	...	250 (101)	250 (101)	250 (101)
Output Feed	...	...	...	...	690 (279)	805 (326)	920 (372)
Output Milling	...	...	...	...	725 (293)	850 (344)	975 (395)

Variable Costs:							
Seed	...	...	...	...	...	47·5 (19)	
Fertilizer	...	...	...	...	...	55·0 (22·5)	
Sprays	...	...	...	...	...	62·5 (25·5)	
TOTAL VARIABLE COSTS	...	...	...		165 (67)	

GROSS MARGIN per ha (acre)							
Feed	...	...	...	...	525 (212)	640 (259)	755 (305)
Milling	...	...	...	...	560 (227)	685 (277)	810 (328)

Notes
1. Prices. See Winter Wheat for CAP Reform details. Prices are the assumed averages for the whole 1995/6 marketing year.
2. *Straw* is not included above. Average yield is 3·5 tonnes per hectare; value £10 to £30 per tonne according to region and season; variable costs (string) approx. £1·05 per tonne.
3. If a *Contractor* is employed, extra variable costs will be as shown for Winter Wheat (p. 4, note 6).
4. *Fuel and Repairs* (per hectare): grain £70, straw £25.
5. *Labour:* see page 98.

SPRING OATS

Production level					Low	Average	High
Yield: tonnes per ha (cwt. per acre)				...	3·50 (28)	4·75 (38)	5·75 (45·5)

Price per tonne (Feed/Milling): £92·50/£100

					£	£	£
Sale Value							
Feed	...	...	...	...	325 (132)	440 (178)	530 (215)
Milling	...	...	...	...	350 (142)	475 (192)	575 (233)
Area Payment	...	...	...	250 (101)	250 (101)	250 (101)
Output Feed	...	...	...	...	475 (233)	690 (279)	780 (316)
Output Milling	...	...	...	...	600 (243)	725 (294)	825 (334)

Variable Costs:							
Seed	...	...	...	...	...	57·5 (23·5)	
Fertilizer	...	...	...	...	...	40·0 (16·5)	
Sprays	...	...	...	...	...	37·5 (15)	
TOTAL VARIABLE COSTS	...	...	...		135 (55)	

GROSS MARGIN per ha (acre)							
Feed	...	...	...	...	440 (178)	555 (224)	645 (261)
Milling	...	...	...	...	465 (188)	590 (239)	690 (279)

Notes
As for winter oats above.

N.B.—The proportion of winter oats increases from north to south and probably exceeds 80% in the south of England in a normal season. Oats now account for only 3% of the total UK cereals area (92,000 ha were grown in 1993). The risk of lodging and thus difficult harvesting remains a drawback.

OILSEED RAPE

A. Winter

Production level	Low	Average	High
Yield: tonnes per ha (cwt. per acre)	2·25 (18)	3·00 (24)	3·75 (30)
	£	£	£
Sale Value	335 (135)	450 (182)	565 (228)
Area Payment	405 (164)	405 (164)	405 (164)
OUTPUT	740 (299)	855 (346)	970 (392)
Variable Costs:			
Seed		40 (16)	
Fertilizer		75 (30·5)	
Sprays		85 (34·5)	
TOTAL VARIABLE COSTS		200 (81)	
GROSS MARGIN per ha (acre)	540 (218)	655 (265)	770 (311)

B. Spring-Sown

Production level	Low	Average	High
Yield: tonnes per ha (cwt. per acre)	1·5 (12)	2·1 (16·75)	2·7 (21·5)
	£	£	£
Sale Value	225 (91)	315 (127)	405 (164)
Area Payment	405 (164)	405 (164)	405 (164)
OUTPUT	630 (255)	720 (291)	810 (328)
Variable Costs:			
Seed		42·5 (17)	
Fertilizer		50 (20·5)	
Sprays		52·5 (21·5)	
TOTAL VARIABLE COSTS		145 (59)	
GROSS MARGIN per ha (acre)	485 (196)	575 (232)	665 (269)

Notes

1. *Prices/Area Payments.* The 1993 harvest crop price increased from £150/tonne at harvest to over £200 during June, then falling to £165 in July. *The price assumed for the 1995 crop, £150/tonne,* is the average for the whole of the 1995/6 marketing season, ranging from £140-145 at harvest to £155-160 towards the end of the season.

   The *area payments* for both the 1994 and 1995 harvest crops, at an ECU value of 93·25p, are as follows, assuming no deductions for excess production and high world prices. England, £437/ha (177/acre); Scotland (non LFA), £489 (198); Scotland (LFA), £403 (163); Wales, £445 (180); N. Ireland, £414 (168). A rounded figure for England is used in the above tables, with an *assumed deduction of 7·5%* through the overshooting of the EU maximum guaranteed area plus possibly also of the regional arable base areas; at the average price assumed there should not be a cut because of price levels, as happened with the 1993 crop.

2. Winter crops are mainly sown between 10th August and 10th September (before the end of August if possible). Spring-sown crops are best sown between late March and mid-April. Winter crops normally are harvested between late July and mid-August, most of the crops either being windrowed and combined from the swath or desiccated by diquat and direct combined. Spring-sown crops are harvested in the first half of September and a desiccant is less often used. Before the flat rate per hectare subsidy was introduced only about 4% of the crop was spring-sown, but the proportion has increased markedly since: approx. 17% in 1992, 27% in 1993 and 30% in 1994—though the increase in the last two years was caused partly by wet late summer and autumn weather. Inputs are lower, pigeons are less trouble and the late summer/autumn workload is eased; however, the later harvesting tends to clash with the winter wheat harvest, there is less time to prepare the ground for, and drill, the following winter cereal crop, and spring droughts are a potential hazard to establishment.

3. *Labour:* see page 104.

for
UNDERGRADUATE DEGREES
and
POSTGRADUATE STUDIES

UNDERGRADUATE DEGREES

- *BSc (Bachelor of Science) in three years*
  - Agriculture D200
  - Agriculture and the Environment D206
  - Animal Agriculture D222
  - Horticulture D250
  - Countryside Management D255
  - Rural Environment Studies F900
  - Animal Sciences D220
  - Applied Biology C110
  - Biochemistry C700
  - Biology C100
  - Environmental Biology C160
  - Environmental Science F910
  - Plant Sciences C200
  - Agricultural Business Management D2N1
  - Horticultural Business Management D2NC
  - Business Studies N120

For full details of these undergraduate degrees, or the postgraduate studies listed overleaf, please return the reply coupon or contact:

Academic Registrar
WYE COLLEGE, University of London
Wye, Ashford, Kent TN25 5AH

Telephone: 0233 812401
Fax: 0233 813320
Telex: 94017832 WYEC G

POSTGRADUATE STUDIES

RESEARCH TRAINING

- *PhD (Doctor of Philosophy) in three years*
- *MPhil (Master of Philosophy) in two years*

POSTGRADUATE COURSES

- *MSc (Master of Science) in one year*
- *Postgraduate Diploma in nine months*

SPECIAL TRAINING

- *Special attachments*
- *Short courses including Advanced Course in Agricultural Business Management (three weeks)*

DISTANCE LEARNING

- *MSc in two years (minimum)*
- *Postgraduate Diploma in one year (minimum)*
- Agricultural Development
- Environmental Management

Name ....

Address ....

....

Telephone ....

Please send me details of:

☐ UNDERGRADUATE DEGREES: ....

☐ POSTGRADUATE STUDIES: ....

Return to: Academic Registrar, **WYE COLLEGE, University of London**
Wye, Ashford, Kent TN25 5AH

LINSEED

Production level	Low	Average	High
Yield: tonnes per ha (cwt. per acre): ...	1·00 (8)	1·75 (14)	2·50 (20)
	£	£	£
Sale Value	120 (48)	210 (85)	300 (121)
Area Payment	480 (195)	480 (195)	480 (195)
OUTPUT	600 (243)	690 (280)	780 (316)
Variable Costs:			
Seed		80·0 (32·5)	
Fertilizer		32·5 (13)	
Sprays		62·5 (25·5)	
TOTAL VARIABLE COSTS		175 (71)	
GROSS MARGIN per ha (acre)	425 (172)	515 (209)	605 (245)

The *price* assumed, £120/tonne, is the average for the whole of the 1995/6 marketing season. Prices have been very variable in recent years. In the four calendar years 1990-1993 they averaged £105/tonne. In the 1992/93 year, the price started as low at harvest as £70 but reached £135 in February. In 1993/94 the price rose quickly from £110 at harvest to reach £140-145 in November; it later rose to £160 but fell back to £130 in July (1994).

The *area payments* for the 1994 crop, at a rate of 87 ECU/tonne, were: England, £481/ha (195/acre); Scotland (non LFA), £452 (£183); Scotland (LFA), £390 (158); Wales (non LFA), £419 (170); Wales (LFA), £269 (109); Northern Ireland, £382 (155). The same, rounded, figure for England is assumed in the above table for the 1995 crop. These payments are now subject to the grower setting aside 15% of the previous year's linseed area.

From 1,165 ha in 1984 the UK area increased to approximately 150,000 ha (94% of the total EC area) in 1993. A considerable reduction has taken place in 1994: the area appears to have roughly halved, to around 75,000 ha.

Advantages: spring-sown; good break crop re pest immunity; normal cereals machinery adequate; does not shed: therefore can harvest late if convenient, but then higher moisture content, and risk of bird damage; safeguard, if low yield, of substantial subsidy *per hectare*.

Drawbacks: needs fine, firm seedbed (may be difficult on heavier soils) and very accurate seeding; small root system, so unsuited to soils prone to drought or waterlogging; competes poorly with weeds, hence careful herbicide treatment needed; disease problems appear to be increasing, particularly botrytis (especially in lodged crops) and alternaria, both wet weather pathogens; pigeons, rabbits and leatherjackets are potential problems; can be difficult to harvest (thorough desiccation very important, done when warm) and harvest can be late, making it difficult to follow with wheat; as the seed flows easily, trailers, etc. need careful sealing and one should not walk on seed stored more than 3 metres (5 feet) deep.

Drilling, mid-March to mid-April (best mid-March to end March). Susceptible to frost. Should not be grown more than 1 year in 5. Care needed re level of nitrogen use: too much (over 75 kg/ha) can cause severe lodging, delayed maturity and excessive weed growth—and hence difficult harvesting, poor quality and lower yields; it should be applied early.

Harvesting (direct-combined): normally not before September and can even be after mid-October in a late season. Moisture content most likely 12-16%: must be dried to 9% for storage.

INDUSTRIAL OILSEED RAPE

Rape for non-food uses may be grown on set-aside land, provided a direct contract with a first *processor* (or collector) is obtained and signed before the crop is sown. The contract must contain specific items of information. The non-food product must be worth more than the total value of any food by-products. Only approved varieties may be grown, or high erucic rapeseed.

The full set-aside area payment is paid but no other EU payments can be claimed. If the rules concerning contracts are broken both the set-aside payment and area payments for other crops could be forfeited, and a further penalty imposed.

The first processor or collector has to lodge a security equal to 120% of the set-aside payments on the fields concerned; this is returned provided an equivalent quantity of raw material has been processed into the final end product in the contract. Area aid is only paid after delivery of the crop to the collector and the weight is declared to the Regional Service Centre.

Two types of industrial rape are grown: high erucic and, mainly, double low, which is primarily spring-sown. The former usually has a lower yield, varying from a little to 15% less; the price is consequently higher: £140/tonne minimum for the 1995 crop.

The following are estimated gross margins for double low industrial rape for the 1995 harvest, given a price of £120/tonne and the same variable costs. The set-aside payments are for England, as estimated on page 43 (1 ECU = 93.25p).

Production level		Winter-sown		Spring-sown	
		Average	High	Average	High
Yield (tonnes per ha (cwt. per acre))	...	3.00 (24)	3.75 (30)	2.1 (16.75)	2.7 (21.5)
		£	£	£	£
Sale Value (at £120/tonne)	...	360 (145)	450 (182)	250 (101)	325 (131)
Set-aside Payment	... ...	315 (128)	315 (128)	315 (128)	315 (128)
OUTPUT	...	675 (273)	765 (310)	565 (229)	640 (259)
VARIABLE COSTS		200 (81)	200 (81)	145 (29)	145 (29)
GROSS MARGIN per ha (acre)	... ...	475 (192)	565 (229)	420 (170)	495 (200)

Mainly because the set-aside payment is well below the area payment for non-industrial rape the gross margins are naturally lower. However, the additional gross margin compared with set-aside should cover any additional fixed costs incurred on most farms, unless substantial fixed cost savings can be made by adhering to fallow set-aside; also, it is widely believed that subsequent crops benefit more from following oilseed rape than from following a (virtual) fallow.

INDUSTRIAL LINSEED

Similar rules apply to those for industrial rape.

Production level					Average	High
Yield (tonnes per ha (cwt. per acre))				...	1.75 (14)	2.50 (20)
					£	£
Sales Value (at £125/tonne)		...	...		220 (89)	315 (128)
Set-aside Payment		...	...	...	315 (128)	315 (128)
OUTPUT	...	...	...		535 (217)	630 (256)
VARIABLE COSTS* ...	...	...	...		155 (63)	155 (63)
GROSS MARGIN per ha (acre)		...	...		380 (154)	475 (193)

*Seed £20/ha less than non-industrial linseed.

The price varies a little depending on the details of the contract, which must be signed before the crop is sown. Some contracts include seed supplied at a special price as well as the purchase price.

Fibre. At present (August 1994) fibre contracts are under review. If the crop is grown on set-aside land it will probably be acceptable to swath, mow or combine the crop. However, if the flax subsidy is being paid it will be necessary to grow an approved variety and pull the crop. Individual contracts must be checked regarding payments and losses but also conditions regarding the management, harvesting and storage of the crop. (For flax see also p. 23).

Acknowledgement. Tony Hardwick gave considerable advice on the above crops.

FIELD BEANS

A. Winter Beans

Production level Yield: tonnes per ha (cwt. per acre)	Low 3·0 (24)	Average 3·6 (28·5)	High 4·2 (33·5)
	£	£	£
Sale Value	265 (106)	315 (128)	370 (149)
Area Payment	360 (145)	360 (145)	360 (145)
OUTPUT	620 (251)	675 (273)	725 (294)
Variable Costs: (3)			
Seed		55·0 (22·5)	
Fertilizer		12·5 (5)	
Sprays		62·5 (25·5)	
TOTAL VARIABLE COSTS		130 (53)	
GROSS MARGIN per ha (acre)	490 (198)	545 (220)	595 (241)

Notes
1. *Price.* The (1995/96) price assumed is £87·50 per tonne. Prices for the 1993 crop were mainly £95-100 from harvest till February, then rose to around £110 in April/May (1994). Tannin-free varieties have fetched about £8 a tonne more but yield some 5% less. Beans for human consumption fetch a premium of around £12/tonne.
   The *area payments* for the 1994 crop, at an ECU value of 93·25p, were as follows: England, £359/ha (145/acre); Scotland (non LFA), £338 (137); Scotland (LFA), £292 (118); Wales (non LFA), £313 (127); Wales (LFA), £201 (81); Northern Ireland, £285 (115). The same, rounded, figure for England is used in the tables for the 1995 crop. For set-aside requirement see page 42.
2. *Physical Input.* Seed: 225 kg per hectare; average cost is approximately £10 less if own seed is sown in alternate years. Fertilizer: 200 kg of no (or low) nitrogen compound where applied, but some crops receive no fertilizer.
3. *Labour:* see page 104.

B. Spring Beans

Production level Yield: tonnes per ha (cwt. per acre)	Low 2·8 (22·5)	Average 3·4 (27)	High 4·0 (32)
	£	£	£
Sale Value	245 (100)	300 (122)	350 (142)
Area Payment	360 (145)	360 (145)	360 (145)
OUTPUT	605 (245)	660 (267)	710 (287)
Variable Costs:			
Seed		60·0 (24·5)	
Fertilizer		12·5 (5)	
Sprays		52·5 (21·5)	
TOTAL VARIABLE COSTS		125 (51)	
GROSS MARGIN per ha (acre)	480 (194)	535 (216)	585 (236)

Notes
1. *Price.* The (1995/96) price assumed is £87·50 per tonne (see above). Spring beans contain more protein than winter beans (except for tannin-free varieties), but large-scale compounders appear to make no distinction between them.
   Winter versus Spring Beans. It used to be assumed that the yield of winter beans was about 0·5 tonnes per hectare above spring beans *provided* a full crop was obtained, that is, where there was no exceptional damage from frost and birds and, in particular, where there was no severe attack of chocolate spot. Thus, whether the average yield over a period of years was higher or lower than spring beans depended mainly upon the incidence of attacks of chocolate spot, which can write off the crop completely. In drier parts of the Eastern counties this may be only one year in six or eight but in South-eastern counties the frequency may be substantially higher. NIAB data indicates an average 8% yield advantage for winter over spring beans.

Other points in favour of spring beans are that: cold, wet seedbeds and winter kill can lead to poor establishment of winter beans; the yield difference between autumn- and spring-sown crops is less than for other crops, especially cereals; there is a longer "near-optimal" period during which they can be sown; and there have been substantial genetic improvements in recent years for spring beans but little for winter beans. However, spring beans are vulnerable to droughts in spring and early summer, especially on light land.

The area of winter beans normally exceeds that of spring beans, except after a wet autumn, but the gap has been narrowing in the last five years; it was approximately 50:50 for the 1993 harvest, following a wet autumn in 1992.

DRIED PEAS

Production level	Low	Average	High
Yield: tonnes per ha (cwt. per acre)	2·8 (22·5)	3·7 (29·5)	4·5 (36)
	£	£	£
Sale Value	265 (108)	350 (142)	430 (173)
Area Payment	360 (145)	360 (145)	360 (145)
OUTPUT (feed)	625 (253)	710 (287)	785 (318)
Variable Costs:			
Seed		110 (44·5)	
Fertilizer		15 (6)	
Sprays		90 (36·5)	
TOTAL VARIABLE COSTS		215 (87)	
GROSS MARGIN per ha (acre)	410 (166)	495 (200)	570 (231)

Notes

1. Dried peas are combine harvested and include peas (especially marrowfats) for human consumption (after processing) and protein peas, for animal feed. About 75% of the crop goes for feed compounding.

2. *Price.* The (1995/96) price assumed above (which is for feed peas) is £95 per tonne. Prices for the 1993 crop were just below £100 from harvest till February, then rose to around £115 in April/May (1994). Feed peas sold on the open market are subject to wide price variations, particularly as poor samples can fetch very low prices. The price for peas for processing (*e.g.*, marrowfats for canning) for *human consumption* obtain a premium of generally £25 to £50/tonne according to quality (size and colour) and the percentage of wastage, but marrowfat yields are generally lower than feed varieties; most peas for human consumption are grown on contract. The premium for peas for the pigeon trade is usually around £12/tonne.

   The *area payments* are as for beans (page 11). For set-aside requirement see page 43.

3. *Physical Inputs.* Seed: 200 to 250 kg. Fertilizer: 250 kg of no nitrogen compound where applied, but some crops receive no fertilizer.

4. *Harvesting* (normally in late July-early August) can be a difficult operation. Most crops are direct combined, although there is a high risk of loss and poor quality, as well as heavy wear and tear on the combine. Drying and handling the crop can be very difficult, much care being needed. Sometimes the crop is desiccated before direct combining, using diquat, to even out maturity and kill green weeds.

5. *Labour:* see page 103.

6. *Peas versus Beans* (for feed). *On average,* yields of peas are slightly above those for beans nationally. Peas are normally spring-sown (winter peas are beginning to be tried) and spring beans are easier to manage than peas. Peas are unsuited to heavier soils and are more vulnerable if the weather is wet during flowering and harvest. They are more sensitive to soil compaction and waterlogging. Their yields are thus more variable than for beans. Their seed costs are also much higher. On the other hand, peas (especially for human consumption) fetch higher prices and are usually easier to sell, given reasonable quality; they are also less sensitive to drought. They are normally ready to harvest well before spring beans.

VINING PEAS

Production level (1)	Low £	Average £	High £
OUTPUT (2), (3)	725 (293)	835 (338)	950 (385)
Variable Costs:			
Seed (4)		120 (49)	
Fertilizer (5)		15 (6)	
Sprays (6)		50 (20)	
TOTAL VARIABLE COSTS		185 (75)	
GROSS MARGIN per ha (per acre)	540 (218)	650 (263)	765 (310)

Notes

1. The categories "low", "average" and "high" are related to the actual growers of vining peas, not to farmers and farm land in general. As the factories will normally only place contracts with the better growers the "average" figure above virtually refers to "premium" farmers on good land. If all farmers had the opportunity of producing this crop the average output would probably be no higher than the "low" figure above, even at present prices.

2. The average sale value equals 4·5 tonnes/ha (36 cwt./acre) @ £185 per tonne (1995 estimate). This is an average over the whole crop where it goes for freezing. Where the peas are for canning yields are likely to be heavier and prices lower. The opposite is true for *petits pois:* the yield is around 20% lower and the price 15% or so higher.

3. The above price excludes payment for harvesting (£55-£60 per tonne) and transport (£22·50-£25 per tonne). Some firms work on a delivered factory price basis. Harvesters cost £225,000-£250,000.

4. *Seed:* this is a "subsidised" price in the sense that the grower pays below the market price for seed but receives a lower price for his product than he otherwise would.

5. *Fertilizer:* many growers use no fertilizer; it is more often used on light land.

6. *Sprays:* both herbicide and aphicides. There are large seasonal variations according to weather conditions and the need for midge control.

7. *Labour:* see page 103.

Note:

For full details (yields, prices, variable costs) of *actual* average Cash Crop Gross Margins in different parts of the country, see the following annual reports:

Report on Farming in The Eastern Counties of England, University of Cambridge, Agricultural Economics Unit, Department of Land Economy.

An Economic Review of Farming in the North-West, University of Manchester, Department of Agricultural Economics.

Farm Management Handbook, University of Exeter, Agricultural Economics Unit.

(Full addresses on page 213-214).

MAINCROP POTATOES

Production level					Low	Average	High
Yield: tonnes per ha (tons per acre)				...	30 (12)	40 (16)	50 (20)
					£	£	£
OUTPUT					2125 (860)	2825 (1145)	3525 (1425)
Variable Costs:							
Seed						485 (197)	
Fertilizer						190 (77)	
Sprays						300 (122)	
Casual Labour for harvesting and grading (3)						300 (122)	
Sundries (P.M.B. levy, sacks, etc.) ...					325 (132)	375 (152)	425 (172)
TOTAL VARIABLE COSTS					1600 (650)	1650 (670)	1700 (690)
GROSS MARGIN per hectare (acre)					525 (210)	1175 (475)	1825 (735)

Notes

1. *Prices.* The price assumed above is £75 per tonne for ware and £17·50 for chats (assumed to be 7½ per cent), which is £70·70 per tonne for the whole crop. The *actual* price in any one season will depend mainly on the national average yield. The five-year average GB price between 1988/89 and 1992/93 was £76 per tonne (£90 at 1995 price levels) but varied from £56 to £99 per tonne. However, while prices have always varied considerably from season to season, there is now even greater uncertainty with the winding up of the Potato Marketing Board, with its regulatory powers, though the average price for the 1994 crop will be well above the level assumed above.
    The average seasonal monthly price indices over the same period (with each annual price = 100) are as follows: July 111, Aug. 89, Sept. 91, Oct. 94, Nov. 91, Dec. 97, Jan. 99, Feb. 102, Mar. 105, April 113, May 129, June 134. As said above, the variation between years is considerable, particularly at the beginning and end of the season.

2. *Physical Inputs.* Seed: 80% planted with certified seed: 2·8 tonnes per hectare at £190 per tonne (the price varies widely from season to season); 20% with once-grown seed: 2·4 tonnes per hectare at £125 per tonne. Sprays: herbicide, blight control, and haulm destruction.

3. *Casual Labour.* The figure in the table above is for assistance during harvesting (£80/ha; machine harvesting is assumed) and for grading/riddling (£220/ha); it is assumed that half the labour for the latter is supplied by casuals, half by regulars. Other jobs for which casual labour may be employed are:
Planting:	£95 per hectare
Picking by hand:	£440 per hectare
Grading/Riddling (all):	£440 per hectare (£11 per tonne).

4. *Contract mechanical harvesting:* £250/hectare (excl. carting, etc.). Other contract work see pages 119-120.

5. *P.M.B. levy* (1994). The proposed new levy, for the diminished Potato Marketing Scheme, is £45/ha, with a further charge of £480/ha on any crop area that exceeds the quota—if still applicable in 1995.

6. *Sacks.* Approx. £6·25 per tonne.

7. *Chitting.* Additional annual cost of chitting is approximately £40 per tonne of seed, or £110 per hectare, including depreciation and interest on the chitting house.

8. *Fuel and Repairs* (per hectare): £150.

9. *Specialized Equipment Prices:* see page 117.

10. *Potato Store Costs:* see page 152.

11. *Labour:* see page 100.

In 1993, the percentages of the total potato area in Great Britain planted in maincrop, second early and first early varieties respectively were 64·6, 25·8 and 9·6; in England and Wales: 63·1, 26·8 and 10·1; in Scotland: 72·2, 20·6 and 7·2. One-sixth of the total GB potato area is in Scotland.

Quota Selling and Leasing. Because of low potato prices in 1992/3 and the first part of the 1993/94 season, together especially with the coming demise of the Potato Marketing Board, quota prices were very low prior to planting the 1994 crop: £20 to £25/ha to lease, £50 to £70/ha to buy.

EARLY POTATOES

Production level					Low	Average	High
Yield: tonnes per ha (tons per acre):				...	18·0 (7·2)	24·0 (9·5)	30 (12)
					£	£	£
OUTPUT	...	...	...	...	2000 (810)	3000 (1215)	4000 (1620)

Variable Costs:					
Seed	...	...	...	...	750 (303)
Fertilizer ...	...	...	...	...	150 (61)
Sprays	...	...	...	...	175 (70)
Casual labour	...	...	...	...	150 (60)
Sundries	...	...	...	...	200 (81)

TOTAL VARIABLE COSTS	...	...	...	1425 (575)

GROSS MARGIN per ha (acre)	...	...	575 (235)	1575 (640)	2575 (1045)

Notes

1. *Prices and Yields.* The price assumed above is £125 per tonne. However, yields increase and prices fall as the season progresses. Thus both depend on the date of lifting, e.g. late May to early June, 7 to 12 tonnes per hectare; July, 20 to 30 tonnes per hectare. Prices in late May to mid June are typically three times those in July; the very earliest crops (early May) can even fetch £1,000 per tonne, but the price may have fallen to £250 or even £200 by the end of May. Thus the average output of £3000 given above could also be obtained from 10 tonnes at £300 per tonne, 15 at £200, 20 at £150 or 30 at £100.

2. *Casual labour* for planting: £95 per hectare.

3. *P.M.B. levy* (1994). The proposed new levy is £12/ha, for crops out of the ground by June 30th. The excess levy is £480 per hectare.

4. *Chitting.* See Maincrop Potatoes.

5. *Fuel and Repairs* (£ per hectare): £125.

6. *Labour:* see page 101.

SECOND EARLY POTATOES

Output (average): 38 tonnes/ha (15 tons/acre) @ £60/tonne = £2275 (920) (lifting July to early September).

Variable Costs: Seed £485 (197), fertilizer £175 (70), sprays £200 (81), casual labour £275 (110), miscellaneous £340 (137); total £1475 (595).

Gross Margin: £800 (325).

Labour: see page 101.

SUGAR BEET

Production level Yield: tonnes per ha (tons per acre)	Low 30 (12)	Average 42·5 (17)	High 55 (22)
	£	£	£
OUTPUT	1260 (510)	1785 (725)	2310 (935)
Variable Costs:			
Seed		90 (37)	
Fertilizer		120 (49)	
Sprays		155 (63)	
Transport (Contract)	170 (71)	250 (101)	330 (136)
TOTAL VARIABLE COSTS	535 (215)	615 (250)	695 (280)
GROSS MARGIN per ha (acre)	725 (295)	1170 (475)	1615 (655)

Notes

1. *Prices.* There are still no signs of the EU sugar regime being substantially altered in the near future. The above table assumes a price, for the 1995 crop, of £38 per tonne, for roots of 17·0 per cent sugar content (*i.e.*, the approximate national average), including any early or late delivery bonuses (see below), plus transport allowance estimated at £4.00 per tonne. This price assumes that most of the crop is paid for at the A and B quota price. Excess production receives a "C beet" price which is very variable—ranging from £6 to £25 a tonne in recent years. If say 5% is C beet paid for at £15/tonne the overall average price drops by over £1/tonne and the average output and gross margin drop by approximately £50/ha (£20/acre) compared with if all the beet were sold at the A and B quota price.

   The price is varied by 0·9 per cent (1 per cent below 15 per cent sugar content) of the contract price for each 0·1 per cent difference in sugar content.

   In addition, early and late delivery allowances are paid as follows (all dates approximate only). Early delivery: In 1992, 18% was added to the basic price if crops were delivered on Sept. 15th; this reduced by one per centage point per day till Oct. 10th, when just the basic price was paid. Late delivery: 26th Dec.-7th Jan.: 0·8% of U.K. minimum price; therafter, the rate rises by 0·2% per day.

2. *Effect of Harvesting Date.* As the season progresses, changes occur in the crop before lifting, approximately as follows, on average:

	early Sept. to early Oct.	early Oct. to early Nov.	early Nov. to early Dec.	early Dec. to early Jan.
Yield (tonnes of washed beet per hectare)	up 3·75	up 1·9	up 1·25	up 1·25
Sugar Content (%)	up 1%	up ¼%	down ¼%	down ¾%
Yield of Sugar (kg per hectare)	up 1000	up 375	up 190	down 60

3. *Contract.* Contract mechanical harvesting costs approx. £135 per hectare excluding carting or £170 per hectare including carting.

4. *Transport.* Contract haulage charges vary widely according to distance from the factory. The figure assumed above is £5·25 per tonne of unwashed beet including cleaner-loader hire (dirt and top tare assumed at 14%).

5. *Fuel and Repairs* (per hectare): £140.

6. *Specialized Equipment Prices:* see page 117.

7. *Labour:* see page 102.

HERBAGE SEEDS

		Italian Ryegrass		Early Perennial Ryegrass	
		Average	High	Average	High
Yield (100 kg/ha)		11·25	15	10·25	14
Price per 50 kg (£)		24		23	
Subsidy per 50 kg (£)		8·25		10·25	
OUTPUT		725	965	680	930
Variable Costs:					
Seed		70		50	
Fertilizer		65		65	
Sprays		65		65	
Cleaning, etc.		125	160	130	170
TOTAL VARIABLE COSTS ...		325	360	310	350
GROSS MARGIN per ha		400	605	370	580
GROSS MARGIN per acre		160	245	150	235

		Intermediate Perennial Ryegrass		Late Perennial Ryegrass	
		Average	High	Average	High
Yield (100 kg/ha)		11·25	15	11	15
Price per 50 kg (£)		25		28	
Subsidy per 50 kg (£)		10·25		13·75	
OUTPUT		795	1055	920	1250
Variable Costs:					
Seed		45		45	
Fertilizer		65		65	
Sprays		65		65	
Cleaning, etc.		125	160	130	170
TOTAL VARIABLE COSTS ...		300	335	305	345
GROSS MARGIN per ha		495	720	615	905
GROSS MARGIN per acre		200	290	250	365

	Hybrid Ryegrass		Kent Wild White Clover & Kent Indig. Perennial Ryegrass	
	Average	High	Average	High
Yield (100 kg/na)	11·5	15·5	0·8(C); 5(R)	1·1(C); 7(R)
Price per 50 kg (£)		24	225(C); 25(R)	
Subsidy per 50 kg (£)		8·25	28(C); 13·75(R)	
OUTPUT	740	1000	790	1100
Variable Costs:				
Seed		35		25
Fertilizer		65		30
Sprays		65		35
Cleaning, etc.	135	175	85	110
TOTAL VARIABLE COSTS ...	300	340	175	200
GROSS MARGIN per ha	440	660	615	900
GROSS MARGIN per acre	180	265	250	365

Notes

1. The following were the estimated number of hectares approved for certified seed production for the main grasses and clovers in England and Wales in 1993:

Italian Ryegrass	1,592	Red Fescue	931
Early Perennial Ryegrass ...	683	Tall Fescue	27
Intermediate Perennial Ryegrass	3,335	Meadow Fescue	18
Late Perennial Ryegrass ...	3,242	White Clover (inc. 166 ha	
Amenity Perennial Ryegrass	955	Kent Wild White)	259
Hybrid Ryegrass	346	Red Clover	23
Cocksfoot	169	Vetch	597
Timothy	17		

The ryegrasses total approx. 10,175 ha (25,150 acres)
All herbage seeds total 12,225 ha (30,200 acres)

2. Average yields are approximate 5-year (1989-93) averages for cleaned seed. The crop is very risky, i.e. yields are highly variable, depending especially on the weather at, and precise timeliness of, harvesting. A considerable amount of skill is necessary to attain the "high" levels. Most grasses give their highest yield in their first harvest year, assuming good establishment.

3. Prices in the table are estimated prices for certified seed. The actual prices received in any one year are very uncertain. The subsidy levels are approximate levels for the 1994 and 1995 harvests, assuming no substantial change in the ECU value prevailing in July 1994.

4. No allowance has been made above for by-products. Some crops produce 4 to 5 tonnes of threshed hay, which is, however, of low feeding value. This could be worth £150 or more per hectare. Some grasses, especially spring-sown ryegrass, also provide substantial quantities of autumn and winter grazing. Clovers can be either grazed or cut for hay or silage and do not have to be "shut up" until mid or late May, or, in some cases and seasons, even early June. More grazing (until end of May) and better quality threshed hay is provided with a combination of ryegrass and white clover than with the specialist herbage seed grasses.

5. If the seed crop is to be undersown, specialist growers often reduce the seed rate for the cover crop by up to half and restrict nitrogen dressing: the cereal yield may thus be reduced by up to 0·6 tonnes per hectare. If this is not done the grass seed yield is usually lower in the first year compared with direct drilling, except for ryegrass.

6. *Labour:* see page 105.

Acknowledgement: Considerable help for this crop has been provided by K. B. Knappett, Seed Production Branch, N.I.A.B. and Mr. W. S. Holliwell, Holliwell Seed and Grain Co. Ltd., Wye.

RYE

Production level				Low	Average	High
Yield: tonnes per ha (cwt. per acre):			...	4·25 (34)	5·25 (42)	6·25 (50)
				£	£	£
Sale Value			...	470 (190)	575 (233)	685 (277)
Area Payment			...	250 (101)	250 (101)	250 (101)
OUTPUT: (Contract price) ...			...	720 (291)	825 (334)	935 (378)
Variable Costs:						
Seed					70 (28·5)	
Fertilizer					65 (26)	
Sprays					95 (38·5)	
TOTAL VARIABLE COSTS					230 (93)	
GROSS MARGIN per ha (acre): ...			...	490 (198)	595 (241)	705 (285)

Largely grown on light, infertile, sandy or stony soils, where yields are poor for other cereals. Yields would clearly be higher on better soils, but then rye has difficulty in competing with wheat and barley; it could never do so on good wheat land. The average yield in England and Wales in the four years 1990-93 was 5·07 tonnes/ha, ranging from 4·6 in 1992 to 5·7 in 1991 (MAFF).

8,100 ha (20,000 acres) were grown in the UK in 1992, mainly in the south, south-east and East Anglia. Rye crispbread is the biggest outlet, Ryvita alone using more than a third of the crop. It is also milled into flour, used in mixed-grain bread and muesli. Increasing concern with dieting means that demand is increasing. About two-thirds of UK requirements are imported, mainly from Canada (which produces the highest quality), Denmark, Germany and Spain.

The price assumed above (£110 a tonne) is an estimated 1995 price at harvest for rye for crispbread. Typically, £3 is added for delivery in October or November and £6 if grown within, say, 80 miles of the processing plant; deductions are made for low quality, particularly if it is only of feed grade (between feed wheat and feed barley price). Only about 15% of the crop is grown for the free market, which is risky. The area payment is as estimated for England (see page 3).

Rye, which is autumn-sown, is drought tolerant and very hardy, can withstand low temperatures and starts growing early in the spring. It has all-round resistance to wheat and barley diseases, e.g. eyespot, and suffers less from take-all than wheat—hence it is a possible replacement for third or fourth wheat. Its vigour keeps weeds down. Its herbicide, fungicide and fertilizer requirements are lower than for other cereals. Harvested earlier than winter wheat (useful for following oilseed rape).

Drawbacks: it sprouts in a wet harvest: must thus harvest early, at relatively high moisture content. It grows very tall and lodges easily: hence high levels of nitrogen are not possible; but growth regulators help. Its heavy straw crop means very slow combining (takes about twice as long per hectare as wheat and barley), and difficult straw incorporation. New hybrid varieties, with shorter, stiffer straw, are being developed; these would improve the comparative profitability of rye on better soils.

Drilling: 2nd and 3rd weeks September.

Harvesting: by mid-August (at relatively high moisture content, then dry to 14-15%).

TRITICALE

Production level	Low	Average	High
Yield: tonnes per ha (cwt. per acre): ...	4·25 (34)	5·25 (42)	6·25 (50)
	£	£	£
Sale Value	375 (152)	465 (188)	555 (225)
Area Payment	250 (101)	250 (101)	250 (101)
OUTPUT	625 (253)	715 (289)	805 (326)
Variable Costs:			
Seed		60 (24·5)	
Fertilizer		60 (24·5)	
Sprays		55 (22)	
TOTAL VARIABLE COSTS		175 (71)	
GROSS MARGIN per ha (acre)	450 (182)	540 (218)	630 (255)

A "man-made" cross between rye and hard wheat. Combines the hardiness of rye and the marketability of feed wheat. The main use is in pig and poultry rations: it contains a superior quality of protein. 9,200 ha were grown in the UK in 1990, 11,000 ha in 1991 and 10,700 ha (26,450 acres) in 1992. In Germany the triticale area has risen tenfold since 1986 to about 280,000 ha and the area in France now exceeds 200,000 ha.

Price is between feed wheat and feed barley and the average throughout the 1995/6 season is taken to be £88·50 per tonne. The area payment is as estimated for England (see page 3).

Its main scope to date has been on light land, especially thin, drought-prone, poorish, marginal cereal-growing soils, where it frequently outyields wheat or barley, especially the former, and it has lower input requirements.

In comparing the average *yields* given above with those of wheat and barley, this point has to be borne in mind, *i.e.* that it is mainly grown at present on poorer soils. Yields appear to be more consistent on such soils than those of barley. The 5-year average yield in Cambridge University's Farm Business Survey in 1988-92 was 4·58 tonnes/ha, with an average of 5·18 in the 1991 and 1992 harvests. MAFF reported a four-year average yield (1990-93) of 5·15 tonnes/ha, ranging from 4·6 in 1992 to 5·4 in 1990 and 1991. Results with newer varieties, both experimental and on-farm, have been good compared with second and subsequent wheats, owing to the crop's resistance to drought and fungal diseases. Thus on average quality soils the newer varieties may yield 6 tonnes/ha or more. An ADAS survey a few years ago on 50 farms gave the average gross margin of triticale exceeding that of winter barley by £52/ha.

Lower levels of fungicide are needed because of its good disease resistance, except for ergot, but including take-all (making it a possible replacement for a third or fourth wheat). It is a tall crop, which helps to suppress weeds, but it is susceptible to lodging; growth regulators are beneficial.

The crop is best drilled early (September) on very light, drought-prone soils; otherwise October is satisfactory.

Harvesting is at approximately the same time as wheat. There is more straw, which slows combining, and incorporation is very difficult; this is less of a problem on poor soils as there is less straw.

NAKED OATS

Production level					Low	Average	High
Yield: tonnes per ha (cwt. per acre):			...		3·5 (28)	4·6 (36·5)	5·5 (44)
					£	£	£
Sale Value	...	...	...	...	490 (199)	645 (262)	770 (312)
Area Payment	...	...	...	...	250 (101)	250 (101)	250 (101)
OUTPUT	...	...	...	...	740 (300)	895 (363)	1020 (413)
Variable Costs:							
Seed	...	...	...	...		55 (22·5)	
Fertilizer	...	...	...	...		55 (22·5)	
Sprays	...	...	...	...		70 (2·8)	
TOTAL VARIABLE COSTS	...	...	...			180 (73)	
GROSS MARGIN per ha (acre)		...	...		560 (227)	715 (290)	840 (340)

Naked oats have a higher protein, energy and oil content than "traditional" oats, but the fibre content is lower—as the husk falls off during harvesting. Because of the high oil content it can go rancid if stored too moist, hence contracts require a maximum moisture content of 14% and 12% is recommended for long-term storage. The crop needs priority treatment at harvest.

Between 6,000 and 8,000 ha are grown in the UK at present and the area is steadily increasing. The traditional markets such as for racehorses and dog foods are increasing, but at least half the crop is now sold for human consumption: for health foods, fancy breads and breakfast cereals.

The (1995/6) *price* assumed is £140 per tonne. Buy-back contracts offering premiums of between £30 and £70/tonne over feed barley, according to husk content, were available for the 1994 harvest. The area payment is as estimated for England (see page 3).

About 85% of the crop is winter sown. MAIB suggests that yeilds average 20 to 25% less than conventional oats, but survey data over several years is as yet unavailable. Like other oats, the variable inputs are lower than for wheat or barley and the crop provides a break in the take-all cycle.

Naked barley, suitable for roasting, flaking or milling as pearl barley, is getting increasingly in the news. It is available on buy-back contracts with a £30/tonne premium over feed grains. Both winter and spring varieties are available. The crop is grown like normal barley, but yields are expected to be some 15% lower.

DURUM WHEAT

Production level			...		Low	Average	High
Yield: tonnes per ha (cwt. per acre):			...		2·75 (22)	3·75 (30)	5·00 (40)
					£	£	£
Sale Value	...	...	...	...	370 (150)	505 (204)	675 (273)
Area Payment	...	...	...	...	250 (101)	250 (101)	250 (101)
OUTPUT	...	...	...	...	620 (251)	755 (305)	925 (374)
Variable Costs:							
Seed	...	...	...	...		80 (32·5)	
Fertilizer	...	...	...	...		65 (26)	
Sprays	...	...	...	...		70 (28·5)	
TOTAL VARIABLE COSTS	...	...	...			215 (87)	
GROSS MARGIN per ha (acre)		...	...		405 (164)	540 (218)	710 (287)

N.B. Extra drying costs estimated at £8 per tonne.

A Mediterranean crop. Used for pasta, semolina (if high quality) and breakfast cereals. Must be grown under contract. The UK demand is relatively small (60,000 tonnes a year); UK consumption per head is approx. 4% that of Italy and 10% that of France. 11,000 ha (27,000 acres) were grown in UK in 1984, but poor results reduced this to approx. 2,000 ha by 1992 and the CAP Reform system reduced this further, to about 400 ha, in 1993. UK production now is only approx. 7% of consumption; imports are mainly from France, Spain and Greece.

Yields well above the average given above are often quoted, but the 5-year average yield in Cambridge University's Farm Business Survey in 1988-92 was only 3·55 tonnes/ha, despite averaging 4·83 in the 1992 harvest. Possibly it has been mainly grown on dry, poorish soils.

The (1995 harvest) *price* assumed is £135 per tonne. Contract prices vary according to quality. At present (July 1993) only growers in Mediterranean type areas get a higher area payment to compensate for the lower yield compared with other wheat. The area payment is as estimated for England (see page 3).

As with milling wheat, there is a risk of rejection if contaminated with excess foreign seeds, especially self-set cereals from previous crop; thus safer as first cereal crop. A poor price is obtained (no EEC subsidy) if quality is too poor for pasta and thus has to go for feed.

The crop is likely to be grown only in the driest parts of the east/south east, where it can best compete with second and third wheats. It is now mainly (approx. 90%) sown in the spring (March) compared with the opposite (October) less than 10 years ago. The crop is very sensitive to stress and frost-kill in severe winters; the spring-sown crop is more reliable, and cheaper to grow. The crop has a higher disease resistance than other wheats, except for eyespot and ergot.

Harvest: spring crop usually mid-August. Critical operation: need to harvest as soon as reaches 20% moisture content, or at most 18%: crop very prone to sprouting and quality for semolina reduced if harvest delayed. Must be dried (slowly) to 15%: easier and quicker to dry than normal wheat. The straw is of poorer quality than wheat straw.

MINORITY CROPS

The following crops have limited possibilities at present, if indeed they can be grown successfully at all, but such factors as the breeding of new varieties could alter the position in the future. Some can be grown, but there is a very limited market, *e.g.*, borage.

Borage

Indigenous to Britain: both grown wild and cultivated for centuries. Grown for use as a dietary food supplement. The oil has a high gamma linolenic acid (GLA) content—more than twice as much as evening primrose. Demand slumped after 1986 owing to overproduction of GLA from non-contract crops of evening primrose in other countries. However, the area contracted in 1993 was approximately 1,000 ha (2,500 acres), mainly in East Anglia.

Compared with evening primrose it has the advantages of spring-sowing (about mid-April), bigger seeds, faster growth, and earlier harvesting (August). Its aggressive growth gives good weed control with a high plant density. It prefers low rainfall. There are no known pests and diseases, except for powdery mildew. It is combinable, after swathing. Harvesting can be difficult. Seed shedding at maturity is a serious problem.

Yields: from virtually nothing to 0·625 tonnes/ha (5 cwt./acre); average 0·375 (3).

Price: £2,000 a tonne. Output at average yield, £750/ha (300/acre).

Variable costs (approx.) (£ per ha (acre)): seed 150 (60); fertilizer 50 (20); sprays 25 (10); total £225 (90).

Gross margin: £525/ha (£210/acre).

Evening Primrose

The seed oil is a good source of essential fatty acids, especially gamma-linolenic acid, which has medicinal properties for many serious diseases and disorders. Brand-named evening primrose oil capsules are widely available in chemists and health food shops.

Grown only in small areas, mainly 2 to 5 ha. About 1,000 ha (2,500 acres) now grown in UK; contract necessary. Wide range of soils suitable, but not acid, high pH, or fen. Good drainage and firm seedbed necessary.

Some growers (especially if on sands) sow in March/April for harvesting early/mid-October, but most sow it late July-early August for harvesting in late September/October the following year—but winter kill is possible. Germination and establishment very difficult (the seeds are tiny); shallow drilling (½") and seedbed consolidation important. Weed control a major problem until established. No significant pest or disease problems known at present. Relatively little fertilizer needed—lush vegetative growth unwanted.

Uneven ripening and pod setting a further problem. Harvesting is difficult. Crop has to be desiccated (perhaps twice) before combining, which needs to be slow to avoid shattering the pods; seeds must be dried quickly, to 10-12%.

Yields: 0·15 to 0·75 tonnes/ha (1·25 to 6 cwt./acre): 0·4 (3·2) a good crop. A high-risk crop best grown on contract.

Price: approx. £1,700 a tonne; 0·35 tonne (2·4 cwt.) = £600/ha (245/acre).

Variable costs (approx.) (£ per ha (acre)): seed 20 (8); fertilizer 50 (20); sprays 80 (33); desiccant 65 (27); cleaning 55 (22); total £270 (110).

Gross margin at 0·35 tonnes/ha therefore approx. £330 (135).

Flax

Linseed for fibre: therefore taller. Long fibres are used for linen, short for industrial purposes. Total EU area is 50,000 ha, mainly in France and Belgium. Expensive plant required for quality linen (the price of which is highly volatile): there are none in Great Britain, one in Northern Ireland. On-farm vetting unreliable. Recent development of a decorticator at Silsoe has revived hopes: for use of the crop for lino, textiles and paper; the waste for fibreboard or farm heating. The attractions are a high EU subsidy, no set-aside requirement and can be grown on land not previously arable. Buy-back contracts now available. For history and further details see 21st edition, page 20.

Output/ha (£, approx): sales 600, subsidy 600. Variable costs: seed 150, fertilisers 30, sprays 120, contract (to pull and bale) 200; total 500. On these assumptions G.M. £700 (285/acre).

Hemp (Cannabis)

Recently approved for growing in UK for industrial purposes, under licence and contract. Its long, strong fibres make fine quality paper. The crop grows 3 to 3·5m (10 to 12 feet) tall. 600 ha were grown on contract (by 32 farmers) in East Anglia in 1993 and averaged around 5 tonnes ha (2t/acre). The target yield is 7·5 t/ha (3t/acre). The area could exceed 1500 ha in 1994. The price is approximately £35/tonne. There is an EU subsidy of approx. £600/ha. Variable costs/ha are, approx.: seed £80, fertiliser £100, contract swathing and baling £150. It may be grown on set-aside land but then without the EU subsidy, only the set-aside payment.

Lupins

Some 1,300 ha were grown in the UK in 1985, but the results were so poor that year that only 260 ha were grown in 1986 and little has been grown in the country since. The area in France has also fallen substantially. Has a high protein content (50% more than peas and beans), making it a good substitute for soya beans in livestock feed compounds, and it is easy to mill. But it has a high fibre content, variable protein ratings and an unbalanced amino acid profile. Some 30,000 tonnes of lupin produce is currently imported per year from Australia.

It is a leguminous, light land crop. Mainly white-flowered varieties grown at present. It is spring-sown (mid-March/early April), nitrogen fixing, has erect growth, is resistant to lodging and shattering, and unmodified cereal machinery is suitable. *But* it is difficult to grow: it needs careful seedbed preparation and free-draining fertile soil; botrytis lower yields, especially in a wet year: there is no certain control at present; late-germinating weeds can cause problems; fairly susceptible to frost damage; possibly uneven ripening; harvested late. To produce a mature crop its heat requirements are even higher than for grain maize: thus many crops have been combined at very high moisture contents or have even failed to mature. Work on a new type of lupin, winter-sown and semi-topless, promising earlier maturity and higher yields, is underway at Rothamsted.

Might average 2 tonnes per ha (16 cwt. per acre) in a good year, though up to 5T/ha claimed in trials of latest varieties of white lupins. Price about £150 a tonne. Area payment approximately £360/ha in England in 1994. Variable costs per ha (approx.): seed £125, fert. £25, sprays £60; total £210.

Maize for Grain

Little scope with present varieties because, as with Sunflowers, our climate is not warm enough. Did reasonably well in good springs and summers for a while, in Southern England, over ten years ago, but results were very poor in late springs and cool summers and harvesting between mid-October and mid-December is grim in a wet autumn/early winter, and drying very costly. Possibly 200 ha are being grown annually in the UK. Do well to average 4 tonnes/ha (32 cwt./acre); price for 1995 crop could be £125-135 a tonne; area payment (England) £250/ha (£101/acre). Seed (120), fertilizer (60) and sprays (30) total approx. £210/ha (£85/acre); drying £100/ha (£40/acre). Forage maize (p. 78) has been much more successful.

Navy Beans

Produced for baked beans. About 100,000 tonnes a year imported, costing around £40 millions. Limited chance of commercial production in the UK in the foreseeable future (*i.e.*, with present varieties) because of insufficient cold tolerance. But new cold and disease resistant varieties better suited to the British climate than American-bred varieties, together with improved harvesting techniques, make it at least a feasible future commercial proposition in the south and south-east of England; its chances are better than for soya beans. Sown mid-May. Very late harvest (end October). Target yield approx. 2 tonnes/ha; price approx., £250/tonne; variable costs £250/ha. At present the crop receives no EU area aid.

Soya Beans

Mainly grown in the USA. In Europe, mainly in the Po Valley (the area of this crop is growing rapidly in Italy) and Southern France (40,000 ha). Very little chance of successful commercial production in the UK, as the crop is unlikely to mature in our climate. Sown mid-May. Yield approx. 1·75 tonnes/ha (14 cwt./acre); price approx. £175/tonne; eligible for oilseeds area payment (approx. £400/ha); variable costs £175/ha. Average EC yield (80% in Italy) 3·0 tonnes (24 cwt./acre).

Sunflowers

Substantial interest still being shown, with extensive field trials in UK, but no significant commercial development as yet. New, earlier varieties are required, together with better pest and disease control. Nevertheless, possibly around 1500 ha were grown in 1993. The demand for the oil is strong and increasing. There is a 15% set-aside requirement.

An estimated 900,000 ha were grown in France in 1994, extending north of Paris. EC average yield in 1988-90 was 1·725 tonnes/ha (13·75 cwt./acre) (2·4 (19) in France), compared with 3·0 (24) for oilseed rape (same average yield in France). Price: approx. £150/tonne, plus approx. £400/ha area aid (as for oilseed rape). Output (at 1·75 tonnes/ha) = £660. Variable costs approx. £230 per ha (seed 120, fertilizer 50, sprays 60). Gross margin £430/ha (£175/acre). Drying costs are high: approx. £50/ha.

Sown in April or early May, when soil temperature exceeds 5°C. Wide range of soils suitable.

Problems: the crop needs a warm climate; in Southern England a "fair" crop might be grown 3 years in 5; susceptible to botrytis, especially in a wet August/September, difficult to control; sclerotina also a major problem in France; birds too can be damaging (thus at least 4 ha (10 acres) need to be grown in one piece); post-emergence weed control is difficult. Harvesting is very late in England; a dry autumn is needed. Dried to 10% for safe storage.

Others

Other crops that have been "in the news" in recent years as possible new crops for the future (or present crops capable of substantial development) include the following: chickpeas and lentils, fenugreek, meadowfoam, cuphea, peppermint, poppies (for cooking oils, not opium), quinoa, buckwheat and sunwheat (a new early maturing short type of sunflower). At present there are no reliable data for these crops on average yield expectations and little on prices or variable costs, when grown on a commercial scale in this country. A number of them are either for the health food market or are sources of oil for industry as replacements for whale oil and light mineral oil. Research continues on many of them.

HOPS

1. *Output data*

Average Yield per ha, 1989-93: 30·0 zentners (50 kg). The 1991 and 1993 crops were particularly high yielding.

Average Price (per zentner): 1989, £125; 1990, £147; 1991, £167; 1992, £167; 1993, £178.

Main varieties (93·7% of total area):

	ha 1993	av. yield 1989-93 (z. per ha)	av. £ per zentner (contract prices)		
			1991	1992	1993
Wye Target	1,613	28·9	153	139	139
Wye Challenger	396	32·2	166	168	200
Wye Northdown	376	31·6	173	177	204
Fuggles	332	28·1	175	193	211
Goldings	288	30·4	185	204	228
Yeoman	88	26·3	156	150	100

Total area of hops (ha): 1984: 5.091; 1988: 3,878; 1993: 3,300.

EC income aid for 1993 (£ per ha): aromatic £346, bitter, £379.

2. *Variable Costs per mature hectare* (materials only)

	£
Fertilizers and Manures...	175
Washes and Powders	1000
Herbicides	125
String	175
Pockets/Bales	50
Drying Fuel	175
Total	1700

3. *Average Direct Labour Costs per mature hectare*

	£
Growing	700
Picking	650
Drying	200
Total	1550

N.B. The above costs are the author's approximations for 1995 based on a limited sample for the 1991-93 crops.

Acknowledgement: T. W. Smith, Grower Liaison Manager, English Hops Limited.

VINEYARDS

At the start of 1993 there were 479 vineyards in England and Wales, covering 1,054 ha (2,605 acres). Of these, 462 (1,035 ha) were in England, with the South-east predominating. 157 of these vineyards have wineries. Production in 1992 was 2·64 million litres: 93·5% white wine, 6·5% red.

Under EC regulations there is a ban on new plantings of vines for producing wine once annual production exceeds 2·5 million litres, but 'quality' wine is exempt. This means that no new areas of the hardy and popular hybrid grape varieties may be planted. A Quality Wine Scheme for England and Wales was introduced in 1991. English wines have to bear the same excise duty and VAT as imported wines, which is not the case in any other EC country. UK wine supplies only 0·5% of the home market. English wine growers, particularly in Kent and East Sussex, have been badly hit, since the introduction of the Single European Market in early 1993, by British people being allowed now to bring virtually unlimited amounts of wine into the country duty-free.

Vineyards need south facing land, less than 100 m. (330 ft.) above sea level, well drained and sheltered, in (at most) the southern half of England and Wales. High level management and marketing are essential, as is expert advice. Good scope for sales to visiting groups farm shops, local restaurants and hotels. A few big producers dominate the national market.

Investment capital of £11,000 to £14,000 per ha (£4,450-£5,675 per acre) typically required. No production for 3 years; full production possibly not until the 6th. Yield and quality highly variable from year to year. At least 5 ha (12 acres) now needed for commercial viability, but many who can afford it produce small areas purely out of interest or personal pleasure. A vinery adds well over £50,000 to initial costs, even for a small unit. Selling to a winery elsewhere entails additional transport costs.

There are two main systems:

Intensive (Double Guyot): 3,450 vines/ha (1,400/acre).
>   *Establishment costs* per ha(acre) (over 2 years): approx. £15,500 (£6,250) inc. materials £10,500 (£4,250) and labour £2,500 (£1,000). (The common system in France and Germany).

Extensive (Geneva Double Curtain): 1,500 vines/ha (465/acre).
>   *Establishment costs* per ha(acre) (over 3 years): approx. £9,750 (£3,950) inc. materials £5,250 (£2,125) and labour £2,100 (£850). (More common system in Britain).

Subsequent annual costs per ha(acre) of growing and harvesting are approximately:

	Intensive System £	Extensive System £
Growing: Materials	1,150 (465)	1,150 (465)
Labour	1,050 (425)	675 (275)
Harvesting	110 (45)	105 (42·5)

Yield: 5 tonnes/ha (2 tons/acre). 1 tonne of grapes = approximately 1,000 bottles of wine. £3·50 a bottle estimated to be needed to break even in an average sized, average cost, commercial unit.

Source: Largely from The Diversification Guide (RASE), including costs adapted from ADAS data.

For further information: English Vineyards Association, 38 West Park, London SE9 4RH (tel. 081-857 0452).

FRUIT

Established crops : per hectare (per acre in brackets)

Note: The *wide range* of yields, prices and costs, both from farm to farm and season to season, has to be stressed. Thus these figures (which are deliberately rounded) can only be considered to be broad guidelines, i.e. yields and prices in any particular year may differ markedly. Similarly, labour requirements, both regular and casual, vary considerably. *Prices* are net of marketing, handling and transport and assume sales in the open market unless otherwise stated and exclude pick-your-own crops. *Yields* refer to *marketed* yields only, of established crops. The figures relate to *average* levels; "high" outputs may be about 50 per cent above those shown; naturally the top producers will achieve still better results, especially in good years.

	Dessert Apples	Culinary Apples	Pears (Conference)	Plums (Vict./M.S.)
Yield (tonnes)	11 (4·4)	18 (7·2)	12 (4·8)	8 (3·2)
Net Price (£/tonne)	350	250	300	600
	£	£	£	£
OUTPUT	3850 (1560)	4500 (1820)	3600 (1455)	4800 (1940)
Variable Costs: [1]				
Fertilizer	50 (20)	50 (20)	50 (20)	50 (20)
Sprays	375 (150)	375 (150)	300 (120)	325 (130)
Packaging	400 (160)	550 (220)	425 (170)	1000 (405)
Casual Labour (picking)	625 (255)	625 (255)	625 (255)	1250 (505)
TOTAL VARIABLE COSTS[1]	1450 (585)	1600 (645)	1400 (565)	2625 (1060)
GROSS MARGIN	2400 (975)	2900 (1175)	2200 (890)	2175 (880)
Regular Labour (hours)	185 (75)	185 (75)	185 (75)	135 (55)

	Strawberries	Raspberries	Blackcurrants
Yield (tonnes)	6·5 (2·6)	4·5 (1·8)	5·5 (2·2)
Net Price (£/tonne)	1050	1600	575
	£	£	£
OUTPUT	6825 (2760)	7200 (2915)	3160 (1280)
Variable Costs: [1]			
Fertilizer	50 (20)	75 (30)	100 (40)
Sprays	450 (180)	250 (100)	300 (125)
Packaging	1750 (710)	1250 (505)	—
Casual Labour	2250 (910)	2500 (1015)	225 (90)
Other	350 (140)	350 (140)	225 (90)
TOTAL VARIABLE COSTS[1]	4850 (1960)	4425 (1790)	850 (345)
GROSS MARGIN	1975 (800)	2800 (1135)	2310 (935)
Regular Labour (hours)	200 (80)	300 (120)	125 (50)

(1) Excluding establishment, storage and transport.

Sources: In particular, for yields and prices, the annual "Economic Results for Horticulture", by Lynn Hinton and Walter C. Housden, Agricultural Economics Unit, Department of Land Economy, University of Cambridge. Supplemented by updated data based on periodic small-scale surveys, mainly in Kent.

FRUIT ESTABLISHMENT

Apples and Pears. Trees, stake, etc., approx. £4/tree. Total establishment costs £3,000–£15,000/ha depending especially on planting density, which varies from 750 to 3,500/ha.

First picking: apples—commonly year 3, 30% of full crop.
pears —commonly year 4, 20% of full crop.

Full picking: apples —generally year 6 to 9; pears—year 7 to 12.

Orchard duration: traditional, apples 20 years, pears 30 years plus; denser bed systems 15 years.

Strawberries. Costs in establishment year approx. £4,000/ha for traditional system, £9,500/ha for intensive systems; 60% of the cost is for plants. 35% pick in year 1 in intensive systems, none in traditional systems, full pick in year 2; generally 3 years cropping.

Raspberries. Establishment costs approx. £2,500/ha, including wirework. 50% pick in year 2, full pick in year 3; 10 years cropping.

Blackcurrants. Establishment costs approx. £5,000/ha using bushes, £2,500/ha using cuttings. Takes 1½ years to establish from 1 year old bushes (i.e. plant Nov. 1992 gives first crop in July 1994), 2½ years from cuttings. Approx. one-third of full crop in first picking year, 75% in second, peak in third, levelling out at slightly lower yield thereafter; 8 or 9 years cropping.

Researcher: Angela Edwards (who assisted further with revising the established fruit and vegetables data). Acknowledgements: Farm Advisory Services Team Ltd. and SmithKline Beecham.

FIELD-SCALE VEGETABLES

Per hectare (per acre in brackets)

Note: The same comments regarding variability apply as to fruit (page 27). The same main source has been used, for most of the crops, plus the annual "Report on Farming", from the same department.

			Carrots	Dry Bulb Onions	Dwarf Beans (for Processing)
Yield (tonnes)	...	...	32·5 (13)	30·0 (12)	6·0 (2·4)
Price (£/tonne)	...	...	75	100	200
			£	£	£
Output	...	...	2450 (990)	3000 (1215)	1200 (485)
Variable Costs: [1]					
Seed	...	...	350 (140)	350 (140)	275 (110)
Fertilizer	...	...	150 (60)	150 (60)	100 (40)
Sprays	...	...	325 (130)	300 (120)	125 (50)
Other*	...	...	650 (265)	750 (305)	—
Total Variable Costs [1]			1475 (595)	1550 (625)	500 (200)
Gross Margin	...	...	975 (395)	1450 (590)	700 (285)
Regular Labour (hours)	...		50-150	40-60	N.A.

					Brussels Sprouts	Cabbage	Spring Greens
Yield (tonnes)	...	...	...	...	12·5 (5)	26	18 (7·2)
Price (£/tonne)	...	...	...	...	275	130	210

					£	£	£
OUTPUT	...	...	...	...	3450 (1395)	3375 (1365)	3775 (1525)

Variable Costs: [1]							
Seeds/Plants ...	...	...	...	475 (190)	500 (205)	325 (130)
Fertilizer	...	...	...	...	130 (55)	150 (60)	150 (60)
Sprays ...	...	...	...	...	220 (90)	200 (80)	250 (100)
Other*	...	...	...	...	950 (385)	1350 (545)	2100 (850)

TOTAL VARIABLE COSTS [1]		...	...	1775 (720)	2200 (890)	2825 (1140)
GROSS MARGIN	...	...	...	1675 (675)	1175 (475)	950 (385)
Regular Labour (hours) ...	...	...	75 (30)	75 (30)	60 (24)

* Other = Casual Labour, Packaging, etc.

			Cauliflower	Broccoli	Calabrese	Sweetcorn
Yield	...	...	1250 (505)	1050 (425)	4·75T (1·9)	N.A.
			(crates of 12)	(crates of 12)		
Price	...	...	£2·75/crate	£2·75/crate	£675/tonne	N.A.

			£	£	£	£
OUTPUT	...	...	3450 (1395)	2900 (1175)	3200 (1295)	2500 (1000)

Variable Costs: [1]						
Seed/Plants ...	...	600 (245)	500 (205)	750 (305)	200 (80)
Fertilizer	...	...	150 (60)	135 (55)	125 (50)	100 (40)
Sprays ...	...	...	150 (60)	165 (65)	250 (100)	75 (30)
Other* ...	...	...	1450 (585)	1000 (405)	1100 (445)	400 (160)

TOTAL VARIABLE COSTS	...	2350 (950)	1800 (730)	2225 (900)	775 (310)
GROSS MARGIN	...	1100 (445)	1100 (445)	975 (395)	1725 (690)

			Lettuce (Outdoor)	Parsnips	Leeks	Rhubarb
Yield (tonnes)	...	...	6·5 (2·6)	25 (10)	15 (6)	20 (8)
Price (£/tonne)	...	...	1150	200	600	225

OUTPUT	...	...	7500 (3035)	5000 (2025)	9000 (3640)	4500 (1820)

Variable Costs:						
Seed/Plants ...	...	1000 (405)	100 (40)	550 (225)	125 (50)
Fertilizer	...	...	150 (60)	175 (70)	125 (50)	75 (30)
Sprays	...	...	250 (100)	400 (160)	425 (170)	50 (20)
Other*	...	...	3500 (1415)	1500 (610)	5500 (2225)	1000 (405)

TOTAL VARIABLE COSTS	...	4900 (1980)	2175 (880)	6600 (2670)	1250 (505)
GROSS MARGIN	...	2600 (1055)	2825 (1145)	2400 (970)	3250 (1315)

* Other = Casual Labour, Packaging, etc.

HORTICULTURE—WHOLE FARM DATA

Comparative whole farm data is less generally available for horticultural holdings than for various types of farm in different regions of the country (see sources of reports listed on page 132). Data from across a wide area of England is presented below. Because the results vary so much from year to year two-year averages are presented: for 1991/92 and 1992/93 (the latest available); these are not updated. The data are collected by eight College/ University centres: Askham Bryan, Cambridge, Exeter, Manchester, Newcastle, Nottingham, Reading and Wye.

All financial figures are *per hectare*. The averages cover a wide range.

Type of Holding	Specialist Glass	Specialist Fruit	Market Gardens
No. of Farms in Sample	75	43	46
Average Size (ha (acres))	1·42 (3·5)	56 (138)	32 (79)
Main Products:	Lettuce (19)	Dessert Apples	Outdoor Veg. (44)
(% Output)	Tomatoes and	and Pears (64)	Glass (9)
	Cucumbers (25)	Culinary Apples (10)	Flowers &
	Flowers and	Soft Fruit (14)	Nurs. Stock (39)
	Nursery Stock (44)		Fruit (3)
	£	£	£
Gross Output	276,380	4,850	30,215
Less:			
Bought Seed and Plants ...	38,665	40	8,870
Market Charges	14,395	725	780
Packing Materials	18,395	295	1495
Net Output	204,925	3,790	19,070
Other Costs:			
Labour (inc. Unpaid Manual)	87,155	1,915	10,845
Glasshouse Fuel	23,030	—	230
Manures	8,850	40	1,050
Sprays and Fumigants ...	2,790	265	355
Horticultural Sundries ...	10,050	170	1,395
Power and Machinery ...	20,555	580	2,560
Land Rent, Glass Deprecn.	20,250	220	1,170
Other Fixed Costs	15,840	335	1,775
Total Other Costs	188,525	3,525	19,380
Management and Inv. Inc. ...	16,400	265	−310
Grower and Wife's Labour (+)	21,015	415	2,145
Net Income	37,415	680	1,835
Tenant's Valuation	202,740	4,600	25,805

Source: Horticultural Business Data, compiled by R. L. Vaughan and R. T. Crane, Department of Agricultural Economics and Management, University of Reading, 1994.

MUSHROOMS

	Per sq. metre bed area per year
Yield: 94·5 kg @ £1·25/kg net	118·10
Spent compost	1·00
TOTAL OUTPUT	119·10
Variable Costs:	
Spawn	4·00
Compost (raw materials delivered)	10·00
Casing (peat and lime)	6·00
Heating	9·00
Sundries (disinfectants, etc.)	2·00
TOTAL VARIABLE COSTS	31·00
GROSS MARGIN	88·10

Notes:

1. Length of cropping period determines:
   (i) number of crops grown per year;
   (ii) volume (and cost) of compost, casing and spawn used per unit area;
   (iii) the weight of mushrooms produced per tonne of compost.
   Assumptions: 5 crops/year; 175 kg mushrooms/tonne compost spawned; 108 kg compost/m²/crop (22 lb/ft²/crop).

2. *Price:* Average annual wholesale price 1984-93 ranged from £1,345 to £1,400/tonne; the average for each year within that period was within 3% of this figure, with no discernible trend. UK production rose from 86,000 to 118,000 tonnes per annum over this period.

3. *Labour:* Total £45-55/m²/year: 30% composting and growing, 70% picking and packing.

4. *Capital intensive:* Composting machinery £20-30,000. Typical building (50m² per tier of trays) £8-10,000 including heating/cooling. Trays £15-20 per sq. metre, useful life 5-10 years (depending on handling). Buildings for composting, peak heating, spawn running, forklift and packhouse/store may also be required, depending on system.

5. Above figures based on tray/movable shelf system; other systems include mechanized shelf, bags and deep trough. Ready spawned compost can be purchased. Mushroom growing NOT recommended as a casual enterprise as expertise required in environment and disease control.

Researcher: Martin Bent.

ORGANIC FARMING

The UK area of organic farming has been estimated to be approximately 32,000 ha (80,000 acres), (approx. 850 farmers), slowly expanding. In mid-1994 there were 18,590 ha (46,000 acres) registered as organic land in England (MAFF).

The benefits to the nation claimed are as follows:
  (i) lower yields = less surpluses = less national and EC expenditure on storage and disposal;
 (ii) environmental benefits of non-use of inorganic fertilizers and agrochemical sprays;
(iii) reduction in use of fossil energy;
(iv) increasing concern over health means a rising demand and thus an expanding market; some 60% of the produce is at present being imported.

Against these points critics argue that:
  (i) it is unproven that inorganic fertilizers and (tested and approved) agro-chemicals harm the environment;
 (ii) it is unproven that organically produced foods are more nutritious, healthier or tastier;
(iii) there is insufficient land available to feed the present population adequately if all farming were organic;
(iv) if organic production became widespread in the UK compared with other countries our competitive position in terms of production costs per tonne would become increasingly eroded.

The economics to the farmer (though this is of secondary interest to many organic farmers) depend *primarily* upon:
  (i) relative yield compared with conventional farming;
 (ii) the price premium compared with conventional farming.

However, there are also the wider whole farm effects to be considered, *e.g.,* unless the farm already has a substantial percentage of its area down to leys this will probably have to be increased in order to maintain yields and this extra grass has to be utilised profitably—which is far from easy, and the extra capital requirements could be heavy.

Furthermore, there is a two year "conversion period" to undergo before full price premiums can be claimed. Also, quality (in the sense of appearance) can be badly affected by pests and diseases.

In order to illustrate the gross margin contrast with conventional farming just one crop will be taken: *Winter Wheat.* The estimates are for the 1995 harvest crop, with national average yields. The price for organic wheat in the table is that required to give the same gross margin as conventionally grown wheat, given all the other assumptions as regards relative yields and variable costs.

| | | | | Conventional | | Organic |
				Feed	Milling	(Milling)
Yield: tonnes/ha (cwt./acre)		...		7·2 (57)	6·5 (51·5)	4·25 (34)
				£	£	£
Price per tonne	...	...	...	90	104	124
Area Payment	...	...	...	250 (101)	250 (101)	250 (101)
Output per ha (acre)		...	...	900 (364)	925 (374)	775 (313)
Seed	...	...	...	45 (18)	50 (20)	55 (22)
Fertilizer/Manures		...	...	70 (28·5)	80 (32·5)	40 (16)
Sprays	...	...	...	105 (42·5)	115 (46·5)	—
TOTAL VARIABLE COSTS	...		...	220 (89)	245 (99)	95 (38)
GROSS MARGIN per ha (acre)			...	680 (275)	680 (275)	680 (275)

Notes on above comparison:

Thus, on the assumptions given, including that £40/ha of inorganic manures are applied, the break-even price for organic wheat in 1995/6 will be approximately £124/tonne, i.e. a premium over the estimated price for conventional feed wheat of £34 (38%) and (more appropriately) conventional milling wheat of £20 (19%). Although future cereal prices are full of uncertainty it is fairly sure that such premiums will be readily achieved, given the likely supply and demand position. Organic wheat prices for recognised breadmaking quality are generally expected to be around £170/tonne in 1994; organic feed wheat could be £30 to £40 less. Hence the gross margin of organic wheat should exceed that of conventional wheat, given the relative yields assumed above: approx. 60% of feed wheat and 65% of milling wheat conventionally grown. However, the rotational aspect referred to above has very much to be borne in mind, as has the cost of the conversion period, though the land to be converted can be included in the set-aside area.

A new *Organic Aid Scheme* for England to encourage new organic producers (but providing nothing for existing producers), with extra help for the conversion period, was introduced in 1994. Participants must register their proposed land for conversion with one of the organic sector bodies or with the United Kingdom Register of Organic Food Standards and provide a conversion plan. There is a minimum eligible size of 1 ha; there is no maximum eligible size but aid will not be paid beyond 300 ha. The rates of aid (£/ha) are:

Year:	1	2	3	4	5
Non-LFA	70	70	50	35	25
LFA	14	14	10	7	5

with an additional £30/ha for the first 5 ha.

As regards relative cultivation costs, in one ADAS monitored study these were reported to be 15 per cent higher on the organically grown wheat (approximately £12·50 more per ha (£5 per acre) at present costs). However no spraying is required. Survey data have indicated overall labour requirements to be 10-30% higher than on conventional farms, with machinery costs generally similar.

As already stated, *the big questions are the relative yields and the price difference*—how likely is it that the required price premiums would be sustained if production of organic wheat should increase substantially?

For considerable further details on organic farming, including gross margin data on many enterprises, see "1994 Organic Farm Management Handbook", by Nic Lampkin and Mark Measures, available from the Department of Agricultural Sciences, University of Wales, Aberystwyth, Dyfed, SY23 3DD, or from the Elm Farm Research Centre (address below). Prices for individual copies £10 including postage.

See also "Organic Farming as a Business in Great Britain" (1992) by M. C. Murphy, Agricultural Economics Unit, University of Cambridge, 19 Silver Street, Cambridge, CB3 9EL.Price £15.

Addresses:

British Organic Farmers, The Organic Growers Association and the Soil Association: 86 Colston Street, Bristol, Avon, BS1 5BB; (Tel. 0272 299666/299800/290661).

Organic Farmers and Growers Ltd.: Abacus House, Station Yard, Needham Market, Ipswich, IP6 8AT; (Tel. 0449 720838).

Organic Advisory Service: Elm Farm Research Centre, Hamstead Marshall, Newbury, Berks., RG15 0HR; (Tel. 0488 58298).

TURF

The recession slowed down what was an expanding market. The fastest growing sector has been the production and sale of 'special' turf, i.e., grass grown specifically for turf production using seed mixtures and highly skilled cultivation techniques appropriate to its final use for sport and amenity areas. The trade is mainly in the hands of specialist companies, rather than direct supply to retailers/consumers by farmers. A number of these companies have, however, been established and developed by farmers.

The main options for farmers are as follows:

1. Selling existing pasture turf to a turf company

This is the main, traditional option. The approach may be by the farmer to the company or vice-versa. Minimum 5-6 year ley/pasture generally needed for spring or autumn lifting, 8-10 year grass better for summer cutting.

Important features: good root structure; number and type of weeds; level, well-drained, stone-free land; good access; timing (farmer wants lifting completing in time to drill next crop).

Payment varies between £675-1350/hectare (£275-550/acre), but mainly £800-1100/ha (£325-450/acre). Usually initial payment plus further payments as turf is lifted. There may be a penalty clause if lifting delays prevent subsequent timely drilling. Lifting can take from two months to even a year. It can be done at any time of year except when there is snow on the ground. The turf company usually sprays against broadleaved weeds, fertilizes and mows before lifting; the farmer may do these tasks, for payment. He may graze the land, for a rent, if lifting is delayed.

Apparently the effect on the land is not detrimental; some say there are benefits (removal of accumulated pests, etc. in the top inch of grass, roots and topsoil).

2. Farmer cutting, lifting and selling pasture turf himself

Not usual. The turf must be treated, as in option 1. A small turf cutting machine can be hired for about £45 a day. This slices off the turf which must then be cut into lengths and picked up by hand. Two or three workers are required. It is slow going even in good conditions. The wastage figure is commonly 10 to 20% of the area, perhaps more.

Turf has a short life once cut and stacked—3 days in summer, 7 days in winter, preferably less. Thus transport and outlets must be well organized: probably to a very local market; may soon be over-supplied.

3. Renting land to a turf company for production of special turf

Some turf companies rent land for special turf production in addition to using their own land. Again, well-drained, stone-free land with good access required. Typically the land is rented for two or three years for about £500/ha (£200/acre) a year, and either one or two turf crops are grown.

No cost to farmer, except for wear and tear on roads, etc.

4. Specialist turf production

On their own land turf producers can apparently grow turf continuously, taking a crop every two years. Where they rent land (as in option 3), they take one or two crops and then move on. A high level of agronomic expertise and considerable investment in machinery are needed, and labour requirements are heavy. Since the business is highly competitive marketing skill is also essential. It appears to be rare (possibly unknown) for a farmer to grow 'special' turf either for a company or "on spec".

Costs and Returns

Approximate Variable Costs (plus Rent)

(Special, hardwearing mix, not very high quality)

	£/ha (acre)
Seed	275-450 (110-180)
Fertilizer	150-190 (60-75)
Herbicide	30 (12)
Fungicide	0-100 (0-40)
Rent (for two years) ...	800 (325)

Labour

Special seed preparation, regular mowing (possibly every five days in May/June), picking up clippings, harvesting (3 men (including one loading lorry), approx. 0·2 ha (0·5 acre) a day, but extremely variable).

Total costs of order of £4,250-5,750/ha (£1,725-2325/acre).

The cost of *specialist machinery* for turf production can be up to £120,000.

Value of Turf (on the field)

	per sq. metre	per sq. yd.	per ha*	per acre*
Pasture turf	44p	37p	£3,950	£1,610
Hardwearing, domestic general contract	£1·20	£1	£10,800	£4,350
Football, hockey, prestige landscape	£1·55	£1·25	£14,000	£5,450
Golf and bowling greens** ...	£1·65	£1·30	£14,850	£5,650

* assuming 90% recovery of turf.

** can be considerably more (£2·25 plus/sq. yd.).

Note, delivered turf will have delivery charges and VAT added, making a total cost of approx. 80p per sq. yd. (£26·65 per 100 turves).

Further Notes

Since turf production is classified as non-agricultural, *planning permission* is usually (but not invariably) required from the local authority.

Tenants mat find themselves in breach of their tenancy agreement; thus obtaining the landlord's permission is very important.

Sources of Technical Advice:

The National Turfgrass Council, 3 Ferrands Park Way, Harden, Bingley, West Yorkshire, BD16 1HZ. (Tel. 0535 273188).

The Sports Turf Research Institute, Bingley, West Yorkshire, BD16 1AU. (Tel. 0274 565131).

Researcher: Angela Edwards. (Figures updated by the author).

GOLF

The popularity of golf is increasing rapidly; it is said to be the fastest growing sport in the world. 274 new courses were built in Britain in the years 1986-93, with many more planning applications than acceptances; however, there are now signs of over supply, at least in some areas of the country; some have gone into receivership.

Between 40 and 60 ha (100 and 150 acres) are needed for an 18-hole course, which takes between 1 and 2 years to construct. A nine-hole par 3 course needs only 4 to 6 ha (10-15 acres), a driving range 4 ha (10 acres) and a pitch and putt course 1½ ha (4 acres).

Four important requirements are: location close to a centre of substantial population, a good distance from other similar courses, good road access, and an attractive, free-draining site. Obtaining planning permission can be difficult.

Development options; the farmer has five:

(i) To sell land with planning permission. Could have twice the agricultural value, possibly much more, if near London and with hotel consent.

(ii) To let land to a developer/operator. Assuming the latter pays for constructing the course, a long lease will be required. This can either be at a premium with a nominal rent or an annual rental, of two to five times the agricultural value, with reviews.

(iii) To form a joint company with a developer/operator. This obviously means the farmer shares the success, or loss. The land would be all or part of the farmer's equity. A well-constructed agreement is essential.

(iv) To develop the course and let the completed development to an operator. This is not recommended: too low a return on the land value and investment.

(v) To develop and operate the course himself. Also not recommended: the farmer needs good knowledge of golf and exceptional management ability.

Construction methods and costs; there are three alternatives:

(i) Contract. Expensive. Approximate costs (excl. the land):
18-hole course: £600,000-£900,000, according to drainage and earthmoving; includes greenkeeper's building and equipment.
9-hole par 3 course: £120,000.
Covered driving range: £120,000.
Clubhouse (approx. 600m²) and car parking: £600,000. (Thus making the total cost (18-holes) £1¼ to 1½ million).

(ii) Direct labour. A golf architect is required. Costs may be reduced by about a third.

(iii) Own (farm) labour. Possible, but very risky, in terms of ultimate quality and cost.

Returns. A well-run 18-hole golf course may given an annual profit of £100,000 plus, but it is more typically £50,000-£75,000 and often less, giving a poor return on capital. It is, however, a long-term investment with capital growth potential. Houses close by, or a hotel, beneficial. A high risk element.

FORESTRY

(Estimated for 1995)

A. Establishment Costs (before grant)

1. Unit cost of operations

Year/s	Operation	Estimated Cost (£)	
1.	Trees for planting		
	(i) Bare rooted:		
	Conifers	55-110 per 1,000	
	Broadleaves ...	150-250 per 1,000	
	(ii) Rooted in small peat blocks:		
	Conifers	125-150 per 1,000	
	Broadleaves ...	200-250 per 1,000	
1.	Tree Protection		
	(i) Fencing (materials and erection)		
	Rabbit	1·50-2·50 per metre	
	Stock	2·00-2·75 per metre	
	Deer	3·00-4·50 per metre	
	Split post and rail	5·50-6·50 per metre	
	(ii) Tree guards/shelters		
	Plastic spiral (600-750 mm)	18-22 per 100	
	Plastic tubes (1200 mm) ...	70-80 per 100	
1.	Planting at approx. 2 m spacing		
	Conifers	130-160 per ha	
	Broadleaves*	450-650 per ha	
2-3.	Replacing dead trees**		
	Operation	30-40 per ha	
	Plant supply ...	35-45 per ha	

	Costs specific to location	Upland	Lowland
1.	Ground Preparation (ploughing) ...	90-110/ha	40-60/ha
1.	Drainage ...	40-60/ha	—
1.	Fertilizing ...	90-150/ha	—
1.4	Weeding per operation***		
	Hand weeding	—	180-200/ha weeded
	Herbicide	70-80/ha weeded	70-90/ha weeded

* Includes cost of erecting guards/shelters.

** Replacing dead trees (beating up) may be necessary once in the second year and again in the third year. Costs depend on number of trees.

*** Up to 2 weeding operations may be necessary in each of the first 4 years in extreme situations. Costs are inclusive of materials.

Access roads may need to be constructed and can typically cost between £6,000 and £20,000 per kilometre (£9,600 to £32,200 per mile) depending on availability of roadstone.

2. Total Establishment Costs up to Year 3.

(i) Conifer—Lowland Sites

On a fairly typical lowland site, requiring little or no clearing or draining, the approximate cost before grant of establishing a conifer plantation would be in the range £1,200-£1,800 per hectare. Up to 8 separate weeding operations may be required.

(ii) Conifer—Upland Sites

Establishing a similar conifer plantation on an upland site could cost £1,100 to £1,500 per hectare. Normally some form of site preparation and drainage is required but only one weeding operation may be necessary. Overall costs tend to be £100-£200 per ha less than on lowland sites.

(iii) Hardwoods

Costs of establishing hardwood plantations could be in the range £1,600-£2,400 per ha. Site conditions normally mean that hardwoods being grown for timber production are restricted to lowland sites.

(iv) Size Factor

Savings in fencing and other economies of scale may reduce average costs per ha by 10 to 20% where large plantations are being established; conversely costs for small woods may easily be 25% higher per ha established.

(v) Method of Establishment

A range of organisations and individuals undertake forestry contracting work and competitive tendering can help to control costs.

B. Maintenance Costs

Once trees have been established they will normally require some maintenance and management work each year. For trees being grown primarily for timber production on a large scale, operations required may include ride maintenance, fence maintenance, pest control, fire protection, management fee and insurance charges. Costs will normally fall within the range £15-£50 per ha per annum (£6-£20 per acre) depending upon the size of the plantation and the complexity of management. One or more fertilizing operations may be needed in the first 20 years in the life of a tree depending on the quality of the site. Estimated cost £90-£150 per ha, depending on elements applied. For trees being grown for sporting and amenity purposes, annual maintenance costs are likely to be less and may range up to about £10 per ha (£4 per acre).

A brashing operation which involves removing branches up to two metres may be required for access reasons as the crop matures. On average 40-50% of the crop may require brashing, at a cost of £150-£300 per ha.

C. Production

Production is usually measured in terms of cubic metres (m^3) of marketable timber per hectare and will vary according to the quality of the site, species planted and thinning policy. Sites in lowland Britain planted to conifers typically produce an average of 12 to 18 m^3 of timber per ha per year over the rotation as a whole and would accordingly be assessed as falling in yield classes 12 to 18. Under traditional management systems thinning begins 18 to 25 years after planting and is repeated at intervals of approximately 3 to 5 years until the wood is clearfelled at between 50 and 60 years. Approximately 40-45% of total production will be from thinnings. Broadleaves typically produce an average of between 4 and 8 m^3 of timber per hectare per year and fall in yield classes 4 to 8.

Prior to a thinning/clearfelling sale the trees normally have to be marked and measured at an estimated cost of £30-£50 per ha depending on species, crop density and age.

D. Prices

Prices for standing timber are extremely variable, depending on tree size and quality, ease of extraction from site, geographical location (nearness to end user) and quantity being sold.

Conifers

Average prices paid for standing coniferous timber sold from Forestry Enterprise areas in the year to 31st March, 1994, were:

Harvesting stage	Average tree size (m³)		Price (£ per m³)	
		England	Wales	Scotland
1st Thinning	Up to 0·074 ...	8·36	6·29	3·36
	0·075-0·124 ...	8·71	7·58	4·23
Subsequent	0·125-0·174 ...	11·38	10·34	8·54
Thinnings	0·175-0·224 ...	14·76	14·38	12·29
	0·225-0·274 ...	15·01	15·59	11·12
	0·275-0·424 ...	18·32	18·23	12·45
	0·425-0·499 ...	22·74	21·03	16·06
Clearfellings	0·500-0·599 ...	23·12	22·72	17·79
	0·600-0·699 ...	23·67	24·93	17·87
	0·700-0·799 ...	29·01	25·41	25·05
	0·800-0·899 ...	30·28	20·50	13·93
	0·900-0·999 ...	26·95	—	19·52
	1·000 and over ...	37·17	25·94	17·32

Hardwoods

The hardwood trade is very complex. Merchants normally assess and value all but the smaller trees on a stem by stem basis. Actual prices fetched can show considerable variation depending on size, form, quality and species.

Some indicative prices for hardwoods are given below, but it is important to note that actual prices fetched can vary quite widely. Wood quality is particularly important in determining prices.

Harvesting stage	Tree size Range (m³)	Price range £ per m³	Possible use
First thinnings	< 0·13	1-12	Firewood, board products and pulp wood. Poles for refineries and turnery.
Subsequent thinnings ...	0·13-0·3	·5-20	Smaller sizes and lower quality material may go for fencing or for use in the mining industry. Trees over 30 cm in diameter and of better quality may go for planking, furniture or joinery.
	0·3 -0·6	8-22	
	0·6 -1·0	10-40	
Clearfellings	1·0 -2·0	15-80	
	2+	25-150	High quality material may go for veneers and can fetch between £150 and £300/m³ depending on species and specifications.

Prices for Oak, Ash, Sycamore, Cherry and Elm tend to be significantly higher than for Beech, which seldom exceeds about £40/m³ standing even for first quality planking.

E. Market Value of Established Plantations and Woods

The value of woods depends on many factors, such as location, access, species, age and soil type. The table below gives an indication of the range of current (1994) market values of commercial woodlands of different ages, based on recent market sales.

Market Value of Commercial Sitka Spruce Woodlands

Age of Commercial Woods and Plantations	Price Range for crop and land £/ha	£/acre
0-5 years	400-1000	(150- 400)
6-10 years	750-1375	(300- 550)
11-15 years	1000-1875	(400- 750)
16-20 years	1500-2750	(600-1100)
21-25 years	1500-3000	(600-1200)

From years 20 to 25 onwards prices of commercial woods will also be increasingly influenced by the quantity of merchantable timber they contain. Depending on the time of clearfelling, the timber may be worth between £3,750 to £10,000 per hectare (£1,500 to £4,000 per acre).

Woods with high amenity can often command a premium over prices fetched for commercial woodlands.

The value of woods containing mature hardwoods will depend on the quality and value of the timber they contain.

F. Grants

(a) Woodland Grant Scheme (WGS)

The WGS is administered by the Forestry Authority (part of the Forestry Commission). Revised terms were announced in July 1994 and the following proposed rates are subject to European Commission approval.

Establishment grants are determined by the type of wood (conifer or broadleaved) and whether new planting or restocking is being undertaken. Levels of payment in £ per hectare are as follows:

New planting: conifers £700 (for any size of wood)
broadleaves £1350 for woods less than 10 hectares
£1050 for woods 10 hectares or more

Payment is 70% after planting and 30% in year 5. A stocking density of 2250 trees per hectare is required unless the woods are native woodlands or amenity woodlands.

Restocking (including natural regeneration):
conifers £325
broadleaves £525

Payment is 100% after planting (or once establishment has been achieved through natural regeneration). A stocking density of 2250 trees per hectare is required for conifers and 1100 for broadleaves. In certain woodlands a discretionary payment towards the cost of work to encourage natural regeneration may be made.

New planting of short rotation coppice:
Set-aside land £400
Non set-aside land £600

A *'better land supplement'* of £600 per hectare for new woodland (excluding short rotation coppice) plantings on arable or improved grassland. A stocking density of 2,250 trees per hectare is required. A *'community woodland supplement'* of £950 per hectare is available to encourage the creation of new woodlands close to towns and cities which will be of value for informal public recreation. The new woodlands must be within 5 miles of the edge of a town or city and be covered by a strategic plan for the locality which has been agreed by the Forestry Authority. To be eligible for this supplement there must be free access to the woods for the public and appropriate car parking facilities must be close at hand.

Management grants, of £35 per hectare per year, are proposed for any age of woodland which has special environmental potential requiring additional management input.

Woodland Improvement Grants are proposed on a discretionary basis in the form of capital payments for work in existing woodlands which will result in significant environmental benefit.

Livestock Exclusion Annual Premia of £80 per hectare per year for up to 10 years are proposed for certain types of woodland in Less Favoured Areas where protection or regeneration is a high priority.

(b) *Farm Woodland Premium Scheme (FWPS)*

This scheme was introduced in April 1992 as a successor to the Farm Woodland Scheme. It is administered by MAFF and offers annual payments to compensate farmers for loss of income from farming where woodlands are established on agricultural land. To qualify for entry to the FWPS the proposed woods must have been approved by the Forestry Authority and attract establishment grants under the Woodland Grant Scheme (WGS).

The magnitude of annual payments depends on the type of land and its location:

	Annual Payment (£ per hectare)
Arable Land/Improved Grassland:	
Outside Less Favoured Areas	250
Disadvantaged Areas of the Less Favoured Areas	190
Severely Disadvantaged Areas of the Less Favoured Areas ...	130
Unimproved Land within Less Favoured Areas (whether Disadvantaged or Severely Disadvantaged Areas) ...	60

For the above purposes arable land is land which has been under arable cropping (including short-term leys when part of a rotation) for a period of at least three years. To qualify as improved grassland outside the LFAs (Less Favoured Areas) over half the sward must comprise, either singly or in mixture, ryegrass, cocksfoot, timothy or white clover. Within the LFAs, to qualify as improved grassland, over one third must comprise the above species *or* alternatively the land must have been "improved" by management practices such as liming and top-dressing which commenced at least three years prior to applying to join the FWPS and WGS.

Arable land and improved grassland will be eligible for the better land supplement under the WGS.

Unimproved land is land other than arable or improved grassland which has been in agricultural use for at least three years prior to the date of the application for the FWPS. Only unimproved land which is in LFAs can be entered in the FWPS.

Annual payments continue for 15 years for woodland containing more than 50 per cent by area of broadleaved trees and 10 years for woodland containing less than 50 per cent broadleaved trees. Woodlands planted for the purpose of agroforestry or coppicing are not eligible for annual payments under the FWPS.

There is a minimum area requirement of 1 hectare to enter the FWPS but no restriction on the minimum size of individual woods created, providing WGS criteria are met. Not more than 50 per cent of an agricultural unit can be entered into the FWPS and not more than 40 hectares of unimproved land per unit in the LFA's.

G. Taxation

Income from commercial woodlands is no longer subject to tax, and tax relief cannot be claimed for the cost of establishing new woodlands.

Woodland Grant Scheme grants are tax free but annual payments under the Farm Woodland Premium Scheme are regarded as compensation for agricultural income forgone and are liable to income tax.

The sale of timber does not attract Capital Gains Tax, although the disposal of the underlying land may give rise to an assessment.

Woodlands which are managed commercially or which are ancillary to a farming business may be eligible for either Business Property Relief or Agricultural Relief for Inheritance Tax purposes.

Acknowledgement. The above estimates are based in part on information supplied by John Clegg & Co.

SET-ASIDE

A. THE "CAP REFORM SCHEME"

(i) *The Provisions*

A new set-aside scheme was introduced as part of the CAP Reform programme starting with the 1993 harvest crop, i.e. as from the autumn 1992 drilling time. The scheme must be complied with in order to obtain the area payments intended to compensate for reduced market price support.

Payments to the nearest £/ha (£0·5/acre) for 1994/5 and 1995/6 (as at 1st July, 1994) are as follows, based on an ECU value of 93·25p (and excluding any penalties for overshooting area limits, except for a small one for Scotland non LFA):

England	Scotland non LFA	Scotland LFA	Wales LFA	Wales non LFA	N. Ireland
315 (127·5)	296 (120)	256 (103·5)	275 (111)	176 (71·5)	250 (101·5)

A simplified scheme with no set-aside commitment is available for those claiming payments on a standardised area that would produce 92 tonnes of grain at average grain yields for the area; this is 15·5 ha (38·3 acres) in England. However, only the area compensatory aid rate for cereals is paid, even on land used to grow oilseeds or protein crops. To claim the higher aid rates for these crops it is necessary to join the general scheme and set aside land. Those growing more than the (approx.) 15·5 ha may opt out of set-aside and claim the cereal aid rate on just the 15·5 ha, but over 20 ha (50 acres) or so the penalty of doing so in terms of the area payments forgone could be prohibitive except perhaps on high-yielding land.

A number of different set-aside options are available in 1995:

1. *Obligatory set-aside*

   Here there is a choice between the following:

   (i) 15% rotational set-aside: different land must be set aside each year over a six-year rotation; it must have been cultivated for harvest the previous year.

   A shorter interval than six years is possible if no other land is eligible, e.g. if the size of holding is altered.

   (ii) 18% flexible set-aside, with three different options:

   (a) non-rotational set-aside,

   (b) some rotational, some non-rotational,

   (c) rotational, in any way the farmer chooses.

   There is no commitment to stay in flexible set-aside for more than one year.

   The 15% or 18% are percentages of the total area of claimed land plus the set-aside area. The claimed land crops will consist primarily of cereals, oilseed rape, linseed, field beans, dried peas and maize. These crops are eligible for aid whether grown for grain, seed or fodder—except in the latter case for any crop(s) grown on land counting towards the forage area under the beef regime (stocking rate restriction).

2. *Voluntary set-aside*

   This is open to all those receiving area aid under the main scheme. However, there is a limit: the extra set-aside area, together with the obligatory set-aside area, must not exceed the total cropped area on which area aid is claimed, plus any *penalty set-aside* (which is imposed if a regional basic area limit is exceeded, and receives no compensation payment). There is no commitment to leave the extra land in set-aside for more than one year.

3. *Additional Voluntary set-aside*

Where land was set-aside under the *old 5-year scheme*, the limit described above for voluntary set-aside may be exceeded right up to 100%, but it has to remain in set-aside for a further five years. However, the set-aside payment is reduced on that area which exceeds the cropped area: this is at 70% of the full rate, i.e. approx. £221/ha (£89/acre) in England (in 1994).

4. *Guaranteed set-aside*

Where the farmer undertakes that the same plots will be set aside for five years the EC will guarantee that the current set-aside payment (at the green ECU rates) on that land will not be reduced for five years, though it may be increased. This only applies up to the 18% limit for non-rotational set-aside or on any ex-5 year scheme set-aside land. May opt out of the agreement to enter a scheme under forestry or agri-environment action programme, or if compulsorily purchased; penalty imposed if withdraw for other reasons.

Transfers of set-aside may shortly be allowed: to within 20 km (normally) but with probably an additional 3% set-aside requirement.

Land must normally have been farmed for two years by the claimant before it can be set aside, with some exemptions.

Land ineligible for area payments or set-aside are permanent grass, permanent crops (e.g. top fruit), woodland or a non-agricultural use.

Whether it is better to choose the 18% non-rotational or part non-rotational option rather than the 15% fully rotational option depends on how variable in quality the land is and whether there are other benefits to the farmer in having non-rotational set-aside, apart from those which will be true for all farmers: easier management and lower costs; however, rotational yield benefits will obviously be forgone.

A range of crops for uses other than human or animal feed may be grown on set-aside land (e.g. for fuel), under contract. Otherwise no cash crop must be planted, nor must any livestock or non-agricultural animals be grazed upon it. Cover crops must not contain more than 5% clover. The minimum size of each set-aside block must be 0·3 ha, with a minimum width of 20 metres. The land must be kept in good agricultural condition.

The rotational set-aside period is from 15th January to 31st August, but from 15th July producers may sow crops for harvest the next year. From 1st September to 14th January producers may not sell any green cover remaining on the land, whether for grazing, hay or silage, but they may harvest these crops for their own use or graze their own animals on it during this period.

Rules. A *cover crop* must be established on set-aside land by 15th December, unless a harvest crop is still in the ground after 1st October; natural regeneration is permitted, legumes are not. *Cutting* is allowed at any time, but it is not advised between April and mid-July; any cover remaining on 15th July must be cut short by 15th August (exemptions granted if birds are still nesting), or destroyed with herbicide by 31st August. Non-residual *herbicides* are allowed to be used provided that green cover is not destroyed before 15th April (unless it is to be replaced); spot applications or selective herbicides are allowed before that date as long as most cover is left intact; there are no restrictions on herbicide use after 15th April. *Cultivations* are allowed after 1st May only to control weeds, although these are not advised before the end of June (all operations are discouraged during the April and May nesting season); cultivations are allowed from 15th June for winter crops to follow set-aside. *Fertilizer and manure* applications are not allowed unless the manure or slurry is generated on the same farm and applied to establish cover; liming is allowed.

(ii) *Gains and Losses*

On the land that has to be set aside the farmer will lose the crop gross margins forgone less the compensation payment and fuel and repair costs saved (approx. £75/ha, £30/acre); contractors' charges, where used e.g. for harvesting, will also be saved. There will also be some saving in interest on working capital. Adding to the (likely) net loss will be the cost of cover crops, if sown, cutting, etc.

If the rotational option is chosen there should be some yield benefit. There should also be some timeliness benefit if the same labour and machinery is available as before. Both are difficult to estimate financially.

On some larger farms at least it has been possible to cut fixed costs, primarily regular labour and machinery depreciation/leasing—possibly by enough to compensate. But for many smaller and medium-sized farms this is impossible. However, some savings in casual labour and overtime, and, given time, machinery depreciation, should be possible on many farms.

Any net loss may also be reduced by crop substitutions: primarily higher for lower gross margin crops. However, unless the farmer has been slack in his choice of crops in the past this possibility is limited and could lead to rotational losses, e.g. if more second and third wheats are grown, but it should at least be possible to put a higher percentage of the land into first wheats.

Inevitably the possibilities and balance of gains and losses will be different on every farm.

(iii) The Countryside Premium Scheme

Announced in June 1989, administered by the Countryside Commission, to benefit landscape and wildlife on set-aside land. The scheme finished in 1993 but payments continue until 1995/6.

Payments additional to the basic rate were made available to farmers in seven counties (Norfolk, Suffolk, Essex, Cambridgeshire, Hertfordshire, Bedfordshire and Northants). Payments vary according to five available options:

(i) Wildlife fallow (£45/ha (£18/acre)). To encourage ground nesting birds and insects.

(ii) Wooded margins (£85/ha (£34/acre)). For wide, rough hedgerows, adjacent strips and belts of broad-leaved trees.

(iii) Winter grazing for Brent geese (£90/ha (£36/acre)). Permanent pasture only.

(iv) Recreational meadow land (£120/ha (£49/acre)). Left rough to encourage mice, rodents and hence barn owls, etc. Must be open to the public, with signs, stiles, etc.

(iv) Habitat restoration. Reconverting land to its original state, e.g., heath, wetland, chalkland sheep grazing. Tenders for estimated cost required.

In 1990, £30/ha supplements were announced for the wooded margins and meadowlands options for additional measures to encourage wildlife.

iv) The Countryside Access Scheme

This proposed new voluntary scheme, open to farmers with land in non-rotational set-aside, is aimed at providing new opportunities for public access to suitable farmland for walking and other forms of quiet recreation. Only particularly suited land will be targeted, e.g. if it provides access to vantage points, attractive landscape or links existing access ways. Farmers entering land into the scheme would continue to manage the land in accordance with set-aside rules and, in addition, observe a range of other conditions regarding maintenance of easy access, etc.

The annual supplementary payments will be based on 10m wide access strips along field margins and/or on whole or part fields. Levels of £90/ha (i.e. £90/km) for access strips and £45/ha for whole or part fields are proposed.

A NOTE ON DIVERSIFICATION

In recent years a whole host of "new" enterprises have attracted farmers' attention, largely in attempts to maintain their total incomes, when those from farming, especially in real terms, were falling substantially. This development has been strongly encouraged by the government.

New enterprises must not be undertaken lightly: most require a substantial amount of capital; many need skills (both in production and marketing) which take time, or a particular type of personality, to acquire; the market may be limited; hence there is often a considerable level of risk attached. Nevertheless, there are many ventures to be seen where entrepreneurial skills have achieved notable success.

Some of these "diversification enterprises" have been included above and there are more in the next section. There are many others. Some are as follows:

Christmas Trees	Barn Conversions
Herbs	Horses*:
Crayfish	Livery
Llamas	Riding School
Ostriches	Trekking
Quails	Tourism:
Rabbits	Bed and Breakfast
Snails	Caravans
Wild Boar	Holiday Cottages
Adventure Games	"Added Value" enterprises:
Clay Pigeon Shooting	Yoghurt, ice cream, etc.

Update on these, and other, enterprises are published periodically in the monthly "Farm Development Review" (MCB University Press Limited, Bradford).

* Horses. See the Horse Business Management Reference Handbook, 4th ed., 1992. Peter Cross, Warwickshire College.

A 1994 series of "Success Within" guides are available free from MAFF Publications (tel. 0645 556000) on: Farm Diversification, Farm-based Tourist Accommodation, Sporting Enterprises on Farms, Marketing Diversified Enterprises.

Area Payments for 1995/96 in ECU/ha

	England	Scotland (non LFA)	Scotland (LFA)	Wales (non LFA)	Wales (LFA)	Northern Ireland
Cereals	266·85	254·25	216·48	232·65	149·40	211·95
Oilseeds	468·53	530·89	432·02	477·65	477·65	441·19
Linseed	516·10	491·74	418·47	449·79	288·84	409·77
Proteins	385·45	367·25	312·65	336·05	215·80	306·15
Set-aside*	338·01	322·05	274·17	294·69	189·24	268·47

*Voluntary set-aside over 50% is 70·175% of the above set-aside figures.

Note. The above figures are subject to cuts if regional base areas are exceeded. The oilseeds payments are also subject to cuts if the total EU base area is exceeded and if prices are above a prescribed level.

3. GRAZING LIVESTOCK
DAIRY COWS

A. Friesians and Friesian Holsteins (per Cow)

	Low	Average	High	Very High
Performance level (yield (1))	Low	Average	High	Very High
Milk Yield per Cow (litres) (2)	5000	5500	6000	6500

	£	£	£	£
Milk Value per Cow (3)	1175	1292	1410	1527
PLUS Value of Calves (4)	120	120	120	120
PLUS Value of Cull Cows (5)	118	118	118	118
LESS Cost or Market Value of Replacements (6, 7)	248	248	248	248
OUTPUT	1165	1282	1400	1517
Concentrate Costs (8)	172	206	241	275
Miscellaneous Variable Costs (10)	90	95	100	105
GROSS MARGIN before deducting Forage Variable Costs (inc. Bought Fodder)* ...	903	981	1059	1137
(Margin of Milk Value over Concentrates (9) ...	(1003	1086	1169	1252)

*No deduction has been made for the annual value of leased or purchased milk quota, which will vary considerably between farms.

Gross Margins per Cow and per Hectare (Acre) at 4 different stocking rates (11) are:

	Low	Average	High	Very High
Performance level	Low	Average	High	Very High
1. At 1·65 cows per forage hectare (low):				
(0·61 forage hectares (1·5 acres) per cow)				
Forage Variable Costs per Cow (11)... ...	69	69	69	69
GROSS MARGIN per Cow	834	912	990	1068
GROSS MARGIN per Forage Hectare ...	1375	1505	1635	1760
GROSS MARGIN per Forage Acre ...	556	609	662	712
2. At 1·9 cows per forage hectare (average):				
(0·525 forage hectares (1·3 acres) per cow)				
Forage Variable Costs per Cow (11) ...	81	81	81	81
GROSS MARGIN per Cow	822	900	978	1056
GROSS MARGIN per Forage Hectare ...	1560	1710	1860	2005
GROSS MARGIN per Forage Acre ...	631	692	753	811
3. At 2·2 cows per forage hectare (high):				
(0·455 forage hectares (1·125 acres) per cow)				
Forage Variable Costs per Cow (11) ...	90	90	90	90
GROSS MARGIN per Cow	813	891	969	1047
GROSS MARGIN per Forage Hectare ...	1790	1960	2130	2305
GROSS MARGIN per Forage Acre ...	724	793	862	933
4. At 2·5 cows per forage hectare (very high):				
(0·4 forage hectares (1 acre) per cow)				
Forage Variable Costs per Cow (11) ...	100	100	100	100
GROSS MARGIN per Cow	803	881	959	1037
GROSS MARGIN per Forage Hectare ...	2005	2200	2400	2590
GROSS MARGIN per Forage Acre ...	811	890	971	1048

1. Performance level refers primarily to milk yield, although increases in this are usually (though not *necessarily*) associated with higher gross margins. Some increase in concentrate feeding (kg/litre) has been assumed as yield rises: see further footnote 8, page 49.

2. *Yield.* The yield referred to is litres produced during a year divided by the average number of cows and calved heifers in the herd. The national average yield for *all* breeds and *all* herds is likely to be approximately 5,250 litres. The average given (5,500 litres) is an estimated figure for sizeable commercial herds of black and white cows.

3. *Milk Price.* This is assumed (as an average for the 1995 calendar year) to be 23·5p per litre, after deducting transport costs. It incorporates all adjustments: for milk composition, hygiene and seasonality.

The average price received by individual producers depends on seasonality of production and compositional quality. Receipts per cow are changed as follows by each 0·25p per litre difference in price at each performance level:

Low	Average	High	Very High
±12·5	±13·75	±15	±16·25

Seasonal Price Adjustments; England and Wales MMB*/Milk Marque**, 1994/5:

	April	May	June	July	Aug.	Sept.	Oct.	Nov.-Mar.
per cent*	−10	−12·5	−5	+15	+15	+10	+5	—
p per litre**	−2·0	−2·5	−1·0	+3·0	+3·0	+2·0	+1·0	−0·7

Compositional Quality Payments

Constituent values (England and Wales MMB, August, 1994):

Butterfat: 2·292 p per litre per 1 per cent.

Protein: 3·580 p per litre per 1 per cent.

Breeds and average milk composition by breed are as follows (England and Wales, MMB recorded herds, 2-year averages, 1990-92):

	% Cows 1988/9	Butterfat %	Protein %
Friesian	74·5	3·98	3·26
Holstein	3·4	3·95	3·19
Friesian/Holstein Cross	16·2	3·97*	3·23*
Ayrshire	1·9	4·01	3·33
Jersey	1·7	5·48	3·84
Guernsey	1·4	4·80	3·58
All Breeds		4·03	3·27

* Estimated.

Within Breed Quality Variation. For Friesians only, the upper and lower deciles in the 1986/87 Milkminder (MMB) sample were as follows:

Upper: Butterfat 4·11%; Protein 3·32%.

Lower: Butterfat 3·75%; Protein 3·17%.

The average difference in milk value is 1·35p per litre (approx. 6%).

Hygeinic Quality Payment Scheme (England and Wales MMB, from 1st April, 1993):

Bacterial count (TBC/ml) (2 month geometric mean)	Band	Milk price deduction (p/litre)
20,000 and less	A	Nil
20,001-100,000	B	0·25
Over 100,000	C (i)*	2
Over 100,000	C (ii)*	6
Over 100,000	C (iii)*	10

(i) If there has been no deduction in previous 6 months.

(ii) If there has been a deduction of 2p in previous 6 months.

(iii) If there has been a deduction of 6p or 10p in previous 6 months.

Mastitis Cell Count Payment Scheme (England and Wales MMB, from 1st April 1993):

Cell count (ml)	Band	Milk price deduction (p/litre)
400,000 and under	1	Nil
400,001-500,000	2	0·5
500,000-1,000,000	3	1·0
Over 1,000,000	4	2·0

All based on a three-month rolling average

Antibiotics. The price of all milk in a consignment that fails a valid antibiotics test is 1p/litre.

4. *Value of Calves.* Average annual value per cow of purebred (mainly) and beef cross heifer and bull calves of all qualities, at 10-20 days old, allowing for mortality and average calving index of 385 days.

5. *Value of Cull Cows.* £525, allowing for casualties (£145); 22·5% per annum replacement rate.

6. *Cost of Replacements.* £1100 per down-calving heifer (purchase price or market value (mainly home-reared)); 22·5% per annum replacement rate.

7. *Herd Depreciation:* thus averages (approx.) £130 per cow per year, *i.e.*, 22·5 per cent of £575 (*i.e.*, £1100-£525).

   Net Replacement Cost = £10 per cow per year, *i.e.*, herd depreciation (£130) less value of calves (£120).

   Bull. AI is assumed in the tables; bull depreciation would be approx. £325 a year (£2,500 purchase price less £875 cull value, 5-year herd life); tight calving pattern: 60 cows per bull, well spread calving pattern: 100; 10 to 20 tonnes silage, 0·75 tonnes concentrates a year.

8. *Concentrate Costs.*

Amounts: Performance level :	Low	Average	High	Very High
kg/litre :	·25	·27	·29	·31
tonnes/cow :	1·25	1·5	1·75	2·0

Price: taken (for 1995) as £137·50 per tonne, which is an average of home-mixed rations at £127·50 and purchased compounds at £147·50 (delivered) of varying nutritive value, averaged throughout the year.

A difference of £10 per tonne has the following approximate effect on margin over concentrates and gross margin per cow, on the assumptions made regarding the quantity fed at each performance level:

Low	Average	High	Very High
±£12	±£14	±£17	±£20

Seasonality. Typically, specialist spring calving herds (60% or more calvings between January and May), compared with autumn calving herds (60% or more calvings between August and December), use 0·9 kg per litre/0·6 tonnes (£82·50) per cow per year less concentrates; their average yield is around 400 litres lower. See further 12 below.

Typical Monthly Variation in Concentrate Feeding (kg per litre)

	Winter				Summer	
	Average	Premium			Average	Premium
October ...	0·32	0·25	April ...		0·25	0·17
November ...	0·34	0·26	May ...	...	0·14	0·09
December ...	0·34	0·26	June ...	...	0·15	0·10
January ...	0·34	0·26	July ...	...	0·19	0·13
February ...	0·33	0·26	August ...		0·24	0·17
March ...	0·32	0·25	September ...		0·28	0·20

Average winter: 0·33
Premium winter: 0·26

Average whole year: 0·27
Premium whole year: 0·20

Average summer: 0·21
Premium summer: 0·14

The actual distribution on any individual farm will obviously vary according to such factors as seasonality of calving, level of milk yield, grazing productivity during the summer, and the quantity and quality of bulk feeds in the winter. The March figure in particular will be affected by type of soil and seasonal rainfall.
Yield with no concentrates and good quality silage: approx. 3900 litres (autumn calvers).

9. *Margin over Concentrates and Concentrates per litre*
   The emphasis in the initial tables should be laid on the differences between the margin of milk value over concentrates per cow; the same large variation can occur with widely differing combinations of milk yield and quantity of concentrates fed.
   In the following table, at each yield level figures are given for (a) *margin of milk value over concentrates* per cow (£) and (b) *concentrates per litre* (kg) at five levels of concentrate feeding.

Yield level Milk Yield per cow (litres)	Low 5,000		Average 5,500		High 6,000		Very High 6,500	
	(a)	(b)	(a)	(b)	(a)	(b)	(a)	(b)
	£	kg	£	kg	£	kg	£	kg
0·75 tonne (£103) concs. per cow	1072	·15	1189	·14	—	—	—	—
1·00 tonne (£137) concs. per cow	1038	·20	1155	·18	1273	·17	—	—
1·50 tonne (£206) concs. per cow	969	·30	1086	·27	1204	·25	1321	·23
2·00 tonne (£275) concs. per cow	900	·40	1017	·36	1135	·33	1252	·31
2·50 tonne (£344) concs. per cow	—	—	—	—	1066	·42	1183	·38

On the same assumptions re the other items of output and variable costs as in the tables on page 47 a very high *margin over concentrates of £1,250 per cow* would give the following results (£):

Stocking rate	Average	High	Very High
Gross Margin per Cow	1054	1045	1035
Gross Margin per Forage Hectare	2000	2300	2585
Gross Margin per Forage Acre	810	930	1045

This could also be achieved with a yield of 7,000 litres obtained with 2·6 tonnes of concentrate per cow (·37 kg/litre).

10. *Miscellaneous Variable Costs* (average)

		£
Bedding*	... ...	10
Vet. and Med.	... ...	35
A.I. and Recording Fees	... ...	25
Consumable dairy stores, etc.	...	25
Total	... ...	95

* *Straw* can vary from 0·4 to 1·5 tonne per cow and from £10 to £30 per tonne.

11. *Stocking Rate and Forage Costs.* **The stocking rates given assume that nearly all requirements of bulk foods—for both winter and summer—are obtained from the forage area,** i.e. little is bought in. On average about 55 per cent of the forage area (or production) is grazed and 45 per cent conserved. It will be observed that as the stocking density increases, gross margin *per cow* falls, but gross margin *per hectare* rises.
The levels of nitrogen are assumed to be as follows: 1·65 cows per forage hectare, 160 kg (128 units/acre); 1·9, 220 (176); 2·2, 275 (220); 2·5, 360 (288). An increase in potash application is also assumed. Seed costs clearly depend on the percentage of permanent pasture, if any, the length of leys, etc. **The following forage costs per hectare (fertilizer, seed and sprays) have been assumed:** 1·65 cows per forage hectare, £105 (£42/acre); 1·9, £135 (55); 2·2, £165 (67); 2·5, £200 (81).
A small amount of purchased bulk fodder/rented keep is assumed, increasing with the stocking rate as follows (per cow): low £5, average £10, high £15, very high £20.

An increase in stocking density can be obtained not only by intensifying grassland production, as above, but also by buying in winter bulk fodder (assuming the same level of concentrate feeding in both cases). This will cause the gross margin *per cow* to fall still further, but will usually result in a higher gross margin *per hectare* than where all forage is conserved on the farm—at any given level of grassland management.

In the table below four examples are given: two policies at two different stocking rates. (A) and (B) assume the land is used for grazing only, i.e. all winter bulk fodder is purchased. (C) and (D) assume the land provides grazing and half the winter bulk fodder, the other half being bought in. (A) and (C) assume a stocking rate equivalent to 1·9 cows per hectare where the land provides both grazing and all the winter bulk fodder, which is an average level of stocking. (B) and (D) assume the equivalent of 2·5 cows per hectare where all bulk food is provided both summer and winter, which is a very high level of stocking. It is assumed that the full winter fodder requirement is 2 tonnes of hay (or other equivalent foods), costing £130 per cow if it is all purchased. (Prices vary widely according to the season and part of the country.) Forage variable costs per hectare are £135 and £200 at the average and high levels of stocking respectively.

| | Margin of Milk Value over Concentrates | | | |
	Low	Average	High	Very High
	Gross Margin per Forage Hectare (Acre)			
	£	£	£	£
(A) All winter fodder purchased; average stocking rate... ...	2575 (1040)	2810 (1135)	3080 (1245)	3350 (1355)
(B) All winter fodder purchased; very high stocking rate ...	3360 (1360)	3670 (1485)	4025 (1630)	4375 (1770)
(C) ½ winter fodder purchased; average stocking rate... ...	1925 (780)	2115 (855)	2305 (935)	2500 (1010)
(D) ½ winter fodder purchased; very high stocking rate ...	2505 (1015)	2755 (1115)	3005 (1215)	3260 (1320)

It must obviously not be forgotten that "fixed" costs per hectare, e.g. labour and depreciation on buildings, will increase considerably as stocking density increases (unless a similar number of cows are kept on fewer hectares), at least when cow numbers outstrip the capacity of existing buildings and labour. Furthermore, husbandry problems such as poaching will multiply, unless zero-grazing is practised—with its further additions to fixed costs and management difficulties.

12. *Seasonality*. Price and concentrate feeding differences according to the seasonality of production have already been outlined in notes 3 and 8.

Typically, autumn calving herds tend to average 6 or 7% (300-400 litres) above spring calving herds but feed 80% (0·6-0·7 tonnes) more concentrates cow/year; spring calving herds should normally only be feeding about 0·15 kg/litre (for the whole year). The average milk price would be expected to be higher for autumn calving herds, but the difference is less than might be supposed and has been reduced in recent years with better prices being paid for summer milk.

13. *Quota*. The price of unused quota has tended to average 35p/litre and leasing 5p to 5·5p, with levels in Scotland significantly higher. However, values rose considerably in late 1993/1994; in mid 1994 they were mainly in the 40p-50p and 7p-8p ranges respectively for average butterfat levels.

14. *Labour:* see page 111.   15. *Building Costs:* see pages 149-150 and 152-3.

B. Channel Island Breeds

Performance level (yield)	Low	Average	High
Milk Yield per Cow (litres)	3600	4000	4400
	£	£	£
Milk Value per Cow	1008	1120	1232
Concentrate Costs per Cow	154	188	225
Margin of Milk Value over Concentrates per Cow	854	932	1007
Herd Depreciation less Value of Calves	40	40	40
Miscellaneous Variable Costs	90	95	100
GROSS MARGIN per Cow before deducting Forage Variable Costs	724	797	867
Forage Variable Costs/Bought Fodder	64	64	64
GROSS MARGIN per Cow	660	733	803
GROSS MARGIN per Forage Hectare (2·25 cows per hectare: 0·45 hectares/cow)	1485	1650	1805
GROSS MARGIN per Forage Acre (1·1 acres/cow)	601	668	730

Notes

1. *Yield.* See Note 2 for Friesians (page 47). Guernseys average some 250 litres more than Jerseys but the latter achieve a higher average price of approx. 2·5p per litre.

2. *Milk Price.* This has been assumed to be 28p per litre, i.e. 4·50p above Friesian milk based on the difference in compositional quality plus the C.I. premium.

3. *Concentrate Costs.*

Amounts: Performance level:	Low	Average	High
kg/litre	·30	·33	·36
tonnes/cow	1·08	1·32	1·58

Price: taken (for 1995) as £142·50 per tonne.

The following table shows for each production level (a) the margin of milk value over concentrates per cow (£) and (b) concentrates per litre (kg) at three levels of concentrate feeding.

Performance level Milk Yield per Cow (litres)	Low 3600		Average 4000		High 4400	
	(a)	(b)	(a)	(b)	(a)	(b)
	£	kg	£	kg	£	kg
0·75 tonnes (£107) concs. per cow	901	0·21	1013	0·19	1125	0·17
1·25 tonnes (£178) concs. per cow	830	0·35	942	0·31	1054	0·28
1·75 tonnes (£249) concs. per cow	759	0·49	871	0·44	983	0·40

4. *Net Annual Replacement Value.* (i.e. Value of Calves less Herd Depreciation) were calculated as follows:

	£ per cow in herd
Cost of replacements: 22·5 per cent of herd per year @ £625 ...	142
LESS Value of culls: 22·5 per cent of herd per year @ £300 (allowing for casualties)*	67
Herd Depreciation	75
Annual Value of Calves**	35
Net Annual Replacement Cost	40

  * Cull cow prices for Guernseys are about £75 higher than for Jerseys.

  ** Allowing for calving index of 390 days and calf mortality; mixture of pure bred calves and beef crosses. Guernsey calves, especially crosses, fetch more than Jersey calves, averaging perhaps £10 more per head—but a lot more for some Guernsey beef crosses.

5. *Miscellaneous Variable Costs.* See Note 10 for Friesians (page 50).

6. *Stocking Rate.* See, in general, Note 11 for Friesians (page 50). The effect of varying the stocking rate on gross margin per forage hectare is as follows:

Cows Forage Hectare	Forage Hectares (Acres) per Cow	GM/Cow before deducting Forage V.Cs.			Forage Var. Costs	
		Low £724	Average £797	High £867	p. Forage Hectare (Acre) £	p. Cow £
		Gross Margin per Forage Ha (Acre) (£)				
1·95	0·51 (1·27)	1305 (528)	1450 (587)	1585 (641)	98 (40)	54
2·25	**0·45 (1·1)**	**1485 (601)**	**1650 (668)**	**1805 (730)**	**124 (50)**	**64**
2·6	0·38 (0·94)	1700 (688)	1890 (765)	2070 (838)	151 (61)	71
2·95	0·34 (0·84)	1905 (771)	2120 (858)	2325 (941)	183 (74)	79

These figures assume that almost all forage requirements—in winter as well as summer—are provided by the farm forage area.

At the average stocking rate given above for combined Channel Island breeds (2·25 cows per forage ha) the average figure for Jerseys would be approximately 2·4 and that for Guernseys 2·1.

C. *Other Breeds* (including Ayrshires)

Performance level (yield)		Low	Average	High
Milk Yield per Cow (litres)		4450	4900	5350
		£	£	£
Milk Value per Cow		1068	1176	1284
Concentrate Costs per Cow		153	182	213
Margin of Milk Value over Concentrates per Cow		915	994	1071
Herd Depreciation less Value of Calves ...		42	42	42
Miscellaneous Variable Costs		90	95	100
GROSS MARGIN per Cow before deducting Forage Variable Costs		783	857	929
Forage Variable Costs/Bought Fodder ...		77	77	77
GROSS MARGIN per Cow		706	780	852
GROSS MARGIN per Forage Hectare (2·0 cows per hectare: 0·5 hectares/cow) ...		1410	1560	1705
GROSS MARGIN per Forage Acre (1·25 acres/cow)		571	631	690

Notes

1. *Yield.* See Note 2 for Friesians (page 48).

2. *Milk Price.* See in general, note 3 for Friesians (page 48). The price assumed in the above table is 24p per litre. The compositional quality of milk from Ayrshires is higher than for the black and white breeds.

3. *Concentrate Costs.* See notes 8 and 9 for Friesians (pages 49-50). In the above table, the levels of feeding per kg (and tonnes per cow) are as follows: low ·25 (1·11 tonne), average ·27 (1·32), high ·29 (1·55); price £137·50 per tonne.

   The following table shows, for each production level, (a) the margin of milk value over concentrates (£) and (b) concentrates per litre (kg) at three levels of concentrate feeding.

Performance level	Low		Average		High	
Milk Yield per Cow (litres)	4450		4900		5350	
	(a)	(b)	(a)	(b)	(a)	(b)
	£	kg	£	kg	£	kg
0·75 tonnes (£103) concs. per cow	965	0·17	1073	0·15	1181	0·14
1·25 tonnes (£172) concs. per cow	896	0·28	1004	0·26	1112	0·23
1·75 tonnes (£241) concs. per cow	827	0·39	935	0·36	1043	0·33

4. *Net Annual Replacement Value.* (i.e. Value of Calves less Herd Depreciation) were calculated as follows (for Ayrshires):

	£ per cow in herd
Cost of replacements: 22·5 per cent of herd per year @ £800 ...	180
LESS Value of culls: 22·5 per cent of herd per year @ £390 (allowing for casualties)	88
Herd Depreciation	92
Annual Value of Calves*	50
Net Annual Replacement Cost**	42

*Allowing for calving index of 385 days and calf mortality; mixture of pure bred calves and beef crosses.

**Higher cull and calf prices should be obtained for Shorthorns.

5. *Miscellaneous Variable Costs.* See Note 10 for Friesians (page 50).

6. *Stocking Rate.* See, in general, Note 11 for Friesians (page 50). The (average) stocking rate of 2·0 cows per forage hectare given above relates to Ayrshires (and compares with 1·9 for Friesians); Shorthorns would have as high a requirement as Friesians.

DAIRY FOLLOWERS *(per Heifer reared)*

A. Friesians

Performance Level	Low £	Average £	High £
Value of heifer (allowing for culls) (1) ...	1050	1050	1050
LESS Value of calf (allowing for mortality) ...	110	110	110
OUTPUT	940	940	940
Variable Costs:			
Concentrate Costs (2)	145	130	115
Miscellaneous Variable Costs (3) ...	55	55	55
TOTAL VARIABLE COSTS (excluding Forage)	200	185	170
GROSS MARGIN per Heifer, before deducting Forage Variable Costs ...	740	755	770
Forage Variable Costs (fert. and seed) ...	55	65	70
GROSS MARGIN per Heifer ...	685	690	700
Forage Hectares (Acres) per Heifer reared (4)	0·95 (2·3)	0·725 (1·8)	0·575 (1·4)
GROSS MARGIN per Forage Hectare (5) ...	720	950	1215
GROSS MARGIN per Forage Acre	290	385	490

B. Channel Island Breeds

Performance Level	Low £	Average £	High £
Value of heifer (allowing for culls) (1) ...	600	600	600
LESS Value of calf (allowing for mortality) ...	25	25	25
OUTPUT	575	575	575
Variable Costs:			
Concentrate Costs (2)	125	110	95
Miscellaneous Variable Costs (3) ...	50	50	50
TOTAL VARIABLE COSTS	175	160	145
GROSS MARGIN per Heifer, before deducting Forage Variable Costs ...	400	415	430
Forage Variable Costs (fert. and seed) ...	45	50	55
GROSS MARGIN per Heifer	355	365	375
Forage Hectares (Acres) per Heifer reared (4)	0·75 (1·85)	0·575 (1·4)	0·45 (1·1)
GROSS MARGIN per Forage Hectare (5) ...	475	635	835
GROSS MARGIN per Forage Acre ...	192	257	338

N.B. On average, Channel Island heifers calve about three months younger than Friesians.

C. Ayrshires

Performance Level...	Low £	Average £	High £
Value of heifer (allowing for culls) (1) ...	765	765	765
LESS Value of calf (allowing for mortality) ...	50	50	50
OUTPUT	715	715	715
Variable Costs:			
Concentrates (2)	140	120	105
Miscellaneous Variable Costs (3) ...	55	55	55
TOTAL VARIABLE COSTS	195	175	160
GROSS MARGIN per Heifer, before			
deducting Forage Variable Costs ...	520	540	555
Forage Variable Costs (fert. and seed) ...	55	60	65
GROSS MARGIN per Heifer	465	480	490
Forage Hectares (Acres) per Heifer			
reared (4)	0·9 (2·2)	0·7 (1·75)	0·55 (1·35)
GROSS MARGIN per Forage Hectare (5) ...	515	685	890
GROSS MARGIN per Forage Acre	208	278	360

Notes

1. The heifer values are based on the purchase price of down-calving heifers, allowing for culls. Most heifers are home-reared. If heifers are reared for sale, the price of whole batches are likely to be lower than the values given in the tables, by perhaps 10 or 15 per cent. On the other hand the purchaser will often take the batch a few months before the average expected calving date, thus reducing feed and area requirements for the rearer.

2. The lower levels of concentrate costs are the combined result of more economical feeding and a lower average calving age. (Other things being equal, however, including the overall level of management, a lower calving age requires higher levels of feeding.)

3. Miscellaneous variable costs exclude straw. Straw requirements average approx. 1 tonne per heifer reared, but are variable, depending on time of year and age when calved, as well as system of housing and extent of outwintering. Vet. and med. approx. £26 per heifer reared.

4. The lower levels of area per heifer reared are the combined result of a higher stocking density and a lower average calving age.

   With an average calving age of 2 years 4 months, a "replacement unit" (i.e. calf + yearling + heifer) equals about 1·25 livestock units. The three stocking rates given above are equivalent to approximately 0·67, 0·58 and 0·5 forage hectares (1·65, 1·45, 1·25 acres) respectively per Friesian cow. The low figure assumes an average calving age of 2 years 6 months (1·4 livestock units) and the high figure one of 2 years 2 months (1·15 livestock units).

5. Much higher gross margin figures per hectare can be combined by intensive grazing methods, particularly if combined with winter feeding systems which involve little dependence on home-produced hay or silage (cf. Note 11, page 47, last three paragraphs).

6. *Contract Rearing:* see page 73.

7. *Labour:* see page 112.

Self-Contained Dairy Herd: Cows and Followers

At average annual replacement rates (22·5 per cent of the milking herd), just over one-quarter of a replacement unit is required for each cow in the herd, i.e. roughly one calf, yearling and heifer for every four cows (including calved heifers)—with a few extra calves reared to allow for culling. At average stocking rates for both this means approximately 1 hectare devoted to followers for every 3 hectares for cows. Since surplus youngstock are often reared and frequently the stocking rate is less intensive the ratio is often 1:2·5 or even 1:2 in practice. 1:3·5 is about the minimum where all replacement heifers are reared, unless their winter feeding is based largely on straw and purchased supplements, or unless there is a combination of long average herd life and early calving, i.e. at 2 years old or just over.

Gross Margin per Forage Hectare (Acre) (£) for the Whole Herd (i.e., Cows and Followers Combined); (at four levels of performance, including four commensurate levels of stocking rate, for the dairy cows; and three levels of performance, including different stocking rates, for the followers) are as follows, *assuming a 3:1 land use ratio* (dairy cow area: followers area); (Friesians only):

		G.M. per Forage Hectare (Acre)			
		Dairy Cows			
		£	£	£	£
		Low	Average	High	Very High
		1375 (556)	1710 (692)	2130 (862)	2590 (1048)
G.M. per Forage	Low	720 (290)	1210 (490)	1460 (591)	1775 (718) 2125 (860)
Hectare (Acre),	Average	950 (385)	1270 (514)	**1520 (615)**	1835 (743) 2180 (882)
Followers	High	1215 (490)	1335 (540)	1585 (641)	1900 (769) 2245 (909)

As an example, the above table indicates that at the average level of performance and stocking rate for both cows and followers, the whole dairy gross margin per hectare (acre) figure falls to £1520 (615) compared with £1710 (692) for the dairy cows alone, a reduction of 11 per cent. If more than the assumed (minimum) number of dairy followers are kept and the ratio is 2:1 the whole forage area figure (on the assumption again of average performance) falls to £1455 (589), which is a reduction of 15 per cent compared with cows only. However, the requirements per hectare for labour, machinery and buildings are of course less for heifer rearing than for dairy cows. Furthermore, the large increase in the value of replacement dairy heifers and cows in recent years has reduced the discrepancy between the gross margins of dairy cows alone and the self-contained herd.

Note that *for a combined, self-contained enterprise budget for the dairy herd and followers* there are the following differences:

Fewer calves for sale (as the required number of heifer calves are retained).

No replacement heifers/cows are purchased. (Thus high prices for replacement heifers reduces the gross margin of the milking herd and raises that of the dairy followers, but they have no effect on the gross margin of the combined, fully self-contained dairy herd breeding all its own replacements (assuming no surplus stock are reared)).

Value of any culled or surplus heifers are included.

Variable costs of replacements are added to those for the cows (on the basis of approximately one in-calf heifer entering the herd each year for every four cows (which allows for mortality and culling)).

BEEF

Finished Cattle Prices

The average UK beef price was around 117p (per kg lw) in the 1993 autumn trough period (having been exceptionally high in mid-summer) and 125-130p in the spring and early summer of 1994.

The prices assumed in the subsequent tables relate either to the *1995 calendar year or 1995/96* as appropriate (*e.g.*, the latter is used for winter fattened beef). The prices assume a spring (March/April) peak of 125p and an autumn (October) trough of 118p.

Beef Special Premium (BSP). Available on male cattle at 10 and 22 months old, but claims can only be made for up to 90 head at each age. Value, at ECU = 92·1p: £69·07 in 1994, £82·89 (90 ECU) in 1995. *However if regional reference herd limits are exceeded in any period the number of claims paid on per producer are reduced. The 1993 payment in England and Wales was reduced by nearly 25%, from £56·34* to around £42, for this reason. However, because the extent of any future overshoot cannot be forecast, *no reductions have been allowed for in the tables below.*

Suckler Cow Premium (SCP). Limited to number on the farm in 1992 base year; otherwise no upper limit to number eligible for premium or number kept. Value, at ECU = 92·1p: £87·49 in 1994, £110·52 (120 ECU) in 1995. Suckler cow *"quotas"* are tradeable: approx. value £120-140/cow to buy, £25-£35 to lease.

The actual value of both the BSP and the SCP are determined by the ECU value in sterling on 1st January each year. Both are subject to a maximum stocking rate, falling from 3 livestock units per ha in 1994 to 2·5 in 1995 and 2 in 1996. Both are supplemented by £27·63 (at ECU (30) = 92·1p) if the stocking rate is less than 1·4 L.U./ha; however, this too is reduced (like the BSP) if regional reference numbers are exceeded; (hence to around £21 for the 1993 payments). (see further p. 72).

Calf prices

Highly variable. It is the balance between three (or four) factors: calf (or store) prices, finished cattle prices and feedingstuff prices (and in some cases stocking rate), that will mainly determine the levels of the gross margin and profit for the different beef systems included in the following pages. Small differences in each factor can cause large differences in the margins. The values assumed below relate *to all qualities*, in all markets, *at 7 to 10 days old*:

	Bulls	Heifers
Friesians	130	115
Hereford × Friesians	160	120
Limousin × Friesians	185	137·50
Simmental × Friesians	205	142·50
Charolais × Friesians	220	150

Note. Results from the Meat and Livestock Commission's Beefplan recording and costing service have been widely used in estimating many of the figures in this section.

Early Weaning—Bucket Rearing (per calf)

	3 months	6 months
Value of Calf	240	340
Less Calf (1)	135	135
Output	105	205
Variable Costs:		
Milk Substitute and Concentrates (2)	47	94
Miscellaneous Variable Costs (3)	14	24
Hay (4)	—	5
Total Variable Costs	61	123
Gross Margin per Calf reared	44	82

Notes

1. £130 per calf (Friesian bull calves, 1 week old, average of all qualities except the poorest); 4 per cent mortality assumed, mainly in first 3 weeks.
2. Milk substitute: 15 kg @ £1225/tonne = £18. Calf concentrates: to 3 months, 165 kg @ £175-£180/tonne = £29; to 6 months, additional 300 kg @ £155-160/tonne = £47. Calves fed less well, i.e. with lower concentrate costs, will fetch proportionally lower market prices, probably resulting in a lower gross margin.
3. Misc. Variable Costs include vet. and med.: 8 (3 months), 11·5 (6 months); and bedding: 3 (3 months), 7 (6 months).
4. Hay: 7 kg to 3 months, 200 kg to 6 months. Variable costs assume made on farm; double the cost if purchased.
5. Weights: at start, 50 kg; at 3 months, 115 kg; at 6 months, 200 kg.
   Contract rearing charge (both 0 to 3 months and 0 to 6 months): £10 per week. Direct labour cost: approx. £15·50 per head to 3 months, £27 per head to 6 months.
   Labour requirements (all beef systems): see page 112.

BEEF

Single Suckling (per cow): Lowland

System Performance Level (1)	Spring Calving		Autumn Calving	
	Average	High	Average	High
	£	£	£	£
Value of Calf (2)	320	356	400	437
Calf Sales/Valn. per Cow (3) ...	288	331	360	407
Headage Payment (1994) (4) ...	111	111	111	111
LESS Cow and Bull Depreciation and Calf Purchases (5)	56	54	64	62
OUTPUT	343	388	407	456
Variable Costs:				
Concentrate Costs (cow and calf)	22	22	45	45
Miscellaneous Variable Costs (6)	36	34	40	38
TOTAL VARIABLE COSTS (excluding forage)	58	56	85	83
GROSS MARGIN per cow, before deducting Forage Variable Costs	285	332	322	373
Forage Variable Costs	40	36	44	39
Purchased Bulk Feed	23	21	23	21
GROSS MARGIN per Cow	222	275	255	313
Cows per ha (7)	2·0	2·4	1·7	2·0
Forage Ha (Acres) per Cow ...	·50	·42	·59	·50
	(1·24)	(1·04)	(1·45)	(1·24)
GROSS MARGIN per Forage Hectare	445	660	435	625
GROSS MARGIN per Forage Acre ...	180	267	176	253

Notes

1. Performance level relates to variations in two factors: weaner calf weight and stocking rate. "High" refers to the average levels likely to be achieved by the better fifty per cent of producers. It is clearly possible to set still higher "targets".

2. Weight of calves (kg) at sale/transfer: spring calving: average 260 (at approx. 7 months old), high 285 (slightly older); autumn calving: average 325 (at approx. 11 months old), high 350 (same age). Price (per live kg): average 123p, high 125p.

3. Calves reared per 100 cows mated: average 90, high 93.

4. Headage payment: see page 59. Numbers are assumed to be within available quota. At the stocking rates assumed the stocking density limit (2·5 LU/ha in 1995) is not exceeded and the extensification premium would not be paid.

5. Assumptions. Herd life: spring calving, 6 years; autumn calving, 5 years. Purchase price £750, average cull value £500. Calves purchased: average, 4 per 100 cows mated, premium 3, at £160. Bull: purchase price £2,500, cull value £1,000.

6. Includes vet. and med. (£18) and bedding (spring calving £11, autumn £14); remainder miscellaneous. Where yarded in winter, straw requirements average 0·5-0·75 tonne per cow for spring calvers and around 0·75 tonne for autumn calvers.

7. The higher stocking density implies better use of grassland. Higher stocking rates can also be achieved by buying in more of the winter bulk fodder requirements, or by winter feeding largely on arable by-products, including straw. Purchased bulk fodder and/or straw balancer concentrates will reduce gross margin per cow but increase gross margin per hectare.

BEEF

Single Suckling (per cow): Upland and Hill

System Performance Level (1)	Upland Spring Calving Average	High	Upland Autumn Calving Average	High	Hill Average	High
	£	£	£	£	£	£
Value of Calf (2)	338	376	430	469	343	376
Calf Sales/Valn. per Cow (3) ...	308	353	391	441	312	353
Headage Payments (4)	158	158	185	185	185	185
LESS Cow and Bull Depreciation and Calf Purchases (5) ...	56	54	64	62	62	60
OUTPUT	410	457	512	564	435	478
Variable Costs:						
Concentrate Costs (cow & calf)	22	22	50	55	40	40
Misc. Variable Costs (6) ...	28	24	40	43	33	33
TOTAL VARIABLE COSTS (excluding forage)...	50	46	90	98	73	73
GROSS MARGIN per cow, before deducting Forage Var. Costs	360	411	422	466	362	405
Forage Variable Costs	37	37	45	45	37	32
Purchased Bulk Feed	23	22	18	20	15	15
GROSS MARGIN per Cow ...	300	352	359	401	310	358
Cows per ha (7, 8)	1·5	1·9	1·15	1·375	·85	1·0
Forage Ha (Acres) per Cow ...	·67	·53	·87	·73	1·2	1·0
	(1·65)	(1·3)	(2·15)	(1·8)	(2·9)	(2·5)
GROSS MARGIN per Forage Ha	450	670	415	550	265	360
GROSS MARGIN per Forage Acre	182	271	168	223	107	145

Notes

1. Performance level relates mainly to variations in two factors: weaner calf weight and stocking rate. "High" refers to the average levels likely to be achieved by the better fifty per cent of producers. It is clearly possible to set still higher "targets".

2. Weight of calves (kg) at sale/transfer: upland spring calving: average 270 (at approx. 7·5 months old), high 285 (same age); upland autumn calving: average 350 (at approx. 11·5 months old), high 375 (same age); hill: average 270, high 285. Price (per live kg): upland spring calving: average 130p, high 132p; upland autumn calving: average 123p, high 125p; hill: average 127p, high 132p.

3. Calves reared per 100 cows mated: upland and hill: average 91, high 94.

4. Suckler cow premium and hill compensatory allowance: see pages 59 and 72. Numbers are assumed to be within available quota. The extensification premium would be available at the stocking rates assumed, except for upland spring calving; no allowance has been made for any overshooting of regional reference herd limits.

5. Assumptions. Herd life: spring calving, 6 years; autumn calving and hill, 5 years. Purchase price £750, average cull value £500. Calves purchased: upland: average, 4 per 100 cows mated, premium 3, at £160; hill: average 3, premium 2. Bull: purchase price £2,500, cull value £1,000.

6. Includes vet. and med. (averages spring calving £15, autumn £18, hill £18) and bedding (averages spring calving £8, autumn £11, hill £7); remainder miscellaneous. Where yarded in winter, requirements average 0·5-0·75 tonne per cow for spring calvers and around 0·75 tonne for autumn calvers.

7. The higher stocking density implies better use of grassland. Higher stocking rates can also be achieved by buying in more of the winter bulk fodder requirements, or by winter feeding largely on arable by-products, including straw. Purchased bulk fodder and/or straw balancer concentrates reduce gross margin per cow but increase gross margin per hectare.

8. Forage Hectares (Acres) per cow and Gross Margin per Forage Hectare (Acre) relate to "in-bye equivalent" (3 hectares of rough grazing are taken as being equal to 1 hectare of in-bye land).

BEEF

Double and Multiple Suckling (per Cow)

	Output level (1)			
	Double Suckling	Multiple Suckling		
No. of calves reared per cow	1·9	2·5	3·5	4·5
	£	£	£	£
Value of Calf	315	310	300	290
Calf Sales per Cow	600	775	1050	1305
Headage Payment (2)	111	111	111	111
LESS Calf Costs (including Replacement Calves) (3)	157	247	412	579
Cow Depreciation	57	57	62	62
OUTPUT (3)	497	582	687	775
Variable Costs:				
Concentrates	63	78	95	112
Miscellaneous Variable Costs (4) ...	52	58	72	87
TOTAL VARIABLE COSTS (excluding forage)	115	136	167	199
GROSS MARGIN per Cow, before deducting Forage Variable Costs	382	446	520	576
Forage Variable Costs	50	59	67	73
Purchased Bulk Feed	23	28	34	39
GROSS MARGIN per Cow	309	359	419	464
Cows per ha	1·7	1·65	1·6	1·55
Forage Hectares (Acres) per Cow ...	·59	·61	·625	·65
	(1·45)	(1·5)	(1·55)	(1·6)
GROSS MARGIN per Forage Hectare ...	525	595	670	720
GROSS MARGIN per Forage Acre ...	213	240	271	291

Notes

1. The different levels of output refer only to different numbers of calves reared per cow. The standards are averages at each level of output. There are wide variations in prices obtained and paid per calf and in concentrate costs: together they can make a very large difference to the gross margin.

2. Headage payment: see page 59.

3. Calf cost assumed: £150 (average steers and heifers, 1 week old). Calf mortality assumed: 5 per cent (double suckling) to 8 per cent (4·5 calves per cow).

4. Miscellaneous variable costs include straw: approx. 1 tonne per cow.

N.B. There is very little survey data available for these enterprises, since multiple suckling in particular is not widely practised. Hence these estimates must be treated with caution.

BEEF

Finishing/Rearing on Suckler-Bred Stores (per head)

	Winter Finishing		Grass Finishing		Overwintering and Grass Finishing		Grazing and Yard Finishing		Overwintering and Selling as Stores	
	Average £	High £	Average £	High £	Average £	High £	Average £	High £	Average £	High £
Sales	634	656	530	534	555	577	625	686	508	548
Less Store (1)	382	372	419	394	342	339	356	332	339	336
Output*	252	284	111	140	213	238	269	354	169	212
Variable Costs:										
Concentrates (2)	89	83	5	3	60	50	57	43	51	46
Miscellaneous (3)	31	26	19	17	33	30	33	30	29	27
Total Variable Costs (excl. Forage)	120	109	24	20	93	80	90	73	80	73
Gross Margin per head before deducting Forage Variable Costs	132	175	87	120	120	158	179	281	89	139
Forage Variable Costs	33	35	22	22	38	38	36	36	23	25
Purchased Bulk Feed	14	16	–	–	15	15	9	6	9	5
Gross Margin per head*	85	124	65	98	67	105	134	239	57	109
No. per ha	9	10	4	5	3·75	4·50	4	5	11	13
No. per acre	3·6	4	1·6	2	1·5	1·8	1·6	2	4·5	5·3
Gross Margin per Forage Ha*	765	1240	260	490	250	475	535	1195	625	1415
Gross Margin per Forage Acre*	310	500	105	198	100	192	217	485	255	575
Weight at start (kg)	320	315	335	320	280	280	285	270	280	280
Weight at end (kg)	520	525	445	445	470	485	500	540	400	425
Purchase Price (p per kg LW)	118	117	125	123	122	121	125	123	121	120
Sale Price (p per kg LW)	122	125	119	120	118	119	125	127	127	129
Concentrates per head (kg)	700	680	40	25	475	425	450	350	400	375
Silage per head (tonnes)	3·4	4·0	–	–	3·6	3·6	2·1	2·3	2·3	2·7

* The output and gross margin figures exclude the beef special premium, as this will depend, per head, on the overall stocking rate on the farm. Where the above beef enterprises represent the only livestock on the farm the full payment per head (see page 59) is likely to be obtained for the centre three systems but not for the first and last.

All-System Assumptions

(1) Allowing for mortality at 1 per cent.
(2) Concentrate costs per tonne: winter: average £127·50, high £122·50; summer: average £117·50, high £112·50.
(3) Including vet. and med. and bedding.

Additional Note: The gross margin per ha figures must be treated with considerable caution, especially with regard to winter fattening/rearing systems: small variations in land requirements and margins per head cause wide variations in the per ha figures, and capital requirements are considerable. Differences in buying and selling prices per kg can be critical.

BEEF

Finishing/Rearing on Dairy-Bred Stores (per head)

	Winter Finishing		Grass Finishing		Overwintering and Grass Finishing		Grazing and Yard Finishing		Overwintering and Selling as Stores	
	Average £	High £	Average £	High £	Average £	High £	Average £	High £	Average £	High £
Sales	597	618	556	584	563	586	615	687	494	533
Less Store (1)	378	334	431	413	351	348	283	293	327	325
Output*	199	284	125	171	212	238	332	394	167	208
Variable Costs:										
Concentrates (2)	60	55	6	5	54	44	75	55	51	46
Miscellaneous (3)	24	24	18	17	41	37	33	30	29	27
Total Variable Costs (excl. Forage)	84	79	24	22	95	81	108	85	80	73
Gross Margin per head before deducting Forage Variable Costs	115	205	101	149	117	157	224	309	87	135
Forage Variable Costs	20	20	22	22	38	38	36	37	23	25
Purchased Bulk Feed	8	7	—	—	15	15	9	6	9	5
Gross Margin per head*	87	198	79	127	64	104	179	266	55	105
No. per ha	7·5	9	4	5	3·5	4·25	3·5	4·5	11	13
No. per acre	3	3·6	1·6	2	1·4	1·7	1·4	1·8	4·5	5·3
Gross Margin per Forage Ha*	650	1780	315	635	225	440	625	1195	605	1365
Gross Margin per Forage Acre*	264	720	128	255	91	178	255	485	245	550
Weight at start (kg)	325	290	350	350	300	300	230	240	275	275
Weight at end (kg)	510	515	475	495	490	505	500	550	395	420
Purchase Price (p per kg LW)	115	114	123	122	117	116	123	122	119	118
Sale Price (p per kg LW)	117	120	117	118	115	116	123	125	125	127
Concentrates per head (kg)	470	450	50	40	425	375	600	450	400	375
Silage per head (tonnes)	3·2	3·3	—	—	3·6	3·6	3·5	4·5	2·6	3·0

* The output and gross margin figures exclude the beef special premium, as this will depend, per head, on the overall stocking rate on the farm. Where the above beef enterprises represent the only livestock on the farm the full payment per head (see page 59) is likely to be obtained for the centre three systems but not for the first and last.

All-System Assumptions

(1) Allowing for mortality at 1 per cent.
(2) Concentrate costs per tonne: winter: average £127·50, high £122·50; summer: average £117·50, high £112·50.
(3) Including vet. and med. and bedding.

Additional Note: The gross margin per ha figures must be treated with considerable caution, especially with regard to winter fattening/rearing systems: small variations in land requirements and margins per head cause wide variations in the per ha figures, and capital requirements are considerable. Differences in buying and selling prices per kg can be critical.

BEEF

Traditional Finishing of Strong Store Cattle (per head) (1)

	Summer Fattening £	Winter Fattening £
Sales	614 (2)	650 (3)
LESS Purchased Store	500 (4)	496 (5)
OUTPUT*	114	154
Variable Costs:		
Concentrates	5	50 (6)
Miscellaneous Variable Costs	20	34 (7)
TOTAL VARIABLE COSTS (excluding Forage)	25	84
GROSS MARGIN per Head before deducting Forage		
Variable Costs	89	70
Forage Variable Costs	17	20
GROSS MARGIN per Head*	72	50
No. per ha (acre)	3·5 (1·4)	8 (3·25)
Forage Hectares (Acres) per Head	·29 (·7)	·125 (·3)
GROSS MARGIN per Forage Hectare*	252	400
GROSS MARGIN per Forage Acre*	102	162

* The (1995) *headage payment* of £110·52 has not been included. Although the animal becomes eligible at 22 months old (if on the farm at that age of course) the stocking rate assumed would limit the numbers eligible per farm for summer fattening and especially for winter fattening. Even where available, the payment is likely to be largely cancelled out under these systems by a higher sum paid for the store.

Notes

1. The financial results of this enterprise are highly dependent on the market margin, i.e. the difference between the price per kg paid for the store and the price per kg obtained for the fat animal. Other important factors are the stocking rate and the degree of dependence on cash-crop by-products and the quality of conserved grass (and hence the quantity of concentrates required in relation to the liveweight gain) in the case of winter fattening.

2. 520 kg @ 118p.

3. 520 kg @ 125p.

4. 400 kg @ 125p.

5. 420 kg @ 118p.

6. 400 kg @ £125/tonne.

7. Including straw: average 0·75 tonne per head.

BEEF

Intensive Cereal Bull Beef (per Head)

	Calves reared on farm		Reared calves purchased	
	Average	High	Average	High
	£	£	£	£
Sales (1)	561	600	561	600
Less Calf (2)	137	134	245	243
Output	424	456	316	357
Variable Costs:				
Concentrates (3)	271	264	224	217
Other Feed	6	6	6	6
Miscellaneous (4)	37	37	33	33
Total Variable Costs ...	314	307	263	256
Gross Margin per Head ...	110	149	53	101

Notes

1. Weight at slaughter (kg): average 460, high 480. Price: average 122p per live kg, high 125p. All year round production is assumed. Days (on farm) to slaughter: calves reared on farm: 345; reared calves purchased: 265.

2. £130 per Friesian bull calf (1 week old average of all qualities except the poorest) + mortality (average 5, high 3 per cent). Reared calves purchased at about 3 months old; average mortality 2 per cent.

3. £47 calf rearing (to 12 weeks: see p. 59) + fattening ration (average £219, high performance £212) + £5 food to losses. Fattening Ration: 17 parts barley @ £94 per tonne (estimated average price, 1995 calendar year), 3 parts concentrate supplement @ £230 per tonne; plus milling and mixing. Total, £122 per tonne.

   Quantity (kg from 12 weeks (115 kg to slaughter): average, 1795 (F.C.R. 5·2); high, 1735 (F.C.R. 4·75).

   A difference of £5 per tonne in the cost of barley changes the feed cost by approximately £7·75 per head.

4. Vet. and med. 7, bedding 13, other 17.

5. *No headage payment is included, because of the stocking rate constraint in the EC Reform package. However, in some farm circumstances it may be available for a limited number.*

Note: Interest on Capital

As examples of the need to be aware of interest paid or forgone on capital invested in beef production, interest on the cost of the calf and variable costs alone, at 10%, are likely to be in the order of £30 a head for intensive cereal beef and £45 a head for 18-month beef (p. 67).

BEEF
18 Month Beef and Grass Silage Beef (per Head)

	18 month Average £	18 month High £	Grass silage Average £	Grass silage High £
Sales	588	625	625	663
LESS Calf	173	170	245	243
PLUS Headage Payments (1995)	83*	55*	37*	28*
OUTPUT	498	510	417	448
Variable Costs:				
Concentrates	138	126	147	123
Other Feed	13	11	13	11
Miscellaneous	49	46	35	33
TOTAL VARIABLE COSTS (excl. Forage)	200	183	195	167
GROSS MARGIN per Head before deducting Forage Variable Costs	298	327	222	281
Forage Variable Costs	45	42	40	37
GROSS MARGIN per Head	253	285	182	244
No. per ha (acre)	3 (1·2)	3·5 (1·4)	7 (2·8)	9 (3·6)
Forage Hectares (Acres) per Head ...	·33 (·83)	·3 (·75)	0·14 (·35)	0·12 (·27)
GROSS MARGIN per Forage Ha (per year) ...	760	1000	1275	2195
GROSS MARGIN per Forage Acre (per year) ...	307	405	515	890

Notes

18 Month Beef

Autumn-born dairy-bred calves, beef crosses.

Slaughter weights (kg): average 490, high 510. Sale price per live kg: average 120p, high 122·5p.

Calf price/value £165 (1 week old bulls); mortality: average 5, high 3 per cent.

Concentrates (kg; average, with high performance in brackets): milk subst. 15; other: first winter 360 (335), at grass 115 (110), second winter 450 (430). Price of concentrates per tonne: first winter (inc. calf rearing) £135 (£127·50); summer £117·50 (£112·50); second winter, £127·50 (£122·50). Silage: 4·5 tonnes (average and high): 0·75 tonne first winter, 3·75 tonnes second.

Miscellaneous (average): vet. and med. £16, bedding £18, other £15.

Intensive grazing of fresh leys and good quality silage are needed—especially to achieve the high performance levels.

*Headage Payment (1995). The full payment (£110·52/head) is only available for all the stock (up to 90 head) if the overall stocking rate on the farm is below 2·5 livestock units per hectare. (This reduces to 2 in 1996). Also, the amounts paid are reduced if regional reference herd limits are exceeded. As a crude approximation only, 75% of the full rate is included for average performance and 50% for high. The actual amount will vary from farm to farm and according to regional production levels.

Grass Silage Beef

Three months old dairy-bred calves fed indoors on grass silage and concentrates, for slaughter at 14 to 17 months old. Good quality silage is the key to high performance per herd (otherwise concentrates per head rise and/or daily liveweight gain falls). High yields of silage per ha raise gross margins per ha.

Slaughter weights (kg): average 510, high 530. Sale price per live kg: average 122·5p, high 125p.

Concentrates per head (kg): average, with high performance in brackets: 1150 (1000); price per tonne £127·50 (£122·50). Silage required: approx. 5·5 tonnes per head.

Miscellaneous (average): vet. and med. £5, bedding £16, other £14.

*Headage payment: see above for 18 month beef. Because of the very high stocking rate with this system the crude approximation included is one-third for average, one-quarter for high..

Note that the gross margin per hectare figures must be interpreted with considerable caution: small differences in silage yields can have a large effect and, more important, the working capital and building requirements per hectare are extremely high: well above even the high needs of 18 month beef.

BEEF

24 Month Beef from Bucket Reared Calves (per Head)

	Autumn-born calf £	Spring-born calf £
Sales (1)	590	620
LESS Calf	170	160
Headage Payments (1995)*	221	221
OUTPUT	**641**	**681**
Variable Costs:		
Concentrates	113	132
Miscellaneous	68	74
Forage	60	50
TOTAL VARIABLE COSTS	**241**	**266**
GROSS MARGIN per Head	400	415
No. per ha (acre)	1·75 (·7)	2 (·8)
Forage Hectares (Acres) per Head	0·57 (1·4)	0·5 (1·25)
GROSS MARGIN per Forage Hectare	700	830
GROSS MARGIN per Forage Acre	283	335

Notes
(1) 500 kg. Autumn-born: 118p per kg; spring-born: 124p.

*Headage payment: 2 payments, at 10 and 22 months old.

VEAL

	£
Sale value (1)	416
LESS Calf (2)	137
OUTPUT	**279**
Variable Costs:	
Concentrates (3)	235
Miscellaneous	14
TOTAL VARIABLE COSTS	**249**
GROSS MARGIN per Head (4)	**30**

Notes
1. Sold at 170 kg liveweight (bought at 45 kg), average 102 kg dressed carcase weight, 15 weeks old. Killing out percentage, 60 per cent. Price assumed: £4·08 per kg d.c.w. (£2·45 per kg liveweight).
2. £130 per calf (Friesian bull calf, 1 week old); 5 per cent mortality assumed, mainly in first three weeks. Cheaper calves, of different breeds, can be purchased (e.g., purebred Guernseys, Ayrshires, Jersey × Continental beef breeds, Hereford heifers), but the fattening period could then be longer and the food conversion rate poorer.
3. Feed: £1,225 per tonne. A conversion rate of 1·5 kg of food per kg liveweight gain is assumed (plus an allowance for losses) = approx. 192 kg total.
4. The gross margin is obviously highly dependent on calf price, the market price of veal, and feed efficiency.

SHEEP

A. Lowland Spring Lambing (per Ewe)

(Selling lambs off grass)

	Low	Average	High
Performance level			
Lambs reared per ewe (1)	1·3	1·45	1·65
Average price per lamb (£) (2)	33·50	34·50	35·50
	£	£	£
Lamb sales	43·5	50·0	58·6
Ewe Premium (2)	17·5	17·5	17·5
Wool (3)	2·2	2·2	2·2
Cull ewes and rams	5·8	5·8	5·8
Sub-total	69·0	75·5	84·1
Less Ewe and ram replacements	16·7	16·7	16·7
Output	52·3	58·8	67·4
Variable Costs:			
Concentrates (55 kg ewes, 12 kg lambs)...		9·3	
Vet. and Med.		4·0	
Miscellaneous and Transport		3·2	
Total Variable Costs (excluding Forage)		16·5	
Gross Margin per Ewe before deducting Forage Variable Costs	35·8	42·3	50·9
Forage Variable Costs (inc. bought forage and keep)	7·0	7·5	8·0
Gross Margin per Ewe	28·8	34·8	42·9
Stocking Rate (Ewes, with lambs, per forage hectare (acre))	8 (3·25)	11 (4·5)	14 (5·75)
Gross Margin per Forage Hectare ...	230	383	600
Gross Margin per Forage Acre	93	155	243

Notes

1. *Lambs reared per ewe* (× 100 = lambing percentage) is derived as follows (*average figures* only):
   Lambs born per 100 ewes lambing = 173
   Lambs born per 100 ewes put to ram = 161
   (93% of ewes put to ram bear lambs: 1·5% deaths, 5.5% barren)
   Lamb mortality: 10% (inc. half dead at birth or before seen)
   Lambs reared per 100 ewes lambing = 156
   Lambs reared per 100 ewes put to ram = 145

2. *Lamb Prices/Ewe Premium.* The price assumed for lambs sold for slaughter *for the 1995 mid-season lamb crop* assumes that most of the lambs are sold between mid-June and the end of October. Prices are normally highest in February-May and lowest in August-October; the pre-1992 guide prices were some 22·5% lower in the autumn trough months compared with the spring peak. Estimating the average price achieved, and the ewe premium, is hazardous. Prices in the spring and early summer of both 1993 and 1994 were exceptionally high, owing to several factors, but particularly a strong export demand. However, prices in the autumn of 1993 only just exceeded 80p/kg lw—but are expected to be well above this level in autumn 1994. An average market price of 95p/kg lw has been assumed, giving approximately £36 per finished lamb (38 kg lw). However, the average price given in the above table allows for a proportion (15 to 20%) sold or retained in the autumn as *store* lambs. Low performance is £1 a lamb less, high £1 more.

A difference in price of £2 per lamb (i.e. a difference of approx. 5·25p per kg lw for a 38 kg lw lamb) causes a difference of £20, £32 and £46 (8, 13, 18·5) to the low, average and high gross margins per hectare (acre) respectively. Exported lambs could average 15-20 per cent above domestic prices.

The "Sheep Annual Premium" payment per ewe is calculated from the shortfall between the basic price set and the average EU market price for lamb marketed at 12 kg or above. The number eligible per farm is based on the number receiving the premium in 1991. The premiums are tradeable, with restrictions; the *quotas* (premium rights) began trading in early July 1993; prices are generally £30 to £37·50/right, around £10 to lease in LFAs, and £22·50 to £27·50/right, £5 to £7 to lease, in non LFAs. The full rate is only paid on up to 500 ewes per farm in lowland areas and up to 1,000 in Less Favoured Areas; only half the premium per head is paid on additional numbers per farm.

3. *Wool.* The government's price guarantee ended on 30th April 1993. The average wool price in 1992/3 was very low, but improved considerably in late 1993 and early 1994. 3kg/herd at 75p has been assumed for 1995.

4. *Breed* will obviously have a large effect on lambing percentage, rate of liveweight gain (reflected in price per lamb), and amount of wool per ewe.

5. *Stocking Density.* The stocking rates assumed are based on land requirements throughout the year. With a given level of management one would expect higher stocking rates to be associated with a lower gross margin per ewe. The assumption made in the initial table, however, is that management performance is affecting both factors together.

N.B. The forage variable costs include *purchased forage* (£0·7, £1·0 and 1·3 per ewe at the three performance levels respectively).

The top one-third gross margin per hectare herds recorded by the Meat and Livestock Commission achieve stocking rates exceeding 15 ewes per hectare. Often such high stocking rates are achieved by substantial use of by-products (e.g. autumn or spring grazing of grass grown primarily for seed) and catch crops (e.g. rape). Otherwise a stocking rate of 15 per hectare (just over 6 per acre) requires a stocking rate of about 24 ewes (with lambs) per hectare in the spring and early summer.

The top few per cent of flocks in the country achieve gross margins per hectare exceeding £650 per hectare (£265 per acre) by a combination of high lambing percentage, high average lamb price and, especially, very high stocking rates.

Where there are no grazing livestock other than sheep on the farm, some ewes, at the higher stocking rates, are often either agisted (away-wintered) or housed indoors, thus reducing the margin. Agistment costs around 31p per week plus transport, i.e. approx. £8 per year. Depreciation and Interest on new Housing (1·2 sq. m per ewe) is approximately £4·50 per ewe per year (10-year life); extra hay and perhaps concentrates will also be required.

On the other hand, with only 7 or 8 ewes per hectare (2·75 to 3·25/acre) on a lowland farm of reasonable quality with no other grazing livestock, there should be surplus grass available in the late spring or early summer; this could be cut for hay or used for seed production.

6. *Flock Depreciation.* (i.e. Market price of replacements less value of culls). It is assumed above that 20 per cent of the ewe flock is culled each year @ £27·50 each and that, allowing for 4 per cent mortality, 24 per cent are purchased or home-reared at £60 each. Rams: 1 per 40 to 45 ewes, 3-year life, purchased @ £300, sold @ £40. The net cost is £10·90 per ewe per year. N.B. Cull ewe prices are approximately £5 per head higher for heavy breeds and £5 lower for light breeds.

No increase in flock valuation through inflation is included.

7. *Miscellaneous Costs* include lambing and shearing bonus. Contract shearing is approximately 85p per head, including rolling (but can be over £1 for small flocks); approx. 45p/ewe for shearing only in upland flocks.

8. *Prices of Specialized Equipment:*

Troughs (2·75 m)	£50 to £55
Racks (2½ to 3 m)	£165 to £185
Foot Baths (3 m)	£80 to £100
Shearer (electric)	£550 to £800
Lamb Creep and Shelter, skids	£500
Netting	60p to £1·10 per metre

9. *Fencing:* approximately £1·35 per metre + 65p labour.

10. *Home-reared tegs* (shearlings). Output: value £57·50 (allowing for culling and mortality) less £32·50 for the lamb, plus £2·0 for wool = £27. Variable costs (including forage) = £12. Gross margin per head = £15, per forage hectare £260 (£105 per acre).

If the figures for home-reared replacement tegs are included in the figures per ewe, the latter are increased approximately as follows: output by £5·50, gross margin (per ewe) by £3·50. The stocking rate in terms of ewes per hectare devoted to sheep will be about 15 per cent less and the overall sheep gross margin per hectare about 5 per cent lower (i.e. averaging approx. £365/ha (£148/acre)).

11. Labour: see page 113.

B. *Other Sheep Systems* (average performance level only)

System	Early Lambing per ewe	Winter Fattening of Store Lambs per head	Upland Flocks per ewe	Hill Flocks per ewe
Lambs reared per ewe	1·4	—	1·3	1·0
	£	£	£	£
Average price per lamb sold	43·0	42·0	33·5	28·5
Lamb sales	60·2	41·2	43·5	21·4
Ewe premium	17·5	—	22·5*	22·5*
Wool	2·2	—	1·8	1·3
Subsidy/Hill Livestock	—	—	3·0*	5·7*
Sub-total	79·9	41·2	70·8	50·9
Less Livestock Purchases (net of cull sales)	9·3	31·2	11·0	(+) 2·5
Output	70·6	10·0	59·8	53·4
Variable Costs:				
Concentrates	21·0	2·1	6·3	3·5
	(135 kg)	(15 kg)	(45 kg)	(25 kg)
Vet. and Med.	4·2	0·3	3·4	2·6
Miscellaneous and Transport ...	3·8	0·6	2·5	1·6
Total Variable Costs (excl. Forage) ...	29·0	3·0	12·2	7·7
Gross Margin per ewe (or head) before deducting Forage Variable Costs ...	41·6	7·0	47·6	45·7
Forage Variable Costs (inc. bought forage)	7·0	1·2	6·1	3·4
Gross Margin per ewe (or head) ...	34·6	5·8	41·5	42·3
Stocking Rate (No. per Forage Ha (Acre))	13·5	50	9·0	—
	(5·5)	(20)	(3·65)	
Gross Margin per Forage Hectare ...	470	290	375	—
Gross Margin per Forage Acre	190	117	151	—

* *The same supplement to the ewe premium (£5·06/ewe) and the same hill sheep compensatory allowances have been assumed as for 1994.*

Notes

Early Fat Lambs. In this system, 60 per cent of the lambs are sold before the end of May, and the remainder before the end of August. This may be compared with *Mid-Season* lamb production (see table on page 68), in which 75 - 80 per cent of the lambs are sold in June, July and August, and *Late* lamb production, in which only two-thirds or so of the lambs are sold for slaughter by the end of the normal grazing season, 60 per cent of total lambs being sold for slaughter or as stores in October/November, or the stores are retained on the farm for winter fattening. The gross margin per ewe tends to be slightly higher with the latter system compared with Mid-Season production, provided the proportion of stores is not too high—but more grass is utilized per ewe, making per hectare results similar.

Winter Fattening of Store Lambs. The gross margin per head is particularly variable, being very dependent on the difference between the purchase and sale price of the lambs.

Hill Sheep. The flock is assumed to be self-maintained; thus only about 0·75 lambs are sold per ewe per annum and the fleece of the yearling ewes are included in wool sales. Only the rams are purchased, costing approx. £2 per ewe per year. Results obviously vary according to the height of the hill and severity of the winter.

Note. The figures for early fat lamb production, upland and hill sheep are largely based on the relative figures for these systems as compared with the lowland spring lambing results obtained from the Meat and Livestock Commission's Flockplan recording and costing service.

GRANTS FOR BEEF AND SHEEP

Beef Cows. The Suckler Cow Premium is £87·49 per cow in 1994 (£105·91 in Northern Ireland) and £110·52 in 1995 (at ECU = 92·1p). Only eligible if calves are reared for meat production, with meat-producing breeds, including bull. The producer must undertake not to deliver any milk or milk products from any of his production units, except that milk producers with less than 120,000 kg (116,540 litres) of quota may apply for the subsidy. Further (1995) details, including quotas, stocking rate limits, extensification premiums, etc., see page 59.

Finished Male Cattle. £69·07 premium per head in 1994, £82·89 in 1995 (at ECU = 92·1p); limited to 90 animals per producer per year. There are no quality criteria. It is payable on male animals only, at the point of slaughter or at the point of sale for slaughter (auction markets). The producer must have finished the cattle over at least the preceding two months. Further (1995) details, including quotas, stocking rate limits, extensification premiums, etc., see page 59. The maximum carcase weight for intervention was reduced to 340 kg from 1st July 1994.

Hill Livestock Compensatory Allowances (1994): (a) Cows. £47·50 a head on eligible cows and in-calf heifers maintained in regular breeding herds on hill land for the purposes of breeding store cattle. Cows kept for selling milk are not eligible. "Disadvantaged areas" cattle: £23·75 a cow.

(b) Sheep (1994). £5·75 per head for hill sheep, £3·00 for upland sheep, £2·44 for special "disadvantaged areas" sheep. Supplement to the ewe premium of £5·06/head paid in less favoured areas.

The maximum rates of payment per hectare are £81·13 in "Severely Disadvantaged Areas" and £60·85 in "Disadvantaged Areas".

GRAZING AND REARING CHARGES:
CATTLE AND SHEEP

Grazing charges vary widely according to the quality of the pasture and local supply and demand. The following figures are typical (estimated for 1995):

Summer Grazing (per head per week)

Store Cattle and in-calf heifers over 21 months, dry cows, and fattening bullocks over 18 months...	£3·70
Heifers and Steers, 12-21 months	£2·85
6-12 months Cattle	£2·20
Cattle of mixed ages	£2·90
Ewes	31p

Winter Grazing (per head per week)

"Strong" Cattle	£2·20-£2·85
Heifers	£1·70-£2·20
Sheep	31p

Note: the above figures assume the farmer whose land the livestock are on does all the fencing and "looking after". Where the owner of the, say, sheep does the fencing, shepherding, etc., the figures may be halved.

Grass Keep (per hectare)

Average £175 (£70 per acre); main range £100-£250 (£40-£100 per acre).

These figures are highly variable, especially between one part of the country and another. The charge can be very high where the pasture is good, the supply scarce and the demand strong. Poor quality keep may fetch only £50/ha, top quality more than £300/ha. Prices were substantially higher in 1994 than in the two previous years; for top quality grassland, fertilized, well-fenced and watered, with stock seen daily, prices even exceeded £400/ha for some lots in the west and north-west. The *average* price can exceed £200/ha in some years in parts of the west and west midlands but often falls below £75 in some south-eastern counties.

Winter Keep (Cattle) *(per head per week)*

Grazing + 9 kg hay and some straw...	£6·30
Full winter keep in yards	£6·80-£8·80
Calf rearing for beef (0 to 12 weeks or 0 to 6 months)	£9·25

Heifer Rearing Charges

Points to clarify in any arrangement are: who pays for transport, who pays the vet. and med. expenses, who bears the losses or pays for replacements, how often are payments made (monthly payments save the rearer interest compared with lump sum payments when the heifer is returned)?

Two possible arrangements are:

1. Farmer X sells calf to Rearer at agreed price; the calf is then Rearer's responsibility and he pays for all expenses and bears any losses. Farmer X has first option on heifers, which he buys back two months before calving. Approx. price: £800 above cost of calf for Friesians, £500 for Channel Islands. Rearer fetches calf; Farmer X supplies transport for heifer.

2. Farmer X retains ownership of calf. Approx. charges: £32 per month from 10 to 14 days old (£35 if two-year old calving), or £28·25 per month from 6 months old (£33 if two-year old calving), (£42 per month from 10 to 14 days to 6 months). As Rearer has no interest on capital to bear, he supplies transport and pays for vet. and medical expenses. Rearer either refunds payments for losses or replaces calf (this means Farmer X and Rearer share a loss averaging approx. £27 each per heifer reared, assuming 10 per cent losses at average 6 months old). Receipts for culls go to Farmer X; he and Rearer share cost of replacement calf equally.

Calf and Heifer Rearing for Shorter Periods

Calf, 10 days to 3 months, £125 (for food, labour and housing) to £140 (all costs, and rearer bearing losses). Heifers, average from 3 months old to steaming up: approx. £14 per month in summer, £40 in winter.

RED DEER

Sales:	Selling at 14-16 months per 100 hinds £	Selling calves per 100 hinds £	Finishing stag calves per 200 stags £
Stag calves	—	3960 (44)	—
Hind calves	—	4440 (37)	—
Stags, 14-16 months	8470 (44)	—	38500
Hinds, 14-16 months	8325 (37)	—	—
Culls (8 hinds, 1 stag)	1560	1560	—
Less purchased stock	500	500	18500
OUTPUT	17855	9460	20000
Variable Costs:			
Supplementary Feed	4580	4305	3355
Forage	1100	700	1100
Vet. and Med.	900	500	720
Miscellaneous	900	600	400
Slaughter Cost	660	135	3000
TOTAL VARIABLE COSTS	8140	6240	8575
GROSS MARGIN	9715	3220	11425
GROSS MARGIN per Hind (Stag) ...	97·15	32·20	57·10
Stocking Rate (No. per ha (acre)) ...	6·5 (2·6)	8 (3·25)	15 (6)
GROSS MARGIN per hectare	630	260	855
GROSS MARGIN per acre	255	105	345

Notes

Numbers of animals sold given in brackets.

Intensive system, on sown pasture. Self-contained herd.

Herd life (years): hinds 12, stags 8. Hinds per stag: 20 to 30.

Calves per 100 hinds: 90 reared (to 4 months).

Supplementary feed: adults: 8·5 kg silage/head/day over 165 days plus 0·5 kg concs./head/day for 30 days; calves: to November, 0·5 kg concs./head/day + ad lib silage 60 days; from November, ad lib silage 120 days, 1 kg concs./head/day + ad lib silage 45 days. Concentrates £160/tonne; silage £18/tonne.

Sale weights and values:

		Stags		Hinds	
		kg	£/kg	kg	£/kg
Calves	... ...	45 LW	2·00 LW	40 LW	3·00 LW
At 14-16 months	... ...	55 DW	3·50 DW	75 LW	3·00 LW

Stock: breeding stags £500 plus, hinds £300 plus, yearling hinds £250 plus hind calves £120, stag calves £90. Prices reflect good quality stock sold in UK. Export prices can be higher. Tb accreditation brings premium.

Venison prices reflect projected sales for 1994/95 to wholesale buyers. Farm shop and local co-operative sales may be higher.

Slaughter costs take into account income from slaughter by-products.

Capital costs: perimeter fencing, £4·20/metre; internal (electric) fencing, £2/metre; permanent fencing, £3·70/metre; handling yard, pens, scales, crush: £6,000—in existing building. Total cost of establishing a 100-hind breeding flock is typically in the order of £40,000, including breeding stock and £10,000 for fencing, housing and handling facilities.

Labour: one experienced stockman can deal with 400 plus head with additional help when yarding.

Comment: Feed costs are based on exploiting summer compensatory growth and reducing overwinter feed rates. Veterinary figures are based on successful minimal regime including biennial Tb testing (now simplified).

A general improvement in the sales volume and prices was achieved in the spring and early summer of 1994; a substantial increase in the demand for livestock for finishing may push up calf prices.

There are now 267 deer farms in England and Wales, 86 in Scotland (MAFF).

Acknowledgement: The above information is provided by J. C. Cordery, Sparsholt College, Hampshire.

SHEEP DAIRYING

(estimates for 1994)

	per Ewe	
Performance level (yield)	Average	High
Milk Yield (litres) (1)	275	350
	£	£
Milk Value (2)	179	227
Value of Lambs (3)	38	43
Ewe Premium	14·5	14·5
Wool	0·5	0·5
Sub-total	232	285
Less Ewe and Ram Depreciation (4)	16	20
Output	216	265
Variable Costs:		
Concentrates (5)	43	50
Miscellaneous (inc. vet. and med.)	25	
Forage Variable Costs	10	
Total Variable Costs	78	85
Gross Margin per Ewe	138	180
Ewes per ha (acre)	10 (4)	12 (5)
Gross Margin per Forage Hectare	1380	2160
Gross Margin per Forage Acre	560	875

Notes

1. *Yield.* For "professional" flocks of a substantial size of British Milksheep and East Friesland ewes. The yields of other breeds may be well below these levels. The yield of milk available for processing is much influenced by the method and age of weaning the lambs. Milking season: April to October inclusive (about 250 days).

2. *Price.* 65p per litre at farmgate.

3. £20 per lamb, with a small percentage sold as breeding sheep. Prices exceeding £100 may be obtained for tegs from pure recorded flocks.

4. *Depreciation.* Assumes £60 per ewe less £10 for cull, 4 lactations. (Much higher prices may be paid for pure recorded flocks). £500 per ram less £30 for cull, 4- ear life, one per 35 ewes.

5. *Concentrates.* Ewe: 0·5 kg/litre at £170/tonne: £23; high £30. Additionally: 100 kg per lamb (artificially reared) at £200/tonne: £20.

Additional Points

Capital Costs of Equipment. Complete milking unit for 100 ewes (including yokes, bulk tank, dairy equipment, installation): £5,000-£8,000. Simple unit for 50 sheep: £2,000 plus. These are likely to be minimum costs; they do not include freezing capacity or building work.

Cheesemaking. 5 litres of milk required to make 1 kg of cheese. Wholesale cheese price: approx. £6.50 per kg. Retail price 40 to 60 per cent higher. Cheesemaking equipment £4,000 to £5,000, excluding building (two rooms plus a store). New environmental health regulations have made all processing much more costly. Require separate processing rooms (minimum cost £5,000-£6,000), pasteuriser (£1,000-£4,000), stainless steel or approved plastic utensils (£400-£500), etc.

Research by Angela Edwards. Additional data supplied by Anthony Hyde, Chairman, British Sheep Dairying Association.

GOAT DAIRYING

Performance level (yield)			Low	per Goat Average	High
Milk Yield (litres) (1)	...	...	500	750	900
			£	£	£
Milk Value (2)	...	...	188	281	338
PLUS Value of Kid(s) (3)	...	...	7	9	18
PLUS Value of Culls (4)	...	...	5	5	5
LESS Cost of Replacements (4)		...	24	24	24
OUTPUT	...	... ...	176	271	337
Variable Costs:					
Concentrates (5)	...	... ...	41	62	74
Forage (6) ...	...	... ...	32	47	57
Miscellaneous (7) ...	...	...	38	38	38
TOTAL VARIABLE COSTS	...	...	111	147	169
GROSS MARGIN per Goat	...	...	65	124	168
Stocking rate: No. per ha(acre) (zero grazed) (8)			6·5 (2·65)	8 (3·25)	9·5 (3·85)
(Equivalent) Gross Margin per ha (acre)			420 (170)	990 (400)	1590 (645)

Notes

1. *Yield.* Per 300 day lactation, kidding every spring.
2. *Price.* 37·5p per litre. 12·5% solids delivered to creamery.
3. *Kid(s).* Prolificacy relates to age and feed level. Assumptions: low (new herds) 140%, average and high 180%. Average week-old kid price for both sexes £5, although many males are unsaleable owing to limited meat trade; premium herds average £10 per kid.
4. *Culls and Replacements.* 20% replacement at £120/head; culls £25, average life 5 years. Bucks: 1 per 40-50 does. Does normally mate in autumn, kid 5 months later; young goats can be mated from 6 months onwards. Rearing costs are higher than the market price of replacements.
5. *Concentrates.* Average 0·55 kg concentrate per litre, at £150 per tonne DM.
6. *Forage.* Average 0·9 kg DM long fibre forage per litre at £70 per tonne DM (part purchased, part home-grown). Goats can be grazed but are normally storage fed to avoid problems with worms, fencing and milk taints.
7. *Miscellaneous.* Bedding £8, vet and med. £24, sundries £6.
8. *Stocking rate.* Based on home-grown forage.
9. *Labour.* 1 full-time person per 100 goats.
10. *Markets.* There is no guaranteed market support for goat produce. Some successful businesses have been built on producer retailing. Bulk purchasers of goats milk are few and far between.

Organisations. The British Goat Society registers pedigree animals and publishes a monthly newsletter. Locally based co-operative milking groups exist and provide a possible stabilising influence on milk prices and contracts.

Acknowledgements. The above information has been supplied by T. Mottram, Institute for Animal Health, Compton, Berks.

ANGORA GOATS

	Breeding Does (2)	Subsequent Shearing (2)
Yield of Fibre (kg/year) (3)	12·90	4·75
Price of Fibre (£/kg) (3)	4·20	2·45

	£ per doe	£ per head
Value of Fibre	54·2	11·6
Value of Kids (1·42 per doe mated (4))	33·5	—
Value of Cull (5)	4·1	9·2
LESS Replacements (5)	9·4	10·0
OUTPUT	82·4	10·8
Variable Costs:		
Concentrates (6)	24·8	5·4
Vet. and Med.	5·0	0·5
Miscellaneous (7)	10·0	1·8
TOTAL VARIABLE COSTS (excl. Forage)	39·8	7·7
GROSS MARGIN per Doe before Forage Costs	42·6	3·1
Forage Variable Costs	8·0	5·3
GROSS MARGIN per Doe/Head	34·6	-2·2
Stocking Rate (Does (inc. followers) per ha (acre)) ...	10 (4)	15 (6)
GROSS MARGIN per ha (acre)	346 (138)	-33 (-13)

Notes:
1. Angora goats produce mohair; angora rabbits produce angora; cashgora is produced by angora cross feral goats; cashmere is produced by improved feral goats (valuable "down" has to be separated from guard hairs; thus, with cashmere production, "yield of down" must not be confused with "weight of clip" as percentage down is low and can vary widely). Goat meat is called "chevon".
2. The data for Breeding Does include output and inputs for a proportion (2%) of a buck and the doe's progeny. Progeny are sold after 2 clips for breeding or after 3 clips for meat. Stock may be retained for further shearing, but the annual margins shown above under "subsequent shearing" indicate that this is currently unprofitable.
3. Angora goats are usually clipped twice a year. Yield increases over first four clips, but quality decreases. Prices can be volatile, being dependent on fashion. Demand and prices for kid fibre are probably more stable than for adult fibre. The following yields and values have been used (recent wholesale values have been lower, but higher values possible by selling direct to handcraft markets):
Clip 1: 1·2 kg, £10/kg; clip 2: 1·8 kg, £7/kg; clip 3: 2·0 kg, £3·50/kg; clips 4-6: 2·2 kg, £2·75/kg; adult: 3·0 kg, £1·70/kg.
4. 1·5 kids born live per doe mated; 2% mortality to each clip. Number of doe kids sold for breeding equal to number of replacements required each year. National flock is expanding at present, therefore higher proportion may be sold for breeding. Value comprises: 0·2 breeders at £100 each, 1·22 kids for meat at £20 each.
5. *Culls.* Breeding stock culled after five years on average. Doe: buck ratio 50·1. Subsequent shearing stock culled after a further 4 clips. Value of all cull stock: £20 each. Replacement costs: does, £45; bucks, £100; shearing stock, £20 (as transfer from breeding enterprise).
6. *Concentrates.* Price: £140 per tonne. Quantities: Kids—12·5 kg to Clip 1, 25 kg to Clip 2, 25 kg to Clip 3; Adults—breeding 90 kg p.a., shearing 40 kg p.a.
7. Miscellaneous costs include 80p per shearing head and bedding materials.
8. *General.* Margins are particularly sensitive to value and numbers of breeding stock sold, yield and value of fibre, kidding percentage and meat values. When comparing with sheep margins the higher average working capital requirement should be recognised. Housing and fencing requirements similar to sheep.

Researcher: Martin Bent.

GRAZING LIVESTOCK UNITS

Dairy Cows	1·00	Ewes and Ewe Replacements	
Beef Cows (excl. calf) ...	0·75	(excl. suckling lambs):	
Bulls	0·65	light * weight	0·06
		medium * weight ...	0·08
Other Cattle (excl. intensive beef):		heavy * weight	0·11
0-1 year old	0·34	Rams	0·08
1-2 years old ...	0·65		
over 2 years old ...	0·80	Lambs:	
Barley Beef	0·47	0 to Fat or Store,	
		and Purchased Stores ...	0·04
		0 to Hoggets	0·08

* most lowland breeds are medium; few are light.

Notes

1. Total livestock units on a farm should be calculated by multiplying the above ratios by the *monthly livestock numbers averaged over the whole year, except* in the case of *lambs,* when *throughput* should be used.

2. The ratios are based on relative requirements of metabolisable energy. Strictly speaking, when calculating stocking density, allowances should also be made for differences in output (e.g. milk yield per cow or liveweight gain per head), breed (e.g. Friesians *v.* Jerseys), and quantities of non-forage feed consumed.

Source: Definitions of Terms used in Agricultural Business Management; (M.A.F.F., Dec. 1977).

Approximations

The following approximations will often suffice in calculating stocking rates, especially in view of the points made in note 2 above:

Dairy Cows	1·00	Lowland Ewes	
Beef Cows (excl. calf) ...	0·80	(inc. lambs under 6 months)	0·15
Other Cattle		Rams and Tegs (over 6 months)	0·15
over 2 years old... ...	0·80	Hill Ewes	0·1
Semi-Intensive Beef			
(6 to 15-18 months old)...	0·70		
Other Cattle 1 to 2 years old...	0·60		
Other Cattle			
under 1 year old ...	0·40		

These livestock units all relate to requirements over a twelve month period: thus in calculating total livestock units the ratios should be multiplied by *monthly livestock numbers averaged over the whole year.*

CAP Reform: Stocking Rate for Beef Premiums

Note that the above units are not those to be used for calculating stocking rates for the purpose of determining eligibility for the new beef premiums. Only dairy cows, beef and sheep animals qualifying for support payments are included in the calculation and the following livestock units are used: dairy and suckler cows (including replacement in-calf heifers) and male cattle over 2 years old, 1; male cattle 6 months-2 years, 0·6; ewes and goats, 0·15. The number of dairy cows used in the calculation are not the actual number on the farm but are based on the farm's milk quota divided by the average yield in the region (5200 kg in England). The total number of units are divided by the land area associated with these enterprises to give the stocking rate in units per hectare.

FORAGE VARIABLE COSTS

(£ per hectare (acre) per annum)

	Grass-Dairying (1)	Grass-Other (1)	Forage Maize (2)	Kale	Fodder Beet
Yield: tonnes/ha (tons/acre)	—	—	40 (16) (silage)	50 (20)	65 (26)
Seed	8 (3)	6 (2·5)	130 (53)	40 (16)	100 (40)
Fertilizer...	100 (40)	60 (24)	50 (20)	70 (28)	95 (38)
Sprays	7 (3)	4 (1·5)	35 (14)	50 (20)	140 (57)
Total	115 (46)	70 (28)	215 (87)	160 (64)	335 (135)

	Rape	Turnips	Rape and Turnips	Stubble Turnips	Swedes
Yield: tonnes/ha (tons/acre)	—	65 (26)	—	—	65 (26)
Seed	15 (6)	8 (3)	20 (8)	25 (10)	15 (6)
Fertilizer...	55 (22)	80 (32)	65 (26)	60 (24)	75 (30)
Sprays	—	37 (15)	—	—	35 (14)
Total	70 (28)	125 (50)	85 (34)	85 (34)	125 (50)

(1) These are *average* figures only. Intensively grazed grass may have much higher fertilizer costs in particular—possibly approaching £140 (57) for dairying. The seed costs will vary according to the proportion, if any, of permanent pasture and the length of the leys. Fertilizer inputs are often less on permanent pasture too, but this depends largely on the attitude of the farmer/manager, which will also be reflected in the stocking rates and productivity levels per animal achieved. Note that the dairying figure is the average for the grass devoted to the *whole herd*, i.e., followers as well as cows; the figure for cows alone will be higher (approx. £135 (55) total forage variable costs per hectare).

(2) Contract work on maize: drilling £37·50 (15); harvesting (inc. carting and clamping) 115 (47). For further details on this crop see "Forage Maize", by Q. Straghan and A. Perry, Genus Management, 1993. The area grown in Britain increased from 14,150 ha (35,000 acres) in 1983 to 77,000 ha (190,000 acres) in 1993.

An area payment (approx. £250/ha (£100/acre) in 1994) is available for forage maize, provided the area is not included in the stocking rate calculation for the beef premiums; the 15% set-aside requirement then applies.

Labour: grass, pages 106-7; kale, page 108; conservation labour, page 106-7. Conservation machinery, page 116.

Silage and Hay

Estimated average costs (for 1995) of producing and harvesting, on a full costs basis (i.e. including rental value of the land, all labour, share of general overheads, etc.) are:

Hay: £67·50 per tonne; Silage: £19 per tonne.

Approximately half the silage cost is for growing the grass and half for harvesting and storage. The % breakdown of total costs is as follows:

Variable Costs	Fertilizer	Seeds and Sprays	Contract	Sundries	
Silage ...	23	1	10	5	
Hay	18	1	2	2	

Fixed Costs	Rent	Labour	Tractors	Deprec. & Reps.	FYM/Lime
Silage ...	21	10	16	9	5
Hay	25	16	19	12	5

Sale Value of hay and (far less common because of its bulk) silage vary widely according to the region and type of season (supply/demand situation), quality and time of year. Silage is typically valued at about £22·50 a tonne.

Ensiled whole crop wheat (50% DM): cost approx. £34 per tonne.

Relative Costs of Grazing, Conserved Grass, etc. (1987)

Source: ICI (M. E. Hutchinson, Henley Manor Farm)

	Yield DM tonnes/ha (acre)	Cost per tonne DM (£)	MJ per kg DM	Pence per MJ of ME in DM
Grazed Grass	11·1 (4·5)	38·6	11·8	0·33
Kale (direct drilled)	6·9 (2·8)	42·0	11·0	0·38
Forage Turnips (direct drilled) ...	6·9 (2·8)	38·1	10·2	0·37
Grass Silage	11·1 (4·5)	69·1	10·9	0·63
Big Bale Silage	11·1 (4·5)	74·1	10·9	0·68
Extra Silage	2·5 (1·0)	37·0	10·9	0·34
Purchased Hay (1)	—	76·5	8·8	0·87
Brewers' Grains (2)	—	108·5	10·0	1·09
Concentrates (3)	—	155·2	12·8	1·21

(1) At £65/tonne. (2) At £24/tonne. (3) 14% CP, delivered in bulk, £133·50/tonne.

Notes

1. In interpreting the above comparative figures for use in planning feed use on the individual farm it is important to remember two points: (a) that own land, labour and capital for equipment are required for home-produced fodder but not for purchased feed, and much more storage is required, and (b) the limitation on the consumption of bulk fodder by ruminant livestock—although this very much depends upon its quality/digestibility.

2. 1992/93 data may be obtained from the Kingshay Farming Trust (Tel. 0460 72977).

Relative Value of Feeds

(based on their energy contents fed to dairy cows)

	Weight equivalent (1)	Relative Value (2)		Weight equivalent (1)	Relative Value (2)
Good hay	154	63	Fresh brewers' grains	589	16·5
Medium hay	165	59	Pressed sugar beet pulp	515	19
Dried grass	143	68	Dried distillers' grains	108	90
Swedes	767	12·5	Molassed dried beet pulp	107	91
Potatoes	449	21·5	Wheat middlings	113	86
Mangolds	857	11·5	Flaked maize	87	112
Cabbage	1030	9·5	Maize germ meal (14%)	88	111
Oats	119	82	Barley straw	218	45
Wheat	98	99	Oat straw	228	43
Sorghum	102	96	Wheat straw	245	40
Maize	97	101	Pea haulm straw	211	46
			Wheat bran	133	73

(1) equivalent to 100 of barley   (2) value (£) compared with barley at £97·50 per tonne (estimated average price, 1994 harvest crop)

Source: A.D.A.S. (D. Morgan)

See also Feedingstuffs: Nutritive Values, page 192.

FODDER CROPS, GRASSES AND CLOVERS: SEED PRICES (1994) AND SEED RATES

Crop	Price	Seed Rate per hectare
Fodder Kale	£8·50 to £11·25 per kg (£12·00 graded)	3·4 to 4·5 kg (1·1 to 1·7 graded)
Swedes	£15·00 to £23·50 per kg (£22·50 graded)	3·0 to 4·0 kg (less if graded)
Turnips	£4·20 per kg (£7·00 graded)	3·0 to 4·0 kg (less if graded)
Mangels	£12·00 per kg (£14 pelleted)	8 to 11 kg (less if graded)
Rape	£1·30 per kg	3·8 kg drilled 7·5 kg broadcast
Mustard	£1·30 per kg	22 to 28 kg
Rape and Turnips	£18 to £28 per hectare	10 to 11 kg rape 1 to 2 kg turnips
Rape, Kale and Turnips	£33 to £44 per hectare	—
Fodder Turnip	£4·00 to £6·25 per kg	7 kg broadcast
Fodder Beet	£104 per hectare	135,000 seeds
Forage Maize—Silage	£90 to £140 per hectare	110,000 to 120,000 seeds
Forage Maize—zero grazed	£100 to £160 per hectare	130,000 to 160,000 seeds
Arable Silage	£100 per hectare	125 kg oats, 60 kg tares
Tares	£55 per 50 kg	—
Italian Ryegrass	£1·20 to £1·30 per kg	33 to 50 kg
Perennial Ryegrass	£1·30 to £1·60 per kg	22 to 33 kg
Cocksfoot	£2·10 per kg	20 to 25 kg
Timothy	£1·20 per kg	7 to 9 kg
Meadow Fescue	£2·10 per kg	11 to 13 kg
Broad Red Clover	£3·00 per kg	18 to 22 kg
Tetraploid Red Clover	£2·20 per kg	18 to 22 kg
White Clover	£3·00 per kg	3·5 kg
Kent Wild White Clover	£6·50 per kg	—
Lucerne	£4·50 per kg	18 to 22 kg
Rye	£20 per 50 kg	220 kg
Rye and Ryegrass	£75 per hectare	125 kg rye, 22 kg Italian ryegrass
1 year leys	£50 to £55 per hectare	—
2-3 year leys	£40 to £45 per hectare	—
3-5 year leys	£40 to £45 per hectare	—
Intensive grazing mixture	£50 to £60 per hectare	—
Cockle Park mixture	£59 per hectare	—
Wye College mixture	£36 to £42 per hectare	—
Horse grazing	£50 per hectare	—
Game Cover mixture	£78 per hectare	—

4. PIGS AND POULTRY

PIGS

1. Breeding and Rearing (to 25 kg liveweight)

Performance Level			Average			High	
		per sow	per weaner			per sow	per weaner
		£	£			£	£
Weaners: 20 (1) @ £29 (3) ...		580	29·00	23·5 (2) @ £29 (3)		680	29·00
Less Livestock Depreciation (4)		25	1·25			30	1·30
Output		555	27·75			650	27·70
Variable Costs:							
Food (5)		370	18·50			370	15·40
Miscellaneous (6)		55	2·75			60	2·50
Total Variable Costs		425	21·25			430	17·90
Gross Margin (per year)		130	6·50			220	9·80

Notes

1. Weaners per sow—average: 9·1 reared per litter, 2·2 litters per year = 20 weaners per sow per year.
2. Weaners per sow—high: 10 reared per litter, 2·35 litters per year = 23·5 weaners per sow per year.
3. Price—assumed pig cycle average. (See footnote (N.B.) on p. 83). Prices for average quality 25 kg weaners have varied from £25 to £40 in recent years.
4. Average livestock depreciation assumes an in-pig gilt purchase price of £160, a cull value per sow of £130 and a 42·5% replacement rate (i.e. approx. 6 litters per sow life). Sow mortality 5%. Boars purchased at £575, sold at £135. "High" compared with "Average"; higher gilt and boar purchase prices and slightly fewer sows per boar assumed.
5. Food—2·0 tonne per sow, including boar (approx. 0·05 tonne per sow) and creep and weaner feed (approx. 35% of total). Price of feed consumed: £185 per tonne; (average of 65% sow feed (at £140-145) and 35% weaner feed (at £260-280), and of home-mixed and purchased compounds). High performance: slightly higher percentage of creep feed but lower feed cost per tonne, as higher proportion home-mixed.
6. Average: vet. and med. £18, transport £5·5, electricity and gas £15, water £3·5, straw and bedding £5, miscellaneous £8.
7. *Direct Labour Cost* per sow: average £130, good £100; per weaner: average £6·50, good £4·15. See further page 113.
8. *Building Costs:* see pages 150-51.

N.B. *Outdoor Breeding:* see page 85.

PIGS

2. *Feeding* (from 25 kg liveweight): per pig

A. *Average Performance*

	Pork £	Cutter £	Bacon £
Sale Value	58·85	66·95	71·75
LESS Weaner Cost*	29·00	29·00	29·00
Mortality charge	0·75	0·90	1·00
OUTPUT	29·10	37·05	41·75
Variable Costs:			
Food	23·30	27·60	30·15
Miscellaneous	1·35	1·90	2·85
TOTAL VARIABLE COSTS	24·65	29·50	33·00
GROSS MARGIN	4·45	7·55	8·75
Liveweight (kg)	77·5	88·5	92·5
Deadweight (kg)	55	65	69
Killing out (%)	71	73·5	74·5
Price per kg deadweight (p)	107	103	104
Price per kg liveweight (p)	75·9	75·6	77·6
Food Conversion Rate (n.b. from 25 kg)	2·65	2·8	2·85
Food per pig (kg)	139	178	192
Average Cost of Food per tonne	£167·50	£155	£157
Food Cost per kg Liveweight Gain	44·4p	43·5p	44·7p
Liveweight Gain per day (kg)	·64	·67	·63
Fattening period (weeks)	11·5	13·5	15·5
Mortality (per cent)	2·8	3·0	3·2
Direct Labour Cost per pig	£2·85	£3·60	£3·75
B. *High Performance* (Food Conversion)			
Food Conversion Rate (n.b. from 25 kg)	2·35	2·5	2·5
Food per pig (kg)	123	159	169
Food Cost per pig	£20·60	£24·65	£26·55
Food Cost per kg Liveweight Gain	39·2p	38·8p	39·3p
Gross margin per pig	£7·25	£10·65	£12·55
Direct Labour Cost per pig	£1·90	£2·40	£2·50

Notes

* Weaner cost assumes on farm transfer. If purchased (i.e., feeding only) transport and purchasing costs have to be added: these are very variable but average about £1 per weaner.

Labour: see page 113.

Building Costs: see pages 150-51.

Acknowledgement: Main data sources: Pig Production (annual, Agricultural Economics Unit, University of Exeter) and Pig Yearbook (Meat and Livestock Commission), but the pig and feed price assumptions are entirely the author's responsibility. Small differences in the relationship between these can of course cause large differences in margins. The weaner price is crucial as regards the relative margins between breeding and finishing.

N.B. No attempt has been made in this section to forecast the actual position of the pig cycle during 1995. The figures represent only what the average trend figures are likely to be in that year, given neither an "up" nor a "down" stage prevailing for much of the year. In recent years the UK Average All Pigs Price has varied from 83p to 138p/kg dwt. For the half year October 1993 to March 1994, the figure was below or very close to the very poor 90p level, having been above 115p in mid-1993. The level assumed above is approx. 105p.

3. Combined Breeding, Rearing and Feeding: per pig

	Pork £		Cutter £		Bacon £	
Level of Performance*	Average	High	Average	High	Average	High
Sale Value	58·85	58·85	66·95	66·95	71·75	71·75
Sow/boar deprecn. ...	1·25	1·30	1·25	1·30	1·25	1·30
Mortality charge ...	0·75	0·65	0·90	0·75	1·00	0·80
OUTPUT	56·85	56·90	64·80	64·90	69·50	69·65
Food	41·80	36·00	46·10	40·05	48·65	41·95
Miscellaneous	4·10	3·85	4·65	4·40	5·60	5·35
TOTAL VARIABLE COSTS	45·90	39·85	50·75	44·45	54·25	47·30
GROSS MARGIN per pig	10·95	17·05	14·05	20·45	15·25	22·35
GROSS MARGIN per sow	220	400	280	480	305	525
Labour	9·35	6·05	10·10	6·55	10·25	6·65

* Performance levels refer to breeding and rearing differences as on page 82 and, for feeding, differences in food conversion rate (and labour cost) only.

4. Further Performance Data

(Meat and Livestock Commission Pigplan results, Sept. 1992/93).

Level of Performance	Average	Top Third	Top 10%
Breeding			
Sow replacements (%)	43·8	43·6	42·4
Sow sales and deaths (%)	40·7	40·5	40·3
Sow mortality (%)	4·8	4·1	4·3
Litters per sow per year	2·24	2·34	2·41
Pigs reared per litter	9·53	9·95	10·38
Pigs reared per sow per year	21·4	23·2	25·1
Weight of pigs produced (kg)	6·5	6·2	6·3
Average weaning age (days)	25	23	24
Sow feed per sow per year (tonnes) ...	1·30	1·28	1·23
Feed per pig reared (kg): sow feed	67	61	55
piglet feed	0·3	0·3	0·3
Sow feed cost per tonne	£149	£148	£150
Piglet feed cost per tonne	£412	£426	£498
Sow feed cost per sow per year	£193	£190	£184
Feed cost per pig reared	£9·97	£9·08	£8·32
Rearing:			
Weight of pigs at start (kg)	6·5	6·5	6·5
Weight of pigs produced (kg)	34·7	35·2	33·2
Mortality (%)	2·8	2·5	1·9
Feed conversion ratio	1·79	1·67	1·52
Daily gain (kg)	·448	·456	·486
Feed cost per tonne	£220	£209	£203
Feed cost per kg gain (p)	39·4	35·0	30·8
Feed cost per pig reared	£11·12	£10·03	£8·23
Feed per pig reared (kg)	50·5	47·9	40·6

Feeding:

Weight of pigs at start (kg)	...	...	...	19·5	17·0	18·4
Weight of pigs produced (kg)	...	...	...	82·2	81·1	77·5
Mortality (%)	...	...	...	...	3·6	3·4	2·9
Feed conversion ratio	...	...	...	2·60	2·40	2·34
Daily gain (kg)	...	...	...	·586	·599	·615
Feed cost per tonne	...	...	...	£167	£160	£151
Feed cost per kg gain (p)	...	...	...	43·4	38·4	35·2
Feed cost per pig produced	...	...	...	£27·21	£24·61	£20·79
Feed per pig reared (kg)	...	...	...	163	154	138
Carcase weight (kg)	...	...	...	63·4	63·4	63·5

Source: Pig Yearbook 1994 (MLC).

5. Outdoor Breeding

The following comparison between Outdoor and Indoor Breeding Herds is from the University of Exeter's Pig Production reports (2-year averages, 1991/2 and1992/3):

	Outdoor	Indoor
Average age at weaning (days)	27	25
Live pigs born per litter	10·3	10·8
Pigs reared per litter	8·8	9·3
Litters per sow per year	2·11	2·23
Pigs reared per sow per year	18·8	20·7
Sow and boar feed per sow per year (tonnes) ...	1·44	1·29
Sow and boar feed per sow per year (£)	212	193
Sow and boar feed per pig reared (kg)	76	62
Sow and boar feed per pig reared (£)	11·4	9·3
Feed cost per tonne of meal equivalent	171	183

Outputs, costs and margin per sow:	£	£
Output	606	717
Feed	366	400
Other Variable Costs	21	27
Gross Margin	219	290
Labour	106	146
(Hours)	(21)	(27)
Land Charges	12	2
Buildings and Equipment	22	31
Other Fixed Costs	33	66
Net Margin	46	45

Piglets, weaners and store pigs sold:		
Liveweight (kg)	28·2	29·9
Price per kg liveweight (p)	123	120
Price per pig (£)	34·33	35·84

Stocking Rate for outdoor pigs is mainly 12·5 to 15 per ha (5 to 6 per acre). Good drainage is essential. A low rainfall and mild climate are also highly desirable.

It is estimated that outdoor pigs now represent around 20% of the UK breeding herd and that the proportion is continually increasing. One estimate is that the cost of establishing a 200-sow herd indoors is £1,280 a head, compared with £210 a head outdoors (PIC).

The MLC also gives comparative results for indoor and outdoor breeding herds.

EGG PRODUCTION

(brown egg layers, 52 week laying period)

Performance Level	Average per bird	Average per doz eggs	Cages High per bird	High per doz eggs	Free Range Average per bird	Average per doz eggs
	£	p	£	p	£	p
Egg Returns	11·67	50·0	12·50	50·0	15·18	66·0
Less Livestock Depreciation	2·12	9·1	2·12	8·5	2·45	10·7
Output (per year)	9·55	40·9	10·38	41·5	12·73	55·3
Variable Costs:						
Food	6·02	25·8	6·02	24·1	7·23	31·4
Miscellaneous	0·90	3·9	0·90	3·6	0·86	3·7
Total Variable Costs	6·92	29·7	6·92	27·7	8·09	35·1
Gross Margin	2·63	11·2	3·46	13·8	4·64	20·2

Notes

Hen-housed data are used throughout, i.e. the total costs and returns are divided by the number of birds housed at the commencement of the laying period.

A. Cage Production

1. The yields assumed are:
   Average ... ... 280 (23·33 dozen)
   High ... ... 300 (25·00 dozen)
2. The average price assumed (for 1995), 50p per dozen, includes all quantity and quality bonuses. Farmer to shop and consumer prices are well above packer to producer levels.
3. Livestock depreciation—the average point of lay pullet is priced at £2·50 (18 weeks old) less £0·48 for culls; (allowance has been made for mortality).
4. The food price assumed (for 1995) is £140 per tonne. The feed cost is dependent on breed, housing and environmental conditions, quantity purchased and type of ration. Quantity of feed used = 43 kg.
5. *Direct Labour Costs:* average £1·17 per bird, premium 95p. See page 113.

B. Free Range Production

1. Egg yields: 276 (23 dozen).
2. Average price: 66p per dozen.
3. Quantity of feed used = 48·2 kg. Price £150 per tonne.
4. *Direct Labour Costs:* average £2·87 per bird, dependent on automation.

Housing Costs: see page 151. Deadstock depreciation averages about £1 per caged bird.

Acknowledgement: see page 89.

REARING PULLETS

(Average per bird reared)

	£
Value of 18 week old bird	2·50
Less Chicks 1·02 (1) @ 50p (including levy)	0·51
Output	1·99
Variable Costs:	
Food: 6·9 kg @ £148 per tonne	1·02
Miscellaneous (2)	0·49
Total Variable Costs	1·51
Gross Margin	0·48

1. Assumes 4 per cent mortality, but 2 per cent allowed in price.
2. Excluding transport (10p), but including gumboro vaccination and in some cases voluntary salmonella testing.

Labour 23p;   *deadstock depreciation* 26p.

TABLE POULTRY

A. *Broilers* (per bird sold at 46 days)

	p
Returns: 2·36 kg per bird @ 60·5p per kg L.W.	142·8
Less Cost of Chick	22·8
Output	120·0
Variable Costs:	
Food: 4·8 kg per bird @ £180 per tonne	86·4
Heat, Light, Miscellaneous	11·1
Total Variable Costs	97·5
Gross Margin	22·5

Capital cost of housing and equipment: £4·25 per broiler space (depreciation cost approximately 3·1p per bird sold).

Labour: 3·5p, excluding catching and cleaning out (3·5p) but includes management; see page 113.

Housing Costs: see page 151.

B. Turkeys (per bird sold) (1)

Size (2)					Light £	Medium £	Heavy £
Returns (Christmas) (3)	...	...	...	...	9·90	13·28	16·01
Returns (All Year Average) (3)	...	...	...	...	8·18	10·97	14·55
Less Cost of Poult	...	...	...	...	1·90	2·05	2·05
OUTPUT (Christmas)	...	...	...	...	8·00	11·23	13·96
OUTPUT (All Year Average)	...	...	...	...	6·28	8·92	12·50
Variable Costs:							
Food (£185 per tonne)	...	...	...	...	2·35	3·72	6·27
Miscellaneous	...	...	...	...	1·44	1·70	2·01
TOTAL VARIABLE COSTS	...	...	...	...	3·79	5·42	8·28
GROSS MARGIN (Christmas)	...	...	...	...	4·21	5·81	5·68
GROSS MARGIN (All Year Average)	...	...	...	...	2·49	3·50	4·22
Killing Age (weeks)	...	...	...	...	14	18	20
Deadweight (kg)	...	...	...	...	4·4	5·9	9·7
Food Conversion Factor	...	...	...	...	2·7	3·2	3·2
Food per bird (kg)	...	...	...	...	12·0	18·6	30·8

(1) 6, 8 and 10% mortality allowed for in cost of poult and feed figures for light, medium and heavy weights respectively.

(2) Light and medium: hen birds; heavy: stags. (As hatched).

(3) Price per kg D.W.: Christmas: hens 210-255p (usually the heavier the bird the lower the price), stags 150-180p; All Year Average: hens 172-200p, stags 135-165p.

Note

Considerable variations occur between individual strains and because of different production systems and feeding regimes. The figures should therefore be used only as rough guidelines.

C. Roasters (Capons) (per bird sold at 12 weeks; Christmas—males only)

									£
Returns 4·6 kg @ £1·85 per kg.	...	...	...	...	...	...	...	...	8·51
Less Cost of Chick	...	...	...	...	...	...	...	...	0·48
OUTPUT	...	...	...	...	...	...	...	...	8·03
Variable costs:									
Food: 14·5 kg per bird @ £180 per tonne	...	...	...	...		2·87
Miscellaneous	...	...	...	...	...	...	...	...	0·49
TOTAL VARIABLE COSTS	...	...	...	...	...	...	...	3·36
GROSS MARGIN	...	...	...	...	...	...	...	...	4·67

10% mortality allowed for in cost of chick and feed figures.

D. *Ducks* (Aylesbury type: per bird sold at 7 weeks)

	£
Returns: 3·2 kg @ £2·10 per kg D.W.	6·72
LESS Cost of Duckling	1·00
OUTPUT	5·72
Variable Costs:	
Food: 9·4 kg per bird @ £195 per tonne	2·01
Miscellaneous	0·75
TOTAL VARIABLE COSTS	2·76
GROSS MARGIN	2·96

E. *Geese*

	£
Returns: 5·5 kg @ £3·90 per kg D.W.	21·45
LESS Cost of Gosling	3·50
OUTPUT	17·95
Variable Costs:	
Food: 18·0 kg @ £190 per tonne	3·76
Miscellaneous	0·96
TOTAL VARIABLE COSTS	4·72
GROSS MARGIN	13·23

N.B. Feed costs for both ducks and geese allow for mortality.

Acknowledgement: The figures in the whole of the poultry section are as estimated by the Poultry Department of ADAS.

RAINBOW TROUT

(per tonne of fish)

							£
Sales: 1 tonne of fish @ £1·87 per kg	...	...	...	...	...		1,870
LESS 3,700 fingerlings @ 4·6p each	...	...	...	...	...		170
OUTPUT	...	...	...	...	...	...	1,700
Variable Costs:							
Food: 1·3 tonnes @ £470/tonne	...	...	...	...	...		610
Vet. and med.	...	...	...	...	...	...	40
Marketing and transport	...	...	...	...	...	...	95
TOTAL VARIABLE COSTS	...	...	...	...	...	...	745
GROSS MARGIN	...	...	...	...	...	...	955

Notes

Fish growing to 300g from fingerlings at 4·5g.

Prices are expected wholesale, 1994, but most fish farmers sell at least some of their production direct to retailers, caterers and consumers at prices up to £4·20 kg, but with added marketing costs.

Fingerlings price: 3·0 to 5·0p each according to quantity ordered and time of year. All female stocks of fingerling are increasing in popularity and will be priced at the top end of the price range.

Average feeding period, 10 months. Mortality, from fingerling to market size, 11%. Food conversion ratio, 1·3 : 1. The price for fish food is an average price for a pigmented expanded pellet. The price of such a pellet varies from £430 to £515 per tonne, plus delivery. Specialist very high oil diets are now available, at £650-£750/tonne, which will give feed conversion ratios better than 1:1. Non-pigmented food is around £70 per tonne cheaper.

Current capital costs for construction of earth pond unit approx. £1,000 per tonne of holding capacity, to include buildings, holding systems and installation of water supply and services, but excluding land.

Labour requirement: the basic norm has in the past been 1 man per 50 tonnes of fish produced per annum on a table fish farm, but with mechanisation this can now be as high as 100 tonnes on some farms.

Acknowledgement: Data provided by Dr. J. R. C. Springate, BOCM PAULS, Renfrew, Scotland.

II. LABOUR

1. LABOUR COST

1. Statutory Minimum Wage Rates
(from June 5, 1994)

The minimum weekly rates relate to a 39-hour standard week of normal hours worked on any five days between Monday and Saturday.(1, 2) The rates apply to both men and women.

Grades I & II Age	Appointment Grade I		Appointment Grade II		NVQ Level 3 (3)		Craftsmen (4)	
	Weekly rate	Overtime per hour	Weekly rate	Overtime per hour	Weekly rate	Overtime per hour	Weekly rate	Overtime per hour
	£	£	£	£	£	£	£	£
20 and over	195·87	7·53	181·36	6·98	171·20	6·58	166·85	6·42

Age	Ordinary Rates					Night work Supplement	Standby Payments
	Whole-time or Part-time workers			Casual workers (5)			
	rate per standard week	rate per hour excluding overtime	overtime rate per hour	rate per hour excluding overtime	overtime rate per hour	rate per hour	rate per day
	£	£	£	£	£	p	£
20 & over	145·09	3·72	5·58	2·76	4·13	74	14·88
19	124·05	3·18	4·77	2·47	3·71	63	12·72
18	110·27	2·83	4·24	2·20	3·30	56	11·31
17	89·52	2·30	3·44	1·78	2·68	46	9·18
16	75·74	1·94	2·91	1·51	2·26	39	7·77
15	68·92	1·77	2·65	1·37	2·06	35	7·07
14	—	1·67	2·51	1·30	1·95	—	—
13	—	1·58	2·38	1·23	1·85	—	—

1. Holidays with pay (Regular Workers): 21 days for workers with 52 weeks' continuous service. The rates of holiday pay for whole-time workers are given on page 92.

2. Rates of pay over the above rates were introduced for flexible working from September 5th, 1993: 5% or 7% higher, according to the working pattern.

3. National Vocational Qualification (NVQ) Level 3 craftsmen (18% premium above the basic rate).

4. In 1993 29·3 per cent of the regular whole-time adult male labour force in England and Wales were classified as craftsmen (plus 4·2 per cent as Grade I and 7·9 per cent as Grade II). However, many other workers receive basic wages above the "ordinary" rates.

5. Casual workers: employed on temporary basis by the hour or day; excludes workers continuously employed for more than 20 weeks.

6. Pre-college students with an approved certificate may be paid 75% of the appropriate minimum rate for age. There are special rates for foreign students for limited periods of employment under an approved exchange scheme.

7. Certain benefits are reckonable in part payment of the minimum wage rates, at specified values, e.g. a cottage or house (£1·50/week—though can be varied on application), board and lodging. There are specified provisions for sick pay.

Holiday Pay for Whole-Time Workers

Age	Appointment Grade I		Appointment Grade II		Craftsman Grade†		Other Worker	
	Weekly rate	Daily rate	Weekly rate	Daily rate	Weekly rate	Daily rate	Weekly rate	Daily rate
	£	£	£	£	£	£	£	£
20 & over	244·83	48·97	226·70	45·34	208·56	41·71	181·36	36·27
19	—	—	—	—	—	—	155·06	31·01
18	—	—	—	—	—	—	137·83	27·57
17	—	—	—	—	—	—	111·90	22·38
16	—	—	—	—	—	—	94·67	18·93
15	—	—	—	—	—	—	86·15	17·23

† NVQ Level 3 craftsmen: £214·00 weekly, £42·80 daily.

2. Average Earnings (1)

Type of Worker	Average Total Earnings				Total Hours (3)
	1993		1995 (est.) (2)		
	Annual	Per Week	Annual	Per Week	Per Week
	£	£	£	£	
All Hired Men	11,475	220·5	12,325	237	46·5
Foremen	13,725	263·5	14,750	284	46·1
Dairy Herdsmen ...	13,650	262·5	14,650	282	51·6
Other Stockmen ...	11,600	223·0	12,450	240	46·4
Tractor Drivers... ...	11,950	230·0	12,850	247	47·9
General Farm Workers	10,800	207·5	11,600	223	46·3
Horticultural Workers ...	9,925	191·0	10,675	205	42·2

1. Hired regular whole-time workers, England and Wales (to nearest £25/year, 50p/week).

2. 1993 earnings, plus approx. 7·5 per cent.

3. Hours worked plus statutory holidays (in 1993).

Source: MAFF Statistics (Survey of Earnings and Hours), with author's adjustments.

3. Typical Annual Labour Cost 1994/95
(regular worker of 20 or more[1]: from June 5, 1994 to (approx.) June 4, 1995)

		Average Annual Cost £	Average Weekly Cost £	Average Hourly Cost (2) £
Minimum Wage (non-craftsman rate) (3)		7690	147·90	4·29
National Insurance Contribution (10·2% of earnings) (4)... ...	785			
Employer's Liability Insurance (1%)	75	860	16·50	
Minimum Cost		8550	164·40	4·77
Overtime, average 7·5 hours per week @ £5·58 (+ NIC, ELI)		2420	46·55	
		10970	210·95	5·02
"Premium" over basic rate, average £27·50 per week (+ NIC, ELI) ...		1590	30·60	
Total Cost (5, 6)		12560	241·55	5·75

(NIC = National Insurance Contributions; ELI = Employer's Liability Insurance)

1. Assuming not paid Craftsman rates (but note "premium" assumed well exceeds Craftsman's "premium" of £21·75 per week).
2. Hours, excluding overtime, based on 46 weeks (of 39 hours) per year, i.e. statutory holidays and a few days' illness have been deducted.
3. Including additional holiday pay.
4. Employer's NIC reduces from 10·2% to 7·6% if the employee's total weekly earnings fall below £200 a week (see page 179).
5. Annual cost (or net value) of cottages, value of perquisites, contribution towards payment of the council tax, etc., would have to be added where appropriate.
6. Total average worker's gross *earnings* on the above assumptions = £11,300 a year, £217·30 a week, £5·17 an hour.

4. Assessing Annual Labour Requirements

The regular labour staff required for a farm is sometimes assessed by calculating the total number of Standard Man-Days (Man-Work Units), as given on page 193. The number of days supplied by casual labour are first deducted, then 15 per cent is added for general maintenance work; it is assumed that 300 Standard Man-Days are provided annually per man; allowance is made for any manual labour supplied by the farmer himself. Alternatively, no addition is made for maintenance work and 300 SMD are assumed to be provided by stockmen and 250 by other workers. (1 SMD = 8 labour hours a year.)

This is a very rough and inaccurate calculation since it makes no allowance for seasonality and the special circumstances of an individual farm, such as soil type, level of mechanization, and condition and layout of the buildings.

The following sections supply the type of data that should be used in assessing labour requirements.

2. LABOUR HOURS AVAILABLE FOR FIELD WORK
(per man per month)

	Total Ordinary Hours (1)	Adjusted Ordinary Hours (2)	% Workable	Available Ordinary Hours (3)	Available Overtime Hours (4)	Total Available Hours	Total Available "8-hour Days" (5)
January	177	148	50	74	28 (61)	**102** (135)	13 (17)
February	160	134	50	67	33 (55)	**100** (122)	12½ (15)
March	172	149	60	89	69 (82)	**158** (171)	20 (21½)
April	161	139	65	90	86	**176**	22
May	171	151	70	106	110	**216**	27
June	170	150	75	112	112	**224**	28
July	177	157	75	118	113	**231**	29
August	169	150	75	112	104	**216**	27
September	172	152	70	106	82 (69)	**188** (195)	23½ (24½)
October	177	153	65	99	63 (83)	**162** (182)	20 (23)
November	172	144	50	72	26 (59)	**98** (131)	12 (16½)
December	161	135	50	67	25 (65)	**92** (132)	11½ (16½)

(1) 40 hour week, less public holidays. No deductions have been made for other holidays because they may be taken at various times of the year.

(2) After deducting (a) for illness (10 per cent Nov. to Feb., 7½ per cent March, April and Oct., 5 per cent May to Sept.), and (b) for contingencies and non-delayable maintenance (½ hour per day).

(3) Adjusted Ordinary Hours × percentage Workable.

(4) Maximum 4 overtime hours per day summer, 3 hours winter, and 12 to 14 hours' work at weekends, according to season. Same adjustments for illness and percentage workable as for ordinary hours. Figures in brackets indicate hours available if headlights used up to limit of overtime stated. The percentage overtime (without headlights) available from weekend work as opposed to evenings = (January to December respectively): 100, 78, 58, 50, 40, 40, 41, 42, 53, 67, 100, 100.

(5) Total available hours ÷ 8.

Notes

1. *These figures relate to medium land. The percentage workability will be higher with light soils and less with particularly heavy soils.* On heavy soils, of course, the land may be virtually 100 per cent unworkable between late November and early March (or still later, according to the season), particularly if undrained. A rough estimate of variations in workability according to soil type (compared with the figures in the above table) are as follows. Heavy land—March, October, November: one-third less; April: one-fifth less; September: 10 per cent less; May to August: no difference. Light land—October to April: one-sixth more; May and September: 10 per cent more; June to August: no difference.

2. When these figures are used for farm planning, it must be remembered that indoor work, e.g. livestock tending or potato riddling, can be continued over the full working-week, i.e. the hours available are the Adjusted Ordinary Hours, plus overtime. Also, some handwork in the field has to continue even in rain, e.g. sprout picking.

3. To be precise, percentage workability varies according to the particular operation, e.g. compare ploughing and drilling.

4. Furthermore, some operations are limited by factors other than soil workability, e.g. combine-harvesting by grain moisture content.

5. Factors touched upon briefly above are discussed fully in Duckham's "The Farming Year".

3. SEASONAL LABOUR REQUIREMENTS FOR CROPS AND GRASS

On the following pages, data on labour requirements for various farm crops and types of livestock are given. Two levels are shown: average and premium. *The average figures relate to the whole range of conditions and farm size. The premium rates do not denote the maximum rates possible,* for instance by the use of especially high-powered tractors under ideal conditions, but relate to rates of work estimated to be obtainable over the whole season, averaging good and bad conditions, with the use of wide implements, largish tractors (75 to 90 kW) (100-120 hp) and high capacity equipment in 8 hectare fields and over, where no time is wasted. **Most farmers with more than 200 hectares (500 acres) of arable land are likely to achieve the premium levels shown. Those with over 400 hectares (1,000 acres) will have still bigger machines and therefore faster work rates, and thus require about 10 to 20 per cent less labour than even the premium levels given.**

The rates of work include morning preparation, travelling to and from the fields, and allow for minor breakdowns and other stoppages. They relate broadly to medium and medium-heavy land; some jobs, such as ploughing, may be done more quickly on light soils. Operations such as combine harvesting can obviously vary according to many factors to do with the topography and other natural features of the farm.

The usual times of year when each operation takes place are shown; these relate to lowland conditions in the south-eastern half of Britain. They will obviously vary between seasons, soil types, latitude and altitude. In particular, on light land, land can be ploughed over a longer winter period and a high proportion of cultivations for spring crops may be completed in February in many seasons. All such factors must be allowed for in individual farm planning. Conditions in different seasons will also affect, for instance, the number and type of cultivations required in seedbed preparation. Typical monthly breakdowns of requirements are given for various crops.

To illustrate the type of questions that need to be asked for full details of seasonal labour requirements on the individual farm, "Critical Questions affecting Timing" are listed for cereals and main crop potatoes. Similar questions would, of course, need to be asked for other crops.

Seasonal Labour Requirements

WINTER CEREALS

Operations	Labour-Hours per hectare Average	Premium	Time of Year
Plough (1)	1·4	1·0	July to October (according to previous crop)
Cultivate (often power harrow)	1·0	0·7	September to October (according to previous crop) (half August if ploughed in July)
Drill (often with power harrows), Roll	1·3	0·9	Mid-September to 3rd week October (according to previous crop and soil)
Apply Fertilizer	0·4	0·3	
Spray ,...	0·3	0·2	October-November
Top Dress (three times (2)) ...	1·2	0·9	March and April
Spray (three or four (2)) ...	1·0	0·7	Spring/early summer
Combine, Cart Grain, Barn Work	2·7	2·1	Mid-August to approx. 10th September
Later Barn Work (3)	0·7	0·4	September to June
Total	10·0	7·2	
Straw: Bale	1·3	0·8	Mid-August to end
Cart	3·7	2·8	September

Typical Monthly Breakdown

Month	Average	Premium	Notes
October ...	2·6	1·9	Approx. 60% of Ploughing,
November ...	—	—	Cults., Drill, Harrow
December ...	—	—	
January ...	—	—	
February ...	—	—	
March ...	0·5	0·3	Part Top Dress
April	1·1	0·8	Part Top Dress, Spraying
May	0·3	0·3	Spraying
June	0·3	0·2	Spraying
July	—	—	
August ...	1·8 (+2·5 Straw)	1·4 (+1·8 Straw)	⅔ of harvesting (4)
September (harvest) ...	0·9 (+2·5 Straw)	0·7 (+1·8 Straw)	⅓ of harvesting (4)
September (prepn. drill)	1·8	1·2	40% of Ploughing, Cults., Drill, Harrow

Notes

1. Some cereal crops are direct drilled or drilled after reduced, or minimal, cultivations, i.e. without traditional ploughing. Direct drilling reduces man-hours per hectare by about 2·5 (average) or 1·8 (premium), and minimal cultivations by about 1·2 (average) and 0·9 (premium).

2. Winter wheat; winter barley will often have one less top dressing and spraying and oats two less.

3. Later barn work excluded from monthly breakdown.

4. Winter wheat (see page 98 for harvest times for winter barley and oats).

SPRING CEREALS

Operations	Labour-Hours per hectare		Time of Year
	Average	Premium	
Plough (1)	1·4	1·0	September-March (according to previous crop and soil type)
Cultivate (often power harrow)	1·0	0·7	March (½ in second half February on light land)
Apply Fertilizer	0·4	0·3	
Drill (often with power harrows), Roll	1·3	0·9	March (¼ at end February on light land)
Top Dress (once, some possibly twice)	0·5	0·3	
Spray (two or three)	0·7	0·5	May
Combine, Cart Grain, Barn Work	2·6	2·0	Last three-quarters of August (affected by variety as well as season)
Later Barn Work (2)	0·6	0·4	September to June
Total	8·5	6·1	
Straw: Bale (unmanned sledge)	1·3	0·8	Mid-August to end
Cart	3·7	2·8	September

Typical Monthly Breakdown

Month	Average	Premium	Notes
October ...	0·4	0·3	Ploughing. How much in
November ...	0·8	0·5	October depends on
December ...	0·2	0·2	area of Winter Wheat, Potatoes, etc.
January ...	—	—	
February ...	—	—	
March ...	2·7	1·9	All Cults. Drilling, Rolling (nearly half in February on light land)
April ...	—	—	
May ...	1·2	0·8	Spray and top dress
June ...	—	—	
July ...	—	—	
August (3) ...	2·6 (+2·7 Straw)	2·0 (+1·9 Straw)	
September ...	— (+2·3 Straw)	— (+1·7 Straw)	

Notes

1. See note 1 on page 96.
2. Later barn work excluded.
3. Spring barley; spring wheat and oats partly September (see page 98).

Seasonal Labour Requirements

In a *normal* (i.e. neither early or late season):

WINTER WHEAT

Drilling mid-September to 3rd week October.
Harvesting mid-August to approx. 10th September.

WINTER BARLEY

As for winter wheat, except that:

Ploughing unlikely to start before cereal harvest, as usually follows a cereal crop.
Harvesting some weeks earlier: mid July to approx. 10th August.

WINTER OATS

As for winter wheat, except that:

Drilling usually first full half of October.
Harvesting earlier (first half of August).

SPRING BARLEY

Drilling end of February to end of March or early April.
Harvesting last half/$\frac{3}{4}$ of August.

SPRING WHEAT

As for spring barley, except that:

Drilling is on average one or two weeks earlier (should be finished in March)—lose more if late than barley.
Harvesting, on average, is two weeks later: last week of August/first half of September (two-thirds in September).

SPRING OATS

As for spring barley, except that:

Drilling is usually a little earlier.
Harvesting is later than spring barley, earlier than spring wheat: end of August/beginning of September.

Seasonal Labour Requirements

Critical Questions affecting Timing (Autumn-sown Cereals)

1. Previous crops (affects time available and need for ploughing and cultivations).
2. Will the crop be ploughed traditionally, chisel ploughed, minimally cultivated, or direct drilled?
3. Earliest and latest drilling date, by choice.
4. Effect on yield if drilling is delayed.
5. Autumn weed control?
6. In the spring: (a) whether crop is rolled, and when.
   (b) whether crop is harrowed, and when.
   (c) time of top dressings.
   (d) Number of spray applications.
7. (a) Average period for harvesting.
   (b) Earliest dates for starting and finishing harvest, and latest dates for starting and finishing harvest, ignoring extreme seasons (one year in ten).

Critical Questions affecting Timing (Spring-sown Cereals)

1. Previous crops.
2. Will the crop be ploughed traditionally, chisel ploughed, minimally cultivated, or direct drilled?
3. Months when winter ploughing is possible, on average. (Where relevant).
4. Is spring ploughing satisfactory? (Where relevant).
5. Average period of cultivations and drilling.
6. Earliest dates for starting and finishing spring cultivations/drilling and latest dates for starting and finishing cultivations/drilling, ignoring extreme seasons (one year in ten).
7. Effect on yield if drilling is delayed.
8. Is the crop rolled (a) within a few days of drilling or (b) later?
9. (a) Average period of harvesting.
   (b) Earliest dates for starting and finishing harvest, and latest dates for starting and finishing harvest, ignoring extreme seasons (one year in ten).

MAINCROP POTATOES

| Operations | Labour-Hours per hectare | | Time of Year |
	Average	Premium	
Plough	1·4	1·0	September to December
Cultivating, Ridging, Destoning/			
Clod sep. (as required) ...	6·5	5·0	March, early April
Plant and Apply Fertilizer (1) ...	4·5	3·5	Last quarter of March, first
Apply Herbicide...	0·3	0·2	three-quarters of April
Spray for Blight (av. 4 times) ...	1·2	0·9	July, first half August
Burn off Haulm	0·3	0·2	End September, early October
Harvest, Cart, Clamp (2) ...	15·0	10·0	End September, October
Work on Indoor Clamp ...	4·8	3·2	November
Riddle, Bag, Load	40·0	30·0	October to May
TOTAL	74·0	54·0	

(1) Automatic planter. Hand-fed planters: approx. 12 hours plus 8 that could be casual labour.

(2) Mechanical harvester, excluding up to 25 hours for picking off on harvester—usually casual labour. None may be needed on clod- and stone-free soils. Hand harvesting: additional approx. 80 hours of casual labour.

Typical Monthly Breakdown

Month	Average	Premium	Notes
October ...	12·2	8·2	80% of harvest, ½ burn off
November ...	5·9	4·0	Clamp work and ¾ plough
December ...	0·3	0·2	¼ plough
January ...	—	—	
February ...	—	—	
March	7·8	6·0	All fertilizer, ½ cults., ¼ plant
April	3·5	2·7	½ cults., ¾ plant
May	—	—	
June	—	—	
July	0·9	0·7	3 blight sprays
August ...	0·3	0·2	1 blight spray
September ...	3·1	2·0	20% harvest, ½ burn off

Note: These figures exclude casual labour and riddling.

Seasonal Labour Requirements

EARLY POTATOES

Operations	Labour-Hours per hectare Average	Premium	Time of Year
Plough	1·4	1·0	September to December
Cultivating, etc.	6·5	5·0	Late February, early March
Plant and Apply Fertilizer ...	4·5	3·5	Late February, early March
Apply Herbicide	0·3	0·2	1st half March (some in February on light land or in early season)
Further Spraying	0·3	0·2	
After-Cultivation/Spray ...	0·3	0·2	April, early May
Harvest, bag, load	30·0(1)	25·0(2)	2nd week June onwards. All June or till mid-July

(1) Excluding 80 hours picking—usually casuals.

(2) Excluding 60 hours picking—usually casuals.

SECOND EARLY POTATOES

Operations	Labour-Hours per hectare Average	Premium	Time of Year
Plough	1·4	1·0	September to December
Cultivating, etc.	6·5	5·0	March
Plant and Apply Fertilizer ...	4·5	3·5	March
Apply Herbicide	0·3	0·2	Half 2nd half March, half 1st half April
Further Spraying	0·9	0·7	End April, May, early June
Harvest	15·0(1)	10·0(2)	Mid-July to end August

(1) Spinner or elevator-digger, excluding picking and riddling—usually casual labour.

(2) Mechanical harvester, excluding picking off on harvester and riddling—usually casual labour.

101

Seasonal Labour Requirements

SUGAR BEET

Operations	Labour-Hours per hectare		Time of Year
	Average	Premium	
Plough	1·4	1·0	September to December
Seedbed Cults	3·4	2·4	Mainly March (some early April. Some late February in good seasons)
Load, Cart, Apply Fertilizer	0·8	0·6	
Drill (and Flat Roll)	2·0	1·3	Late March and April, especially early April
Spray (herbicide: pre- and post-emergence)	0·6	0·4	Late March/April
Spray (× 2)	0·6	0·4	May/June
Spray (aphis)	0·3	0·2	July
Harvest (machine)	15·0	10·0	End September, October, November
Load	3·4	2·7	End September to early January
TOTAL	27·5	19·0	

Typical Monthly Breakdown

Month	Average	Premium	Notes
October ...	7·7	5·2	45% harvest; + loading
November ...	8·7	5·9	45% harvest; ¾ ploughing; + loading
December ...	1·0	0·8	¼ ploughing; + loading
January ...	0·5	0·4	Loading
February ...	—	—	
March ...	4·1	2·8	Fertilizer, most of cults., some drilling
April	2·7	1·9	Some cults., most of drilling
May	0·3	0·2	Spray
June	0·3	0·2	Spray
July	0·2	0·2	Spray
August ...	—	—	
September ...	2·0	1·4	10% harvesting; + loading

Seasonal Labour Requirements

VINING PEAS

Operations	Labour-Hours per hectare		Time of Year
	Average	Premium	
Plough	1·4	1·0	September to December
Cults., Fert. and Drill	2·5	1·8	Mid-Feb. to April
Post Drilling and Spraying ...	1·5	1·0	
Harvesting	20·0	15·0	July and early August

Note

Drilling is staggered in small areas through the season, ranging from early varieties to late varieties.

DRIED PEAS

Month	Labour-Hours per hectare		Operation
	Average	Premium	
October	1·4	1·0	} Stubble cult.; Plough
November ...	0·9	0·6	
December ...	0·2	0·2	
January	—	—	
February	0·2	0·1	Cult. twice, harrow; drill and fert. (80 per
March ...	3·4	2·4	cent March); light harrow and roll;
April	0·6	0·4	spray
May	2·5	1·8	} Scare pigeons; spray
June	0·2	0·2	
July	2·2	1·4	} Possible spray desiccant; combine and
August	2·5	1·6	cart; dry
September ...	1·0	0·5	} Stubble cult.

Assumes direct combining.

FIELD BEANS

A. Winter Beans

Operations	Labour-Hours per hectare Average	Premium	Time of Year
Broadcast Seed	0·6	0·4 ⎫	
Apply Fertilizer	0·4	0·3 ⎪	
Plough	1·4	1·0 ⎬ September/October	
Power Harrow	1·0	0·8 ⎪	
Spray (pre-emergence) ...	0·3	0·2 ⎭	
Spraying (two or three times)	0·8	0·5	Spring
Combine and cart and barnwork	3·6	3·0	August

B. Spring Beans

Operations	Labour-Hours per hectare Average	Premium	Time of Year
Plough	1·4	1·0	September to December
Cultivate (often power harrow)	1·0	0·7 ⎫	
Apply Fertilizer	0·4	0·3 ⎬ End Feb., early March	
Drill, Roll	1·3	0·9 ⎪	
Spray (two or three times) ...	0·8	0·5 ⎭	
Combine and cart and barnwork	3·6	3·0	September

OILSEED RAPE

(Autumn Sown)

Month	Labour-Hours per hectare Average	Premium	Operation
October ... ... ⎫			
November ... ⎬ 0·6		0·4	Spray herbicide and insecticide if necessary
December ... ⎭			
January	—	—	
February	—	—	
March ... ⎫			
April ... ⎬ 1·0		0·6	Top dress twice
May ... ... ⎭			
June	—	—	
July	2·9	2·1 ⎫	Windrow (1st half July); combine (½ 2nd
August	2·6	1·8 ⎬	half July; ½ 1st half Aug.); straw, dry
August	2·0	1·3 ⎫	Cults. (× 2), spray, drill, fert.; harrow, roll,
September ...	3·3	2·1 ⎭	barn work (0·5)

HERBAGE SEEDS (first production year)

A. Undersown

Operations	Labour-Hours per hectare Average	Premium	Time of Year
Undersow	0·6	0·4	March, April
Roll	(0·6	0·4)	Straight after drilling
Load, Cart, Apply Fertilizer ...	0·4	0·3	September
	0·4	0·3	Late February, March
Harvest (by Combine): Mow	1·4	0·9	3 to 4 days before combining
	4·5	3·5	*Ital. Ryegrasses and Early Perennials: late July. Intermed Perennials: late July/early August.*
Combine and Cart			*Late Perennials/White Clover: mid-August.*
	6·0	4·5	Meadow Fescue: early July
	7·0	5·0	Cocksfoot: early July
	10·0	7·0	Timothy: mid-August Red Clover: late September

B. Direct Drilled in Autumn

Operations	Labour-Hours per hectare Average	Premium	Time of Year
Plough	1·4	1·0	} Depends on previous crop— Usually July or August
Seedbed Cults.	2·2	1·6	
Load, Cart, Apply Fertilizer	0·4	0·3	
Drill (with harrows behind) ...	0·8	0·6	As early as previous crop allows. This may be up to mid-September for rye-grasses without detriment to the subsequent yield.
Roll (soon after drilling) ...	0·6	0·4	Meadow fescue and cocksfoot are best sown
Harvest ... ... See above (Undersown)			no later than July and it is risky to sow timothy much later than this.

GRASS

A. Production

Operations	Labour-Hours per hectare Average	Premium	Time of Year
Plough	1·4	1·0	Autumn drilling: may not plough
Seedbed Cults.	2·2	1·6	
Load, Cart, Apply Fertilizer	0·4	0·3	
Drill*	0·7	0·5	Mid-March to mid-April (1) or end July to mid-Sept.
Roll	0·6	0·4	Soon after drilling
Load, Cart, Apply Fertilizer*:			
(three lots)	1·2	0·9	March to mid-August (2)
Top*	1·4	0·9	Mid-June to mid-July; if grazed only

Notes

1. Direct drilling in spring may continue to mid-May to enable extra cleaning cultivations or the application of farmyard manure.

2. P. and K. may be applied in September—especially on undersown ley in year sown.

* Only these operations apply where the seeds are undersown in a spring cereal crop soon after drilling. One extra harrowing and rolling are needed if undersown in an autumn-sown cereal crop.

B. Conservation

Operations	Labour-Hours per hectare Average	Premium	Time of Year
Hay (5·5 tonnes per hectare)			
Mow	1·2	0·9	
Turn, etc.	2·6	1·9	Two-thirds June, one-third
Bale	1·3	0·9	July
Cart	6·0	4·5	
Total per hectare	11·1	8·2	
Total per tonne	2·0	1·5	
Silage (17 tonnes per hectare)			
Mow	1·2	0·9	
Turn, etc.	0·7	0·5	Two-thirds May, one-third
Load	2·3	1·7	June
Cart	3·0	2·3	
Clamp	2·3	1·7	
Total per hectare	9·5	7·1	
Total per tonne	0·56	0·42	

Specialized Equipment Prices for Grass Conservation: see page 116.

Seasonal Labour Requirements

Typical Monthly Breakdown

A. Production (figures averaged over the life of the ley)

	1-year ley undersown		3-year ley undersown		1-year ley direct drilled in spring		3-year ley direct drilled in autumn (1)	
	Av.	Prem.	Av.	Prem.	Av.	Prem.	Av.	Prem.
March	0·9	0·5	0·7	0·5	0·6	0·3	0·6	0·3
April	0·9	0·5	0·7	0·5	0·6	0·3	0·6	0·3
May	0·6	0·3	0·6	0·3	0·6	0·3	0·6	0·3
June	0·6	0·3	0·6	0·3	0·6	0·3	0·6	0·3
July	0·6	0·3	0·6	0·3	0·6	0·3	0·6	0·3
August	0·3	0·2	0·3	0·2	5·0	3·4	1·9	1·4
September ...	0·6	0·3	0·3	0·2	3·2	2·2	1·4	1·0

Note
1. On land ploughed after a cereal crop, drilled early August to mid-September.

	1-year ley direct drilled in autumn (1)		3-year ley direct drilled in spring		Permanent Pasture	
	Av.	Prem.	Av.	Prem.	Av.	Prem.
March	3·0	2·1	1·4	1·0	0·6	0·3
April	1·8	1·2	0·9	0·7	0·6	0·3
May	0·3	0·3	0·6	0·3	0·6	0·3
June	0·6	0·3	0·6	0·3	0·6	0·3
July	0·6	0·3	0·6	0·3	0·6	0·3
August	0·3	0·2	0·2	0·2	0·3	0·2
September ...	—	—	—	0·2	0·2	0·2
October	0·9	0·5	0·6	0·3	—	—
November ...	1·4	1·0	1·0	0·3	—	—
December ...	0·7	0·5	0·6	0·2	—	—

B. Conservation

	Hay				Silage			
	per hectare		per tonne		per hectare		per tonne	
	Av.	Prem.	Av.	Prem.	Av.	Prem.	Av.	Prem.
May ...	—	—	—	—	6·3	4·7	0·37	0·28
June ...	7·4	5·6	1·3	1·0	3·2	2·4	0·19	0·14
July ...	3·7	2·6	0·7	0·5	—	—	—	—

Seasonal Labour Requirements

A. Maincrop
KALE (growing only)

Operations	Labour-Hours per hectare Average	Premium	Time of Year
Plough	1·4	1·0	September onwards
Seedbed Cults.	2·2	1·6	March, April, early May
Fertilizer	0·4	0·3	April, early May
Drill	1·3	1·0	May
Roll	0·6	0·4	Straight after drilling
Spray (weedkiller)	0·3	0·2	6 weeks after drilling

B. Catch Crop

Kale may be drilled up to the first week of July; the crop will be smaller but either an early bite or silage crop may have been taken from a ley earlier in the year, or the ground may have been fallowed and thoroughly cleaned during the spring and early summer. The smaller crop is also easier to graze using an electric fence.

The above operations will still apply although the times of the year will obviously be different, but there may be an additional three or so rotavations and two or three heavy cultivations if fallowed for the first half of the year or ploughed after an early bite. This means approximately an extra 10 (average) or 8 (premium) man-hours per hectare in April, May, June.

FIELD-SCALE VEGETABLES

(Labour hours per hectare unless otherwise stated)

Cabbage Transplanting. Hand 150-160. Spring cabbage, Sept.-Oct.; summer, April; autumn, May-June.

Machine (3·5 gang). Spring cabbage 75, summer 85, autumn 100.

Pulling and dipping plants. 20 per hectare transplanted.

Cabbage Harvesting. Early spring cabbage, 210, Feb.-April; hearted spring, 250, April-June; summer, 220, June-July; autumn, 220, Oct.-Dec.

Brussels Sprouts Transplanting. 45 (machine) to 55 (hand), May-June.

Brussels Sprouts Picking. 320-400: picked over 3-5 times, maximum approx. 3 hectares per picker per season. Early sprouts, Aug.-Dec.; late, Nov.-Mar.

Peas Hand Pulling. 475-525 (150 per tonne). Early, June; maincrop, July-Aug.

Runner Beans (Picked) Harvesting. 625 (175 per tonne), July-Sept.
Runner Beans (Stick) Harvesting. 675, July-Sept.
Runner Beans (Stick) Erecting Canes and String. 100-150, May-June.

Carrot Harvesting. Elevator-digger: 260 (1 man + 12 casuals, 20 hours per hectare). Earlies, July-Aug.; maincrop, Sept.-Feb. Harvester: 30 (3 men, 10 hours per hectare). Riddle and Grade: 1½ per tonne), Dec.-Feb.

Beetroot Harvest and Clamp. 25, Oct.-Dec. 12-15 man-hours per tonne to wash and pack.

Source: The Farm as a Business, Aids to Management, Section 6: Labour and Machinery (M.A.F.F.). (N.B. This data is now very dated, but it is still the latest known to the author.)

4. LABOUR FOR FIELD WORK: Gang Sizes and Rates of Work

Basic information on *Rates of Work* is given on pages 119 to 121, where both "average" and "premium" rates for many operations are listed.

The following data relate to rates of work with gangs of different sizes. The rates of work are *averages* for good and bad conditions throughout the season, including preparation time and travelling to the field, and *assume an 8-hour day, unless otherwise stated.* Obviously these rates can be exceeded by overtime work in the evenings.

Combine Harvesting

Gang size can vary from 1 to 4 men per combine (excluding straw baling) according to the number of men available, size and type of combine, distance from grain store, crop yield, type of grain drier, and degree of automation in the grain store. The main possibilities are:

1 man: all jobs (trailer in field)
2 men: 1 combining, 1 carting and attending to grain store
3 men: 1 combining, 2 carting and attending to grain store
3 men: 1 combining, 1 carting, 1 attending to grain store
4 men: 1 combining, 2 carting, 1 attending to grain store

Three men is most typical, although two is quite feasible with a fully automated grain store with in-bin or floor drying, unless transport times are excessive owing to distance or lack of good connecting roads. Four men is most usual with two combines, but an extra man may be needed with a continuous drier.

Except in the case of the small area cereal producer operating on his own, the rate of work will normally depend on the speed of the combine, sufficient tractors and trailers being provided to ensure that combining does not have to stop because of their absence.

Assuming an 9-hour combining day, typical rates of work are:

Size of combine (metres cut)					No. of Men	Ha/day
3 to 4·2	...	...	...	...	...	1	4·5 to 7·75
					2 or 3	6 to 10
4·25 to 5·4	...	...	...	...	...	2 or 3	8 to 12
5·5 and over	...	...	...	...	...	3 or 4	10 to 15

Straw Carting

2 men, 1 or 2 tractors and trailers	"traditional" system	2·5 to 3·25 ha a day
3 men, 1 to 3 tractors and trailers		3·25 to 5 ha a day
1 man, 1 tractor with front and rear carriers		2·5 ha a day
2 men, flat 8/10 accumulator mechanised system		10 to 15 ha a day
2 or 3 men, big bale system		8 to 15 ha a day

Potato Planting

Hand planting (chitted seed) 3 men, 16 women	2 ha a day
Hand planting (unchitted seed) 2 men, 12 women	2 ha a day
(women working a 6-hour day only)	
2-row planter (chitted seed) 3 workers	1 ha a day
3-row planter (chitted seed) 4 or 5 workers	1·75 ha a day
2-row planter (unchitted seed) 3 workers	1·5 ha a day
3-row planter (unchitted seed) 4 workers	2·25 ha a day
2-row automatic planter (unchitted seed) 1 worker	2·5 ha a day
(part-time help loading and carting seed additional; this may be full time if fertilizer is applied with an attachment to the planter)	

Potato Harvesting

Hand harvesting (piecework) 3 to 5 men, 10 to 15 women	0·65 to 0·85 ha a day
(women working a 6-hour day only)	
Machine harvesting (1-row) 4 men, 3 women	0·65 to 0·9 ha a day
Machine harvesting (2-row) 5 men, 3 women	1 to 1·5 ha a day
(lower end of range for heavy land, upper end for light land and good work organization)	

Potato Riddling

3 to 5 workers	10 to 15 tonnes a day

Sugar Beet Harvesting (1-row)

Gang can vary from 1 to 5 (1 or 2 on harvester, 2 or 3 carting, 1 at clamp) but is usually 3 or 4.

3 or 4 men	0·9 ha a day
2 men	0·8 ha a day
1 man	0·7 ha a day
(add 20 per cent for light loams and silts)	

Vining Peas

Drilling (2 men)	7 to 10 ha a day
2·5-3 m. cutter (1 man)	2 ha a day
Pea pod picker, and carting, 5 or 6 men	0·4 ha a day
(large-scale growers: two 12 hour shifts worked per day)	

Carting Hay Bales

2 men, 1 or 2 tractors and trailers	7 to 9 tonnes a day
3 men, 1 to 3 tractors and trailers	9 to 14 tonnes a day

Silage-Making with Forage Harvester (excl. mowing, but inc. clamping; 15 tonne/ha crop)

1 man gang (1)	1·25 ha a day
2 man gang (1,3)	2·25 ha a day
3 man gang (1,3)	3·5 ha a day
4 man gang (2,3)	4·5 ha a day
(1) trailers towed behind, in line	
(2) trailers towed alongside	
(3) man with buckrake at clamp full-time	

Farmyard Manure Spreading

1 man: front loader and mechanical spreader	28 tonnes a day
4 men: front loader and 3 mechanical spreaders	90 tonnes a day

5. LABOUR FOR LIVESTOCK

DAIRY COWS

Herd size (no. of cows)	60	80	100 or more
	hours per cow per month		
January	3·3	2·9	2·5
February	3·3	2·9	2·5
March	3·3	2·9	2·5
April	3·0	2·7	2·4
May	2·7	2·4	2·2
June	2·7	2·4	2·1
July	2·7	2·4	2·1
August	2·7	2·4	2·1
September	2·7	2·4	2·2
October	3·0	2·8	2·4
November	3·3	2·9	2·5
December	3·3	2·9	2·5
Total per cow per year	36	32	28
Total hours per year	2160	2560	2800
„ „ per week	42	49	54
Total cost per annum	£13,260	£16,120	£18,460
„ „ per week	£255	£310	£355
„ „ per cow per annum	£221	£202	£185
Cost per litre: 5000 litres/cow	4·42p	4·03p	3·69p
„ „ „ : 5550 „ „	4·02p	3·66p	3·36p
„ „ „ : 6000 „ „	3·68p	3·36p	3·08p
„ „ „ : 6500 „ „	3·40p	3·10p	2·84p

Note

These *costs* (note, not *earnings*) are *estimates for 1995* and are based on the average number of *direct* hours of work per cow for different herd sizes obtained from University costings; they do not include fieldwork, such as hay and silage making. The costs include craftsman addition and any other premiums paid, overtime, national insurance payments, and holidays with pay. They also include the cost of relief milking, including during annual holidays.

Earnings. The average earnings of all "dairy herdsmen" in 1993, according to MAFF Statistics, were £262·27/week (£13,640/year), for a 51·6 hour week. Wage inflation is likely to raise this to approximately £282 (£14,650) in 1995.

DAIRY FOLLOWERS AND BEEF

A. Calves (per head, early weaning)

Age Group	Labour hours per month Average	Premium
0-3 months	2·6	1·9
3-6 months	1·0	0·7
(av. 0-6 months	1·8	1·3)
6-12 months, yarded	1·3	0·6
6-12 months, summer grazed	0·3	0·2
(av. 0-12 months, during winter (1)	1·5	1·0)
(av. 0-12 months, during summer (1)	1·0	0·8)

Note
1. Assuming 6- to 12-month olds yarded in winter and grazed in summer, and calvings or calf purchases fairly evenly spaced throughout the year.

B. Stores (per head)

Yearling, yarded	1·2	0·7
2 year olds and over, yarded	1·9	1·0
Outwintered store	0·9	0·7
12 months and over, summer grazed	0·2	0·1

C. Dairy Followers

(Per "replacement unit", i.e. calf + yearling + heifer.) (1)

During winter	3·7	2·1
During summer	1·4	0·9

Note
1. Assuming calvings fairly evenly spaced throughout the year.

D. Beef Fattening (per bullock fattened)

Yarded	2·1	1·2 (0·9 Self-feeding)
Summer Grazed	0·2	0·1
Intensive Beef	0·8	0·6

E. Suckler Herds (per cow)

Single suckling (av. whole year)	0·9	0·6
Multiple suckling (av. whole year)	2·9	2·5

F. Veal Calves

130-150 per worker	1·5	1·2

SHEEP
(per ewe)

							Labour hours per month Average	Premium
January	...	...	...	...	...	...	0·3	0·25
February	...	...	...	...	...	...	0·3	0·25
March	...	...	...	...	...	...	1·0 (1)	0·75
April	...	...	...	...	...	...	0·4	0·3
May	...	...	...	...	...	...	0·3	0·25
June	...	...	...	...	...	...	0·4 (2)	0·3
July	...	...	...	...	...	...	0·2	0·15
August	...	...	...	...	...	...	0·2	0·15
September	...	...	...	...	...	...	0·25	0·15
October	...	...	...	...	...	...	0·25	0·15
November	...	...	...	...	...	...	0·2	0·15
December	...	...	...	...	...	...	0·2	0·15
Total	...	...	...	...	...	...	4·0 (3)	3·0

Notes
1. Assuming mainly March lambing.
2. 0·3 if shearing is by contract.
3. A full-time shepherd can look after 400 ewes, with lambs (average), to 600 (premium), with help of extra man at lambing time (4 to 6 weeks) and extra men during dipping (one day) and at shearing time. The above labour-hour figures would thus be higher if only full-time shepherds were considered, since 400 ewes per man equals more than 5·5 hours per ewe per year. (With a full-time assistant a shepherd can look after 1,000 ewes or more.)

PIGS

	Labour hours per month Average	Premium
Breeding only, per sow ... ... (Average 110 sows per worker, Premium 150)	2·0	1·5
Fattening only, per 10 pigs ... ... No. at a time, per worker: Average 1,200 per man, Premium 1,600	1·9	1·4
No. per year, per worker: Average: 5,000 porkers, 4,000 cutters, 3,500 baconers Premium: 6,750 porkers, 5,500 cutters, 4,750 baconers		
Breeding and Fattening, per sow Porkers, average 70 sows per worker (with progeny), premium 95	3·2	2·4
Cutters, average 65 sows per worker (with progeny), premium 90	3·5	2·6
Baconers, average 60 sows per worker (with progeny), premium 80	3·7	2·8

POULTRY
(large-scale, automated)

	Labour hours per month
Laying hens: 12,000 per full-time worker	1·65 per 100
Broilers: 32,500 at a time per full-time worker* (225,000 a year)	1·0 per 100

* N.B. additional help needed for catching and cleaning out (included in labour hours per month).

III. MACHINERY

1. AGRICULTURAL MACHINERY PRICES

(Estimated Spring 1995 prices for new machinery, net of discounts
and excluding V.A.T.)

1. Tractors

(a) Two-Wheel Drive

	£
27-34 kW (36-45 hp)	12,000-14,000
35-40 kW (47-54 hp)	14,000-15,000
43-49 kW (57-66 hp)	15,000-16,000
50-56 kW (67-75 hp)	16,000-17,000
57-66 kW (76-89 hp)	17,000-20,000
67-75 kW (90-100 hp)	20,000-25,000

(b) Four-Wheel Drive

43-50 kW (57-67 hp)	16,000-19,000
56-65 kW (75-87 hp)	19,000-24,000
66-75 kW (88-100 hp)	24,000-29,000
76-90 kW (101-120 hp)	29,000-36,000
95-100 kW (127-134 hp)	36,000-43,000
115-134 kW (154-180 hp)	43,000-50,000
140-165 kW (187-220 hp)	50,000-58,000

(c) Crawlers

53-60 kW (70-80 hp), inc. linkage	20,000-22,000
75-94 kW (100-125 hp), inc. linkage	45,000-50,000
150-215 kW (200-287 hp), rubber track	90,000-115,000

2. Cultivating Equipment

(a) Ploughs

Mounted 3-furrow	2,300-2,600
4-furrow	2,500-3,600
Semi-mounted 5-furrow	7,000-8,000
Reversible 2-furrow	3,400-4,400
3-furrow	4,000-5,000
4-furrow	5,000-7,000
5-furrow	7,000-9,000
6-furrow (semi-mounted)	11,000-13,000

(b) Furrow Presses

3-furrow	1,800-2,000
4-furrow	1,900-2,100
5-furrow	2,000-2,200
6-furrow	2,200-2,500

(c) Front Presses

1·5 m single row	1,400-1,500
3·0 m single/double row	2,000-2,400/2,500-2,900
4·0 m single/double row— hydraulic folding	3,000-3,500/3,750-4,250

(c) Other Cultivating Equipment

Sub Soiler 2-3 leg	1,700-2,200
Vibrating Compaction Breaker (2·5-3·0 m)	4,000-5,000
(3·7-4·5 m)	6,000-7,000
Straw Incorporating Cultivator (3-4 m)	3,500-4,500
Straw Incorporating Disc Harrows (2·8-4 m)	8,000-9,000
Spring-tine Cultivator (3 m)	1,800-2,000
(4 m):	2,000-2,500
(5 m): 3 section hydraulic folding ...	3,000-3,500
Combination Harrows (2·5-4 m)	2,000-2,500
(3-4 m): hydraulic folding ...	3,000-3,500
Disc Harrows (2-3 m): mounted	2,000-2,500
(3-4 m): mounted	3,000-3,500
(4·5-5·5 m): trailed, heavy duty	10,000-11,000
Harrows (3-5 m): light-medium	600-1,000
Rotovator (up to 80 kW tractor)	4,000-5,000
(80-100 kW tractor)	5,000-6,000
Power Harrow (2·5-3 m)	4,500-5,500
(3·5-4 m)	7,000-8,000
(4·5-5 m, with crumbler roller)	14,000-15,000
Roller Packer for power harrow (2·5-4 m)	800-1,200
Rolls: triple gang, hydraulic folding (6 m)	5,000-6,000
five gang, „ „ (12m)	11,000-12,000

3. Fertilizer Distributors, Seed Drills, Sprayers

(a) Fertilizer Distributors

Mounted Spinner (600-800 litre hopper)	1,400-1,600
(800-1200) litre hopper): twin disc ...	2,000-2,500
Pneumatic Spreader: mounted (12m)	3,500-5,000
trailed (12m)	9,000-10,000
trailed (18m)	16,000-18,000

(b) Seed Drills

Grain: mounted 3-4 m, 25-33 row	4,500-6,000
trailed 3 m, 18-24 row	6,000-7,000
4 m, 24-32 row	7,000-8,000
3-4 m, pneumatic	7,000-8,000
6-8 m, pneumatic	17,000-26,000
Mounted grass seed broadcaster (2·4-4·6 m)	650-900

(c) Combine Grain Drills

Trailed, 3 m, 18-24 row	6,500-7,500
4 m, 24-32 row	7,500-8,500
6 m, pneumatic	18,000-24,000

(d) Sprayers

Mounted, 200-300 litre tank, 6-8 m boom	800-1,100
Mounted, 400-500 litre tank, 8-10 m boom	1,100-1,300
Mounted, 600-800 litre tank, 12 m hydraulic boom ...	3,000-3,500
Mounted, Air Assisted, 600-800 litre tank, 12 m boom ...	7,000-10,000
Trailed, Air Assisted, 2,000-2,500 litre tank, 12 m boom ...	14,000-18,000
Trailed, 1,500-2,000 litre tank, 12 m boom	9,000-12,000
Trailed, 2,500-3,000 litre tank, 24 m boom	15,000-20,000
Self-propelled, 12 m boom, lightweight	20,000-25,000
Self-propelled, 24 m boom, 4-wheel drive	40,000-50,000

4. Grass Conservation and Handling Equipment

(a) Forage Harvesters and Buckrakes

Double chop	5,500-7,000
Fine and Precision chop (trailed)	10,000-14,000
Metal Detector	4,000-5,000
Self-propelled (2·2-3 m pick-up 165-265 kW)	70,000-100,000
Loader Wagon (18-25 m³)	13,000-16,000
Silage Trailer, 4 tonne	1,800-2,000
Silage Trailer, 6 tonne	2,500-3,000
Silage Trailer, 10 tonne, tandem axle	4,500-5,000
Buckrake (push off)	1,100-1,200

(b) Haymaking Equipment

Mower (1·6-1·8 m, rotary type)	2,000-2,500
Mower Conditioner mounted (2-2·4 m)...	5,000-6,000
Tedder (5-7 m, 4-6 rotors)	4,000-6,000
Windrower, (3-4 m)	2,000-2,400

(c) Silage Handling Equipment

Silage cutters (for front loader): (0·6-0·8 m³)	1,400-1,600
Silage grab	900-1,100
Forage Feeder Wagon (6-7 m³)	6,000-7,000
Mixer-feeder Wagon (7-12 m³)	14,000-19,000

5. Grain and Straw Harvesting and Handling Equipment

(a) Combines

	Engine size kW (hp)	Cutterbar width metres (feet)	
Conventional:	75-89 (100-119)	3·0-4·6 (10-15)	45,000-53,0C0
	90-111 (120-149)	3·6-6·0 (12-19)	55,000-65,000
	112-148 (150-199)	3·6-6·0 (12-19)	65,000-80,000
	Over 150 (over 200)	4·2-6·1 (14-20)	90,000-100,000
Rotary:	120-150 (160-200)	4·3-5·5 (14-18)	90,000-100,000
	150-187 (200-250)	5·5-6·1 (18-20)	100,000-110,000
	187-225 (250-300)	6·1-7·3 (20-24)	115,000-130,000

(b) Straw Disposal Equipment

Straw Chopper (trailed)	3,500-4,500
Straw Chopper attachment for combines	3,500-4,500

(c) Pick-up Balers (twine tying)

Small rectangular bales	6,000-7,000
Small rectangular bales, heavy duty models	7,500-8,500
Big round bales, twine tying	11,500-12,500
net wrap	13,000-15,000
High density rectangular bales	40,000-45,000

(d) Bale Handling Equipment

Big Bale Wrapper: mounted	3,500-4,500
trailed	6,500-7,500
Bale Trailers, 5-6 tonne	1,700-2,000
Accumulator, flat 8, mechanical	1,400-1,600
Loader, flat 8	650-750
Big Bale Spike	200-250
Big Bale Handler	500-700
Big Bale Shredder	3,000-3,500

(e) Drying, Handling, Food Processing Equipment
Grain driers and Grain storage: see pages 124, 143

Cleaner/grader, 10-20 tonnes/hour	6,000-9,000
Grain augers 100 mm, 3·3-7·3 m	400-500
Grain augers 150 mm, 6-8·5 m, with trolley	1,400-1,600
Grain conveyors (200mm) (inc. motor)	1,600-1,800 + 80-90 per m
Hammer Mill, 4-7·5 kW automatic	2,000-2,300
Mill and Mixer, 1000kg, 3·7-5·5 kW	4,000-4,500
Mixer, 750-1,000 kg	2,200-2,500
Crushing Mill, 2-5·5 kW	1,500-2,000
Seed Dresser, 3 tonne	2,000-2,700

6. Potato, Sugar Beet and Vegetable Machinery

(a) Potato Machinery

Declodder, 1·8 m	15,000-17,000
Stone separator , 1·5-1·8 m	20,000-23,000
Bedformer, 1·5-2 m	2,300-2,600
Bed cultivator, 1·8 m	4,500-5,000
Planter: 2 row automatic, mechanical drive	4,000-5,000
2 row automatic, electrical belt feed	5,000-6,000
3 row automatic, electrical belt feed	9,000-10,000
Fertilizer attachment, 2 row	1,300-1,500
Haulm Pulveriser: 2 row	5,000-6,000
4 row	7,500-8,500
Elevator-Digger, 1 row	3,000-3,500
Elevator-Digger, 2 row	4,000-4,500
Harvesters: mounted, 1 row, manned/unmanned	12,000-14,000
trailed, 1 row, manned	17,000-22,000
trailed, 2 row, manned/unmanned	40,000-45,000
Elevator (rubber belt)	5,000-5,500
Flat belt conveyor, 3-8 m	1,500-2,500
Swinging head elevator	9,000-10,000
Soil Elevator (rubber belt)	3,000-3,500
Self-unloading hopper, 3-5 tonnes	5,500-7,000
Hopper Cleaner, 2-4 tonnes	3,000-4,250
Stone and clod extractor, 7-30 tonnes/hour	9,000-10,000
Sizer, 5-10 tonnes/hour	5,500-7,500
Roller inspection table, 1·2 × 2·4 m	2,500-3,000
Weigher, automatic, 8-10 tonnes/hour	4,500-5,500
Box tipper	3,250-4,000
Box filer, automatic	9,000-10,000
Bag stitcher (hand held)	700-800

(b) Sugar Beet Machinery

Precision Drill: 6 row-12 row (mechanical)	7,000-13,000
6 row-12 row (pneumatic)	10,000-13,000
Hoe: 6 row-12 row (heavy duty)	3,300-6,500
Harvesters: Trailed, 1 row, tanker	19,000-21,000
Trailed, 2-3 row, tanker	30,000-35,000
Self-propelled, 6 row (including power unit)	100,000-110,000
Cleaner-loader, with engine, 2 tonnes per minute	12,000-13,000
Fodder beet harvester	4,000-4,500

(c) Vegetable Machinery

Onion windrower	6,500-7,000
Root crop digger: 1 webb	4,000-4,500
2 webbs	5,000-6,000
Top lifting vegetable harvester: single row, bunker ...	30,000-35,000
twin row, bunker/elevator ...	50,000-57,000
four row, elevator ...	80,000-90,000
Leek harvester	10,000-11,000

7. General

Trailer, 4 tonne tipping; grain/silage	1,500-1,600/1,800-2,000
Trailer, 6 tonne tipping; grain/silage	2,200-2,500/2,500-3,000
Trailer, 10 tonne tipping, tandem axle; grain/silage	4,000-4,500/4,500-5,000
F.Y.M. Spreaders, (4-6 m^3)	2,250-2,750
F.Y.M. Spreaders, (7-9 m^3)	3,500-4,200
Loaders, front mounted	3,000-4,500
Pallet loader: self levelling (1,000-1,600 kg)	4,500-5,500
Fork Lift Truck: fixed mast (1·5-2·0 tonne)	17,000-20,000
telescopic boom (2·5-3·0 tonne)	27,000-32,000
Slurry Stores (metal), including base but before grant (assumes large store for 200 cows with a 15-week storage period; stores for 70-80 cows are £150-170 per cow)	£125 per cow
Slurry Tanker-Spreaders (4,000-5,000 litre)	3,500-4,000
Slurry-Tanker-Spreaders, tandem axle (6,000-10,000 litre) ...	6,000-8,000
Slurry pump	2,500-3,000
Cattle crush	500-700
Cattle crush with weigher	1,000-1,200
Cattle trailer (twin-axle)	1,700-2,000
Yard scrapers	350-450
Grassland Roll, ballastable (2·5-3 m)	700-800
Pasture topper (2·0-3·0m)	1,500-2,000
Hedger: hydraulic angling; flail head	4,500-5,500
Ditcher: fully slewing	3,750-4,500
Carrier box	300-400
Post hole digger/driver	1,000-1,300
Saw bench	500-600
Log splitter	400-500

2. TYPICAL CONTRACTORS' CHARGES, AVERAGE FARMERS' COSTS AND RATES OF WORK FOR VARIOUS FARM OPERATIONS

Contractors' charges vary widely according to many factors: those given below are estimates for 1995. Farmer-contractors often charge less, since their overheads and machinery fixed costs are largely covered by their own farming operations, but the service may not always be so complete, including specialist advice.

Farmers' own costs vary even more widely; those given below (estimated for Spring 1995) are averages in every respect—covering different types of soil, size of farm, and so on; they are based on accounting cost procedures in that labour, tractor and machinery fuel, repairs and depreciation are included—but no allowance has been added for general farm overheads, interest on capital, supervision or under-occupied labour during slack times. They assume four-wheel drive 75-90 kW (100-120 hp) tractors for ploughing, heavy cultivation and other work with a high power requirement. Four-wheel drive 55-65 kW (75-87 hp) tractors are assumed to be used for most other operations. The figures should on no account be used for partial budgeting.

For a typical set of farm operations, excluding harvesting, the breakdown of the farmers' costs averages approximately 30% labour, 45% tractors and 25% implements/machines. The larger the farm the lower the labour element and the higher the machine element, and vice-versa.

The contract charges and average farmers' costs are put side-by-side for tabular convenience, not to facilitate comparisons. Apart from the fact that contractors' charges must cover expenses omitted from the farmers' cost, the advisability or otherwise of hiring a contractor for a particular job depends on many factors, varying widely according to farm circumstances; furthermore, there are advantages and disadvantages not reflected in a cost comparison alone.

Four-wheel drive 120-150 kW (150-200 hp) tractors are assumed where appropriate to achieve the "Premium" rates of work (which will be achieved on most farms with more than 200 hectares (500 acres) of arable land); obviously, still larger wheeled tractors and crawlers could achieve still faster rates of work, particularly on light land. See further page 95, first paragraph.

All charges and costs below are *per hectare* unless otherwise stated.

Operation	Contract Charge	Average Farmers' Cost	Rate of Work (hectares per 8 hr. day)	
			Average	Premium
	£	£		
Ploughing (light/heavy soils) ...	33·00-42·00	29·00-38·00	5-6½	7½-9
Deep Ploughing (over 300 mm)	47·00-58·00	46·00-57·00	3-3¾	5-6½
Rotovating	45·00-55·00	50·00 (ploughed land)	4½	6
		75·00 (grass)	3	4

Operation	Contract Charge	Average Farmers' Cost	Rate of Work (hectares per 8 hr. day)	
			Average	Premium
	£	£		
Subsoiling	45·00	27·75	6	10
Stubble Cultivating	25·00	14·75	12	16
Heavy Disc Cultivating	25·00	20·25	10	15
Medium/Light Disc Harrowing ...	16·00	11·25	12	16
Power Harrowing	30·00	25·00	9	12
Spring tine Harrowing	17·00	11·00	12	18
Seedbed Harrowing	13·00	8·25	12	20
Rolling (flat 3-4 tonne)	18·00	15·75	6	10
(ring, set of 3, 6 m) ...	10·00	9·25	14	22
Fertilizer Distributing (including loading and carting):				
Broadcast (125-375 kg/ha) ...	9·00-11·00 (fert. in field)	6·75	20	30
Broadcast (500-1,250 kg/ha) ...	—	11·00	15	20
Pneumatic (125-375 kg/ha)	—	7·75	30	45
Drilling:				
Cereals (Direct into stubble) ...	31·00 seed & fert. in	28·75	8	10
Cereals (Plain, 1 man)	18·00 field	14·50	12	16
Grass (broadcast)	15·00	10·75	11	15
Roots (4-row)	—	45·75	3½ (4 row)	5 (6 row)
Sugar Beet—precision drill ...	32·00	27·50	6 (6 row)	10 (12 row)
Power Harrowing and Drilling Cereals	38·00	30·00	8	11
Destoning potato land	160·00	130·00	3·25	4
Potato Planting automatic	—	87·00	2½ (2 row)	3¼
Potato Ridging	33·00	20·50	5½	7
Spraying (excl. materials):				
Low Volume (up to 175 l/ha) ...	10·00	5·25	35	55
Medium Volume (200-300 l/ha)	12·00	6·25	30	45
High Volume (over 800 l/ha) ...	—	11·25	25	35
Tractor Hoeing Sugar Beet ...	—	25·50	5	8
Combine Harvesting Cereals:			(hectares per hour)	
100 ha/year	80·00	80·00	¾-1	1-1½
200 ha/year		65·00		
Carting to barn add	16·00	11·00		
Combine Harvesting:				
Oilseed rape (direct)	90·00	as cereals + 10%	¾-1	¾-1¼
Beans	80·00	as cereals + 10%	¾-1	¾-1¼
Peas	100·00	as cereals	¾-1	1-1½
Windrowing Oilseed Rape	35·00	—	1·2	1·4
Pick-up Baling (incl. string) ...	19-22p per bale	13·75 per tonne	0·8 per hour	1·25 per hour
Big Baling (round)	1·30-1·85 per bale	9·75 per tonne	—	—
Crop Drying—Cereals (per tonne)				
by 6 per cent	12·50	8·50	—	—
by 10 per cent	16·00	10·00	—	—
Oilseed Rape				
by 5 per cent	15·00	10·50	—	—
by 10 per cent	18·00	13·00	—	—
Cleaning without drying (per tonne)	8·00	—	—	—
Mobile Seed Cleaning (cereals) (per tonne)(excluding chemicals)	40·00	—	—	—
Grain Storage (per tonne per month)	£1	(see page 132)	—	—

Operation	Contract Charge	Average Farmers' Cost	Rate of Work (hectares per 8 hr. day)	
			Average	Premium
	£	£		
Potato Harvesting	—	900–1,000 (incl. carting, store, casuals)	0·75	1
Sugar Beet Complete Harvesting (3 row tanker)	—	135 (excl. carting)	3	4
	—	170 (incl. carting)		
Grass Mowing/Topping (inc. Set-aside)	20·00	17·50	7	10
Swath Turning/Tedding	13·00	11·25	11	15
Forage Harvesting (inc. mowing): Full chop harvester, 17·5 tonnes/ha (driver only)	48·00	—	—	—
Forage harvesting, carting and ensiling grass 17·5 tonnes/ha	100	—	—	—
Forage harvesting, carting and ensiling maize 25–30 tonnes/ha	115	—	—	—
F.Y.M.: Tractor and Spreader ...	20·00 per hour	—	—	—
F.Y.M.: Tractor and Loader	18·00 per hour	—	—	—
Lime Spreading	2·50 per tonne	—	—	—
Hedge Cutting (flail head)	16·00 per hour	—	—	—
Tractor Hire (inc. driver and fuel):				
2 wheel drive, 56 kW (75 h.p.) ...	102 ⎫	—	—	—
2 wheel drive, 75 kW (100 h.p.)	106 ⎪ per	—	—	—
4 wheel drive, 56 kW (75 h.p.) ...	115 ⎬ 8-hour	—	—	—
4 wheel drive, 90 kW (120 h.p.)	125 ⎪ day	—	—	—
Crawler, 90 kW (120 h.p.) ...	150 ⎪	—	—	—
Trailer (with driver and tractor) ...	120 ⎭	11·25 per hour	—	—

Contract Charge for All Operations (Cereals and Combinable Break Crops, "stubble to stubble", i.e. up to and including Combine Harvesting and Carting the Grain to Store): £220 to £270/ha (£90-110/acre). (Variation according to such factors as distance away, area contracted, size of fields, type of terrain, quality of soil and level of inputs (as affecting weight of crop to be harvested and carted). The charge usually ranges from £175 (£70) to £210 (£85) where a major proportion of the profit is also taken by the contractor or a neighbouring farmer after payment of a rent.

Tractor Power Requirements

		hp/acre		hp/ha		kW/ha	
		av.	prem.	av.	prem.	av.	prem.
Combinable crops:	heavy land	·75	·6	1·85	1·5	1·4	1·1
	light land	·5	·4	1·25	1	·9	·75
Mixed cropping:	heavy land	1	·8	2·5	2	1·85	1·5
	light land	·75	·6	1·85	1·5	1·4	1·1

Grain Haulage Costs
Averaged 13p/tonne/mile for journeys over 40 miles in 1993. Average cost per tonne of grain £4.80. (Home-Grown Cereals Authority).

3. TRACTOR HOURS
(per annum)

Crops

	per hectare Average	Premium
Cereals	9	7
Straw Harvesting	3·5	2·5
Potatoes	25	15
Sugar Beet	20	12
Vining Peas	20	12
Dried Peas	10	8
Field Beans	9	7
Oilseed Rape	9	7
Herbage Seeds:		
1 year undersown or 3 year direct drilled	7	5
1 year direct drilled	11	8
Hops (machine picked)	125	—
Kale (grazed)	8	6
Turnips/Swedes: folded/lifted	12/35	10/25
Mangolds	50	35
Fallow	12	7
Ley Establishment:		
Undersown	2	1
Direct Seed	7	4
Making Hay	12	8
Making Silage:		
1st Cut	12	8
2nd Cut	9	6
Grazing:		
Temporary Grass	3	2·5
Permanent Grass	2	1·5

Livestock

	per head Average
Dairy Cows	6
Other Cattle over 2 years	5
Other Cattle 1-2 years	4
Other Cattle ½-1 year	2·25
Calves 0-½ year	2·25
Yarded bullocks	3
Sheep, per ewe	1·25
Store sheep	0·8
Sows	1·75
Other pigs over 2 months	1
Laying Birds	0·04

Notes

1. For Livestock, annual requirements are the per head requirements above multiplied by average numbers during the year (i.e. average numbers at end of each month).

2. As with labour, the number of tractors required by a farm depends more on the seasonal requirements and number required at any one time than on total annual tractor hours. These can be calculated from the seasonal labour data provided earlier in this book. The soil type and size/power of tractors purchased are obviously other relevant factors.

4. TRACTOR COSTS

(Estimates for Spring 1994)

	Two-Wheel Drive			
	27-34 kW (36-45 h.p.)		43-49 kW (57-66 h.p.)	
Initial Cost	£13,000		£15,500	
	per year £	per hour £	per year £	per hour £
Depreciation	1,040	2·08	1,240	2·48
Tax and Insurance	159	0·32	175	0·35
Repairs and Maintenance	650	1·30	775	1·55
Fuel and Oil	330	0·66	550	1·10
Total	2,179	4·36	2,740	5·48

	Four-Wheel Drive			
	56-65 kW (75-87 h.p.)		76-90 kW (101-120 h.p.)	
Initial Cost	£22,000		£32,000	
	per year £	per hour £	per year £	per hour £
Depreciation	1,760	3·52	2,560	5·12
Tax and Insurance	218	0·44	283	0·57
Repairs and Maintenance	1,100	2·20	1,600	3·20
Fuel and Oil	900	1·80	1,200	2·40
Total	3,978	7·96	5,643	11·29

	Crawlers			
	53-60 kW (70-80 h.p.)		75-94 kW (100-125 h.p.)	
Initial Cost	£21,000		£47,500	
	per year £	per hour £	per year £	per hour £
Depreciation	1,680	3·36	3,800	7·60
Tax and Insurance	175	0·35	335	0·67
Repairs and Maintenance	1,050	2·10	2,375	4·75
Fuel and Oil	880	1·76	1,280	2·56
Total	3,785	7·57	7,790	15·58

Depreciation is based on the assumption that a tractor is sold or traded in for one-fifth of its original cost after ten years. Annual Repair Costs have been calculated at 5 per cent of initial cost. No interest on capital has been included.

The hourly figures are based on a use of 500 hours a year. A greater annual use than this will mean higher annual costs but possibly lower hourly costs. Early replacement at a given annual use will increase depreciation costs per hour but should reduce repair costs. The hourly figures are averages for all types of work: heavy operations such as ploughing obviously have a higher cost than light work.

5. ESTIMATING ANNUAL MACHINERY COSTS

Annual machinery costs consist of depreciation, repairs, fuel and oil, contract charges, and vehicle tax and insurance. These can be budgeted in three ways, assuming there is no available information on past machinery costs on the farm:

(a) *Per hectare,* by looking up an average figure for the district, according to the size and type of farm. Approximate levels are shown in the tables of fixed costs (pages 133-138). This is obviously a very rough and ready measure.

(b) *Per standard tractor hour.* The crop area and livestock numbers can be multiplied by the appropriate standard (average) tractor hours per hectare and per head as given on page 122. The total can then be multiplied by the machinery cost per standard tractor hour as calculated from farm surveys. The following average figures (estimated for mid-1995) are based on 1990-93 levels in South-East England.

Farm Type	Cost per Standard Tractor Hour
Mainly Sheep/Cattle, over 100 ha	£8·00
Sheep/Cattle and Arable, over 100 ha... ... ...⎫	
Dairy, Sheep/Cattle and Arable ... ...⎬	£10·00
Mainly Sheep/Cattle, under 100 ha ... ...⎭	
Mainly Arable, over 200 ha ... ...⎫	
Dairy and Arable, over 200 ha ... ...⎬	£13·50
Mainly Dairying, over 60 ha ... ...⎫	
Dairy and Arable, under 200 ha ... ...⎬	£14·00
Mainly Dairying, under 60 ha ... ...⎫	
Sheep/Cattle and Arable, under 100 ha ...⎬	£14·50
Mainly Arable, 100-200 ha	£17·50
Intensive Arable—Field Vegetables	£20·00
Mainly Arable, under 100 ha	£24·00

Premium levels are about 10 per cent lower.

Depreciation is based on the current (i.e. replacement) cost of the machinery and equipment. The capital element of leasing (but not the interest) is included in depreciation. *With depreciation calculated on the 'historic' (i.e. original) cost the above figures are reduced by approximately 10%.*

The percentage composition of the total cost varies with size and type of farm but averages approximately:

	Depreciation	Repairs	Fuel/Elec.	Contract	VTI*
A.	32·5	25	17·5	20	5
B.	40	22·5	15	17·5	5

A = Depreciation based on historic cost
B = Depreciation based on current cost
*Vehicle tax and insurance

This method may be used as a check on the per hectare calculation.

(N.B. The standard tractor hour is used only as a convenient measure of machinery input. *The costs incorporate not only tractor costs but all other power and machinery expenses, including field machinery and implements, fixed equipment, landrovers, vans, use of farm car, etc.)*

(c) *Fully detailed calculation,* costing and depreciating each machine in turn, including tractors, estimating repairs and fuel costs for each, and adding the charges for any contract work.

The following tables, giving, for different types of machine, estimated life, annual depreciation, and estimated repairs according to annual use, are taken from "Profitable Farm Mechanisation", by C. Culpin.

ESTIMATED USEFUL LIFE (YEARS) OF POWER OPERATED MACHINERY IN RELATION TO ANNUAL USE

Equipment	Annual Use (hours)				
	25	50	100	200	300
Group 1: Ploughs, Cultivators, Toothed harrows, Hoes, Rolls, Ridgers, Simple potato planting attachments, Grain cleaners	12+	12+	12+	12	10
Group 2: Disc harrows, Corn drills, Binders, Grain drying machines, Food grinders and mixers	12+	12+	12	10	8
Group 3: Combine harvesters, Pick-up balers, Rotary cultivators, Hydraulic loaders	12+	12+	12	9	7
Group 4: Mowers, Forage harvesters, Swath turners, Side-delivery rakes, Tedders, Hedge cutting machines, Semi-automatic potato planters and transplanters, Unit root drills, Mechanical root thinners	12+	12	11	8	6
Group 5: Fertilizer distributors, Combine drills, Farmyard manure spreaders, Elevator potato diggers, Spraying machines, Pea cutter-windrowers	10	10	9	8	7

Miscellaneous:

Beet harvesters	...	...	...	...	11	10	9	6	5
Potato harvesters	...	...	...	...	—	8	7	5	—
Milking machinery	...	...	...	...	—	—	—	12	10

	Annual Use (hours)					
	500	750	1,000	1,500	2,000	2,500
Tractors	12+	12	10	7	6	5
Electric motors	12+	12+	12+	12+	12	12

DEPRECIATION: AVERAGE ANNUAL FALL IN VALUE

(per cent of new price)

(Source: V. Baker, Bristol University)

Frequency of renewal. Years	Complex. High Depreciation Rate e.g. potato harvesters, mobile pea viners, etc.	Established machines with many moving parts, e.g. tractors, combines, balers, forage harvesters	Simple equipment with few moving parts, e.g. ploughs, trailers
	%	%	%
1	34	26	19
2	24½	19½	14½
3	20*	16½*	12½
4	17½†	14½	11½
5	15‡	13†	10½*
6	13½	12	9½
7	12	11	9
8	11	10‡	8½†
9	(10)	9½	8
10	(9½)	8½	7½‡

* Typical frequency of renewal with heavy use.
† Typical frequency of renewal with average use.
‡ Typical frequency of renewal with light use.

VALUATION AND DEPRECIATION OF MACHINERY
BY TYPE

(% of totals per farm, 1992/93; both based on replacement costs; depreciation in brackets)

Type of Farm:	Mainly Cereals	Mixed Cropping	Dairy & Arable	ALL FARMS
Tractors	30 (31)	29 (30)	30 (31)	27 (28)
Vehicles	11 (11)	10 (11)	13 (14)	14 (14)
Harvesters	14 (18)	13 (17)	9 (11)	9 (12)
Other Equipment and Plant	45 (40)	48 (42)	48 (44)	50 (46)

Source: M. C. Murphy, Report on Farming in the Eastern Counties of England, 1992/93. University of Cambridge, Agricultural Economics Unit, 1994.

DEPRECIATION: PERCENTAGE RATES

A. *Straight-Line*

Years Retained	Trade-in, Second-hand or Scrap Value as % of New Price							
	5	10	20	25	33	40	50	60
3	—	—	—	—	—	20	16½	13½
4	—	—	—	—	17	15	12½	—
5	—	—	—	15	13½	12	—	—
6	—	—	13½	12½	11	10	—	—
8	—	11	10	9½	—	—	—	—
10	9½	9	8	—	—	—	—	—
12	8	7½	—	—	—	—	—	—
15	6½	—	—	—	—	—	—	—

Example: If a machine costing £10,000 is retained for 8 years, at the end of which the trade-in value is 20% of the new price (i.e. £2,000), the average depreciation per annum has been £8,000 ÷ 8 years = £1,000 (i.e. 10% of the new price).

B. *Diminishing Balances*

Years Retained	Trade-in, Second-hand or Scrap Value as % of New Price							
	5	10	20	25	33	40	50	60
3	—	—	—	—	—	26	21	16
4	—	—	—	—	24	20	16	—
5	—	—	—	24	20	17	—	—
6	—	—	23	20	17	14	—	—
8	—	25	18	16	—	—	—	—
10	25	20	15	—	—	—	—	—
12	22	17	—	—	—	—	—	—
15	18	—	—	—	—	—	—	—

Example: If a machine costing £10,000 is retained for 4 years, at the end of which the trade-in value is 40% of the new replacement price, the annual depreciation on the diminishing balances method is: Year 1, £2,000 (i.e. 20% of £10,000); Year 2, £1,600 (i.e. 20% of £8,000 (the written-down value)); Year 3, £1,280 (i.e. 20% of £6,400); Year 4, £1,024 (20% of £5,120). The total written-down value at the end of Year 4 is therefore £4,096 (i.e. £10,000 less the total depreciation of £5,904). This is approximately 41% of the new price. (Taking the percentages in the above table to decimal places would give the trade-in prices stated more precisely).

Note. The trade-in value taken for purposes of the calculation must exclude any "disguised" discount on the price of the new machine.

Calculations of data collected as part of the Farm Management Survey in 1982/83 found the following to be the best estimates of the real diminishing balance rates of depreciation for machines sold during that year: (source: S. Cunningham, University of Exeter, Agricultural Economics Unit, 1987):

Tractors	15%	Potato harvesters	21%
Combine harvesters	15%	Forage harvesters	21%
Balers	18%	Beet harvesters	23%

For other machinery and equipment an average rate of 15% is suggested (author).

Tax Allowances on Machinery. See page 173.

ESTIMATED ANNUAL COST OF SPARES AND REPAIRS AS A PERCENTAGE OF PURCHASE PRICE* AT VARIOUS LEVELS OF USE

	Approximate Annual Use (hours)				Additional use per 100 hours
	500	750	1,000	1,500	ADD
	%	%	%	%	%
Tractors	5·0	6·7	8·0	10·5	0·5

	Approximate Annual Use (hours)				Additional use per 100 hours
	50	100	150	200	ADD
	%	%	%	%	%
Harvesting Machinery:					
Combine Harvesters, self-propelled and engine-driven ...	1·5	2·5	3·5	4·5	2·0
Combine Harvesters, p.t.o. driven, metered-chop forage harvesters, pick-up balers, potato harvesters, sugar beet harvesters	3·0	5·0	6·0	7·0	2·0
Other Implements and Machines:					
Group 1:					
Ploughs, Cultivators, Toothed harvows, Hoes, Elevator potato diggers — Normal Soils	4·5	8·0	11·0	14·0	6·0
Group 2:					
Rotary cultivators, Mowers, Binders, Pea cutter-windrowers	4·0	7·0	9·5	12·0	5·0
Group 3:					
Disc harrows, Fertilizer distributors, Farmyard manure spreaders, Combine drills, Potato planters with fertilizer attachment, Sprayers, Hedge-cutting machines	3·0	5·5	7·5	9·5	4·0
Group 4:					
Swath turners, Tedders, Side-delivery rakes, Unit drills, Flail forage harvesters, Semi-automatic potato planters and transplanters, Down-the-row thinners	2·5	4·5	6·5	8·5	4·0
Group 5:					
Corn drills, Milking machines, Hydraulic loaders, Simple potato planting attachments	2·0	4·0	5·5	7·0	3·0
Group 6:					
Grain driers, Grain cleaners, Rolls, Hammer mills, Feed mixers, Threshers	1·5	2·0	2·5	3·0	0·5

* When it is known that a high purchase price is due to high quality and durability or a low price corresponds to a high rate of wear and tear, adjustments to the figures should be made.

6. IRRIGATION COSTS
(Estimated for 1995)

A. Capital Costs
(before deducting grant)

1. *Pumps* (delivering from 27 to 110 cubic metres per hour from a surface water source)

Tractor driven, with accessories	£2,600-3,300
Diesel units	£7,700-19,500
Electrically driven units (excluding power supply)	£5,100-11,500

2. Pipelines (per m)

   Portable: (excl. valves) 75 mm, £8·90; 100 mm, £11·50; 125 mm, £15·50; 150 mm, £21·50; (incl. valves) 75 mm, £11·80; 100 mm, £14·00; 125 mm, £18·20; 150 mm, £25·10.

   Permanent (P.V.C. pipe and laying, before grant): 100 mm, £18·30; 150 mm, £21·20. Hydrants: 100 mm, £415; 150 mm, £480.

3. Application Systems

Self travellers: hose reel equipment capable of irrigating 20-25 hectares in a 10-day cycle (two moves each day and operating for 22 hours per day) cost approximately £10,500. Larger machines capable of irrigating 32, 50 and 60 hectares in a 10-day cycle cost approximately £15,000, £19,250 and £23,500 respectively.

Sprinkler lines: a 1 hectare setting of a conventional sprinkler line costs approximately £6,200 to £6,400. For each hectare cover of sprinklers 30 to 40 hectares can normally be irrigated in a 10-day cycle.

4. Total

If no source works are needed, as with water from a river, or pond, total capital costs can be as low as £900 for each hectare requiring irrigation at regular intervals, but are more typically £1,300 to £2,000.

5. Source Works

Boreholes typically cost £150 to £190 per m depth and require expensive submerged pumps. An overall cost, including electricity supply, pump and well head, to irrigate 4 hectares with 25 mm of water per day would be in the region of £20,000 to £30,000. £500 to £800 per hectare can easily be added to capital costs.

The least expensive large reservoirs typically cost £1 per cubic metre of storage capacity, with smaller reservoirs costing as much as £4.00 per cubic metre where lining is required. £1 per cubic metre equals £1,000 per hectare irrigated if enough water is stored to apply 100 mm per hectare.

B. Operating Costs

A typical depreciation and interest cost for a self traveller capable of covering 25 ha in a 10-day cycle where only limited source works are provided would be £49 per application of 25 mm per hectare. Running costs, including labour (2 man-hours per hectare), repairs, fuel, etc. would cost £28.

Abstraction charges vary widely, depending on the region, season and whether or not the source is supported by National Rivers Authority operations. Winter abstraction charges typically range from £2 to £5 per 1,000 m^3 and summer rates from £10 to £20 per 1,000 m^3 for sources which are not supported by National Rivers Authority operations. Abstraction charges during the summer can be up to £70 per 1,000 m^3 in areas where supplies are supported by National River Authority operations. A charge of £4 per 1,000 m^3 equals £1 per 25 mm per hectare, whilst a charge of £16 per 1,000 m^3 would cost £4 per hectare per 25 mm application. Mains water at 50p per m^3 would cost £125 per application of 25 mm per hectare

Total costs per application of 25 mm per hectare, based on limited source works and summer abstraction rates, would be in the region of £80 to £85 for a self traveller system. Costs for sprinkler lines are likely to be between 10 and 20 per cent higher, largely because of greater labour requirements (5 man-hours per hectare).

Source works at £1,200 per hectare, together with mainly permanent pipelines, would increase the above figure for depreciation and interest to £84 per 25 mm per hectare, but abstraction and variable costs would be lower, giving a total cost of £100 to £105 per application of 25 mm per hectare.

Where irrigation capacity is underutilised the effective cost per 25 mm of water applied per hectare can be very much higher.

Note:

The (approximate) imperial equivalents for metric values commonly used in irrigation are as follows:

1 cubic metre=1,000 litres=220 gallons.

A pump capacity of 100 cubic metres per hour is equivalent to 22,000 gallons per hour (366 gallons per minute).

In terms of water storage 1,000 cubic metres (1 million litres) is equivalent to 220,000 gallons (1 million gallons=4,546 cubic metres).

1,000 cubic metres is sufficient to apply 25 millimetres of water over 4 hectares, which is approximately equivalent to applying 1 inch over 10 acres.

7. FIELD DRAINAGE

(Estimated for 1995)

(Costs before deducting grant*)

1. Installation (costs per metre of excavating a trench, supplying and laying the pipe and backfilling with soil).

		£ per metre
Plastic pipes:	60mm diameter	0·80—1·00
	80mm diameter	1·05—1·25
	100mm diameter	1·60—1·90
	125mm diameter	2·30—2·70
	150mm diameter	3·10—3·20
	300mm diameter	5·50—7·50

The above rates apply to schemes of 5 hectares or more; smaller areas and patching up work can cost up to 50% more.

Supplying and laying permeable backfill to within 360mm of ground level will add between £1·40 and £1·80 per metre to costs.

Digging new open ditches (1·8m top width, 0·9m depth) costs £1·50-£2·00 per metre compared with improving existing ditches at £1·00 to £1·20 per metre.

Subsoiling or mole draining will cost in the region of £45-£60 per hectare.

2. *Total*

Costs per hectare for complete schemes will vary depending on the distance between laterals, soil type, size of area to be drained, region of the country and the time of year when the work is to be undertaken. The cost of a scheme with 20m spacing between laterals and using permeable backfill will typically be in the range £1,300 to £1,500 per hectare (£520-£600 per acre). Backfilling with soil, rather than with permeable material such as washed gravel, may reduce the cost by almost half but is only possible on certain types of soil. Equally, certain soil types which are particularly suitable for mole drainage may permit spacing between laterals to be increased to 40m or even 80m in some instances. Where this is possible costs will be reduced proportionately.

* Grant aid is available through the Farm and Conservation Grant Scheme. It is confined to the replacement and renewal of existing field drainage systems and is only available when an approval plan is submitted (see page 180). Rates of grant are currently 25% in Less Favoured Areas and 15% elsewhere.

8. GRAIN DRYING AND STORAGE COSTS
(Estimated for 1995)

A. Drying

Capital Costs: vary widely according to type and capacity of drier; a typical range is £26 to £39 per tonne dried annually.

Annual fixed costs: depreciation and interest £3·00 to £4·50 per tonne.

Running costs: fuel and repairs, approx. £3·00 per tonne (6 per cent moisture extraction) for oil-fired driers or where little heat is used in ventilated plants; £7·50 to £10·00 for electrically-heated driers. Labour, £1·15 to £2·90 per tonne.

Total operating costs: average £7·00 to £10·00 per tonne (6 per cent) for cereals; costs for oilseed rape are likely to be £2 to £3 per tonne higher when drying in ventilated bins, because of higher labour requirements.

B. Storage

Capital Costs: from less than £60 per tonne (inexpensive storage in an existing building) to £200 per tonne for an elaborate plant, including pit, elevator, conveyors etc. in a new building.

Typical costs are given on page 151.

Depreciation and Interest: £150 per tonne depreciated over 10 years, with 10 per cent interest, equals £24·25 per annum; over 15 years, at 7 per cent interest, £16·50. (In highly mechanized bulk plants, part of this may be charged against harvesting rather than entirely against storage).

Fuel and Repairs: £1·75 per tonne.

Extra Drying: Additional drying costs will be borne if storage necessitates further moisture reduction. Average £1·50 per tonne where own drier, £3·50 if dried on contract, for an additional 4 per cent moisture extraction.

Loss of Weight: the value of the weight of grain lost should be charged if storage requires extra drying. 2 per cent = £1·75 to £2·20 per tonne.

Interest on Grain Stored: from 52p (£90 per tonne grain, at 7 per cent) to £1·00 (£120 per tonne grain, at 10 per cent) per month.

Contract Storage: typically £1 per tonne per month with a handling charge of around £1·50 per tonne for loading into store and out of store.

IV. OTHER FIXED COSTS DATA

1. WHOLE FARM FIXED COSTS

The following are a *broad indication* of the levels of fixed costs (£) per hectare (acre) for various types and sizes of farm, estimated for 1995, *including the value of unpaid family manual labour,* including that of the farmer and his wife.

All of these costs can of course vary widely according to many factors, especially the intensity of farming, e.g. the number of cows per 100 farm hectares on the mainly dairying and dairying and arable farms, or the hectares of intensive crops such as potatoes, sugar beet and vegetables per 100 farm hectares on the mixed cropping farms.

Furthermore, *the figures provided are only averages. "Premium" farms of the same level of intensity can have labour, machinery and general overhead costs at least 20% lower.* However, the most profitable farms are often more intensive and therefore have higher fixed costs associated with the great intensity—but with substantially higher total farm gross margins; it is the net amount (TGM-TFC) that matters.

More specific data relating to local types of farm can be derived from reports published annually by the agricultural economics departments of certain Universities and Colleges; those in England and Wales (based on the Farm Business Survey) are given below (all have been consulted in compiling the data presented).

North: Farming in Northern England (University of Newcastle-upon-Tyne).

Yorkshire: Farming in Yorkshire (Askham Bryan College).

North-West: An Economic Review of Farming in the North-West (University of Manchester).

East Midlands: Farming in the East Midlands (University of Nottingham).

Eastern Counties: Report on Farming in the Eastern Counties (University of Cambridge).

South-East: Farm Business Statistics for S.E. England (Wye College, University of London).

South: Farm Business Data (University of Reading).

South-West: Farm Incomes in South-West England (University of Exeter).

Wales: Farm Management Survey in Wales (University College of Wales, Aberystwyth).

The addresses and telephone numbers of the above are given on pages 213/214.

Data for Scotland and Northern Ireland are available from the Scottish Agricultural College and Department of Northern Ireland respectively. Their addresses are given on page 214.

The term "fixed costs" is used here as it is in gross margin analysis and planning: a full explanation of the differences between fixed and variable costs in this context is given on pages 1 and 2. *Note that all casual labour and contract work have been included under fixed costs.* In calculating enterprise gross margins on the individual farm these costs are normally allocated as variable costs if they are specific to a particular enterprise and vary approximately in proportion to its size, i.e. are approximately constant per hectare of a particular crop or per head of livestock. Otherwise they are included as fixed costs. In both cases, however, they could be regarded as substitutes for regular labour and/or the farmer's own machinery—which are both items of fixed cost. It is therefore simpler if both are included, fully, as fixed costs. If one is comparing results from accounts set out on a gross margin basis, and some or all of the casual labour and contract work have been included as variable costs (especially on cropping farms, e.g. for potato harvesting by casual labour or contractor's machine), the necessary adjustments need to be made in making the comparisons.

Notes

Unpaid Labour. Refers to the value of family manual labour, including that of the farmer and his wife.

Depreciation. This is based on the "historic" (i.e. original) cost of machinery, not on the current (i.e. replacement) cost. Although the latter is a truer reflection of the *real* loss of value of machinery (as is apparent when replacement becomes necessary), virtually all farm accounts use the historic cost method. The change therefore facilitates efficiency comparisons. It should however be noted that depreciation is based on current costs in the University/College reports listed on the previous page; on average this increases the figure by about one-third. Both this item and *Repairs* include vehicles.

Leasing Charges: The capital element, but not the interest, is included in depreciation; the proportion paid as interest varies according to the rate of interest paid and the length of the leasing period, but is typically 15 to 20 per cent.

Rental Value. Estimated rent for owner-occupied land, based on actual rents of farms of similar type and size (established tenancies). 'Landlord-type' expenses average about 40 per cent of the estimated rent.

General Overheads include general farm maintenance and repairs, office expenses, water, insurance, fees, subscriptions, etc. 'Farm maintenance', i.e. repairs to property (buildings, roads, etc.), average approximately one-quarter of total general farm overhead expenses.

In making comparisons with fixed costs taken from farm accounts it is important to note that in the figures below unpaid manual labour and a rental value for owner-occupied land are included; (but not paid management or interest charges).

Labour, machinery and buildings are the main items of "fixed" costs subject to change with major alterations in farm policy. Each is the subject of a separate section in this book.

	Mainly Dairying		
	Under 50 ha (Under 125 acres)	50-100 ha (125-250 acres)	Over 100 ha (Over 250 acres)
Regular Labour (paid)	130 (53)	210 (85)	250 (101)
Regular Labour (unpaid) ...	400 (162)	205 (83)	85 (34)
Casual Labour	20 (8)	10 (4)	15 (6)
Total Labour	550 (223)	425 (172)	350 (141)
Machinery Depreciation ...	115 (47)	100 (41)	95 (39)
Machinery Repairs	80 (33)	72·5 (29)	70 (28)
Fuel, Elec., Oil	65 (26)	60 (24)	50 (20)
Contract	80 (32)	60 (24)	70 (28)
Vehicle Tax and Insurance ...	15 (6)	12·5 (5)	10 (4)
Total Power and Machinery ...	355 (144)	305 (123)	295 (119)
Rent/Rental Value	165 (67)	155 (63)	150 (61)
General Overhead Expenses ...	180 (72)	130 (53)	125 (51)
Total Fixed Costs	1250 (506)	1015 (411)	920 (372)

	Dairying and Arable		
	Under 100 ha	100-200 ha	Over 200 ha
	(Under 250 acres)	(250-500 acres)	(Over 500 acres)
Regular Labour (paid)	195 (79)	225 (91)	195 (79)
Regular Labour (unpaid) ...	195 (79)	65 (26)	40 (16)
Casual Labour	10 (4)	10 (4)	10 (4)
Total Labour	400 (162)	300 (121)	245 (99)
Machinery Depreciation ...	90 (37)	85 (35)	85 (35)
Machinery Repairs	55 (22)	55 (22)	55 (22)
Fuel, Elec., Oil	50 (20)	50 (20)	40 (16)
Contract	47·5 (19)	45 (18)	22·5 (9)
Vehicle Tax and Insurance ...	12·5 (5)	10 (4)	7·5 (3)
Total Power and Machinery ...	255 (103)	245 (99)	210 (85)
Rent /Rental Value	145 (59)	140 (57)	135 (55)
General Overhead Expenses ...	110 (44)	100 (41)	80 (32)
Total Fixed Costs	910 (368)	785 (318)	670 (271)

	Mainly Cereals*		
	Under 100 ha	100-200 ha	Over 200 ha
	(Under 250 acres)	(250-500 acres)	(Over 500 acres)
Regular Labour (paid)	50 (20)	85 (34)	105 (43)
Regular Labour (unpaid) ...	175 (71)	100 (41)	30 (12)
Casual Labour	5 (2)	5 (2)	5 (2)
Total Labour	230 (93)	190 (77)	140 (57)
Machinery Depreciation ...	70 (29)	75 (31)	70 (29)
Machinery Repairs	37·5 (15)	37·5 (15)	35 (14)
Fuel, Elec., Oil	32·5 (13)	30 (12)	27·5 (11)
Contract	47·5 (19)	27·5 (11)	15 (6)
Vehicle Tax and Insurance ...	12·5 (5)	10 (4)	7·5 (3)
Total Power and Machinery ...	200 (81)	180 (73)	155 (63)
Rent/Rental Value	130 (53)	125 (51)	120 (48)
General Overhead Expenses ...	85 (34)	70 (28)	60 (24)
Total Fixed Costs	645 (261)	565 (229)	475 (192)

* With combinable break crops.

	Mixed Cropping*		
	Under 100 ha (Under 250 acres)	100-200 ha (250-500 acres)	Over 200 ha (Over 500 acres)
Regular Labour (paid)	95 (38)	135 (55)	170 (69)
Regular Labour (unpaid) ...	160 (65)	75 (30)	20 (8)
Casual Labour	25 (10)	10 (4)	10 (4)
Total Labour	280 (113)	220 (89)	200 (81)
Machinery Depreciation ...	90 (37)	85 (35)	80 (33)
Machinery Repairs	50 (20)	50 (20)	50 (20)
Fuel, Elec., Oil	40 (16)	35 (14)	35 (14)
Contract	35 (14)	27·5 (11)	25 (10)
Vehicle Tax and Insurance ...	15 (6)	12·5 (5)	10 (4)
Total Power and Machinery ...	230 (93)	210 (85)	200 (81)
Rent /Rental Value	140 (57)	135 (55)	135 (55)
General Overhead Expenses ...	85 (34)	75 (30)	70 (28)
Total Fixed Costs	735 (297)	640 (259)	605 (245)

* With potatoes and/or sugar beet and/or field vegetables.

	Mainly Sheep/Cattle (lowland)		
	Under 100 ha (Under 250 acres)	100-200 ha (250-500 acres)	Over 200 ha (Over 500 acres)
Regular Labour (paid)	60 (24)	80 (32)	95 (39)
Regular Labour (unpaid) ...	225 (91)	105 (43)	70 (28)
Casual Labour	15 (6)	5 (2)	5 (2)
Total Labour	300 (121)	190 (77)	170 (69)
Machinery Depreciation ...	50 (21)	45 (18)	40 (16)
Machinery Repairs	45 (18)	35 (14)	32·5 (13)
Fuel, Elec., Oil	30 (12)	25 (10)	25 (10)
Contract	30 (12)	20 (8)	15 (6)
Vehicle Tax and Insurance ...	10 (4)	10 (4)	7·5 (3)
Total Power and Machinery ...	165 (67)	135 (54)	120 (48)
Rent/Rental Value	120 (49)	115 (47)	110 (45)
General Overhead Expenses ...	85 (34)	65 (26)	55 (22)
Total Fixed Costs	670 (271)	505 (204)	455 (184)

	Sheep/Cattle and Arable		
	Under 100 ha (Under 250 acres)	100-200 ha (250-500 acres)	Over 200 ha (Over 500 acres)
Regular Labour (paid)	50 (20)	85 (34)	105 (43)
Regular Labour (unpaid) ...	155 (63)	90 (37)	50 (20)
Casual Labour	10 (4)	5 (2)	5 (2)
Total Labour	215 (87)	180 (73)	160 (65)
Machinery Depreciation ...	65 (27)	65 (27)	55 (22)
Machinery Repairs	35 (14)	30 (12)	25 (10)
Fuel, Elec., Oil	22·5 (9)	20 (8)	17·5 (7)
Contract	25 (10)	20 (8)	15 (6)
Vehicle Tax and Insurance ...	12·5 (5)	10 (4)	7·5 (3)
Total Power and Machinery ...	160 (65)	145 (59)	120 (48)
Rent /Rental Value	125 (51)	120 (48)	115 (47)
General Overhead Expenses ...	75 (30)	65 (26)	55 (22)
Total Fixed Costs	575 (233)	510 (206)	450 (182)

	Arable and Pigs/Poultry*		
	Under 100 ha (Under 250 acres)	100-200 ha (250-500 acres)	Over 200 ha (Over 500 acres)
Regular Labour (paid)	325 (131)	360 (146)	215 (87)
Regular Labour (unpaid) ...	200 (81)	70 (28)	15 (6)
Casual Labour	25 (10)	20 (8)	20 (8)
Total Labour	550 (222)	450 (182)	250 (101)
Machinery Depreciation ...	105 (43)	95 (39)	95 (39)
Machinery Repairs	85 (34)	85 (34)	75 (30)
Fuel, Elec., Oil	120 (49)	80 (32)	60 (24)
Contract	45 (18)	32·5 (13)	30 (12)
Vehicle Tax and Insurance ...	15 (6)	12·5 (5)	10 (4)
Total Power and Machinery ...	370 (150)	305 (123)	270 (109)
Rent/Rental Value	170 (69)	155 (63)	140 (57)
General Overhead Expenses ...	220 (89)	175 (71)	100 (40)
Total Fixed Costs	1310 (530)	1085 (439)	760 (307)

* The number of pigs in relation to the total farm area varies widely, and so, therefore, can these per hectare (per acre) figures.

						Livestock Rearing	
						Upland	Hill
						(per *adjusted* hectare (acre))*	
Regular Labour (paid)	...	...	...	...	...	60 (24)	40 (16)
Regular Labour (unpaid)	...	...	...	...	...	85 (35)	70 (29)
Casual Labour	...	...	...	...	...	10 (4)	5 (2)
Total Labour	...	...	...	...	...	155 (63)	115 (47)
Machinery Depreciation	...	...	...	...	...	30 (12)	20 (8)
Machinery Repairs	...	...	...	...	...	22·5 (9)	12·5 (5)
Fuel, Elec., Oil ...	...	...	...	...	...	15 (6)	10 (4)
Contract	...	...	...	...	...	17·5 (7)	5 (2)
Vehicle Tax and Insurance	...	...	...	...	...	5 (2)	2·5 (1)
Total Power and Machinery	...	...	...	...	...	90 (36)	50 (20)
Rent/Rental Value	...	...	...	...	...	65 (26)	35 (14)
General Overhead Expenses ...	...	...	...	...	...	50 (20)	30 (12)
Total Fixed Costs	...	...	...	...	...	360 (145)	230 (93)

* Divisors for per *actual* area figure = upland 1·5, hill 2·25.

Note: Large (Lowland) Farms

Data included in the Cambridge University Farm Business Survey sample (reference M. C. Murphy's annual "Report on Farming in The Eastern Counties of England", Agricultural Economics Unit, Dept. of Land Economy) for farms of 400 to 500 ha and over 500 ha give no clear indication of their having lower fixed costs per hectare than the figures presented in this section for farms over 200 ha in size. One difference, however, as would be expected, is that a lower proportion of the manual labour is supplied by the farmer. This element falls to average approximately £10/ha for farms of 400-500 ha and becomes neglible over 500 ha. Paid labour costs rise to compensate, giving a similar total value of labour input per hectare.

N.B. **Horticultural holdings**—see page 30.

2. RENTS

Average Rent per hectare (acre) of Crops, Grass and Rough Grazing.

Farm rents have almost stabilised in recent years, the average level rising by only about 5% in the last five years, a reduction of approximately 20% in real terms. Farms in England due for a rent review in 1993 (34% of the total) had an average increase of 5·0%; (44% had an increase, 49% a standstill and 7% a decrease); this meant an increase over *all* farms of 1·4%. These percentage increases are 1·6 and 0·4 percentage points respectively above those in the two previous years.

The figures below, which are the rent levels for all farms which were due for a rent review in the year to October 1993 (rounded to the nearest 50p per hectare or 25p per acre) can be taken as approximate average levels in 1995.

Region			£ per ha	£ per acre
North West	...	...	156·00	63·00
West Midlands	...	...	130·00	52·75
East Anglia	...	...	119·50	48·50
South West	...	...	116·50	47·00
East Midlands	...	...	116·00	47·00
South East	...	...	115·50	46·75
Yorks/Humberside	...		91·00	36·75
Northern	...	...	48·00	19·50
England ...	...	...	106·50	43·25
Wales	...	...	76·50	31·00

It has to be borne in mind that rough grazing, including upland, is included in the above: hence the low figure (most notably) for the Northern farms. **The average rent for lowland, excluding woodland and rough grazing, is likely to average approximately £130 per ha, £52·50 per acre.** The levels on large mixed arable farms (i.e. including potatoes, sugar beet and/or vegetables) on good soil, or well-equipped dairy farms, will tend to average £150 to £175 per ha, £60 to £70 per acre, especially where the landlord is anxious to obtain a good rent. Variations according to soil type (land classification) and size are shown below.

In the case of new lettings by tender the levels are likely to be higher still, owing to the scarcity factor. Farmers who already own land, with little or no mortgage, can afford to offer a higher figure than bidders with no other farm. However, the difference between average and tender rents has declined substantially in recent years owing to falling profitability, especially on arable farms, until very recently.

Land Quality Differences (England)
(Agricultural Land Classification)

Land Class				£ per ha	£ per acre
1	...	...	...	178·00	72·00
2	...	...	...	124·50	50·50
3	...	...	...	111·00	45·00
4	...	...	...	63·50	25·75
5	...	...	...	14·00	5·75

Size Differences (England)

Area in ha			£ per ha	£ per acre
less than 10	...	...	238·50	96·50
10-19·9	...	...	136·00	55·00
20-29·9	...	...	139·00	56·25
30-39·9	...	...	134·00	54·25
40-49·9	...	...	119·50	48·25
50-79·9	...	...	110·00	44·50
75-99·9	...	...	109·00	44·00
100-249·9	...	...	104·00	42·25
250 & over	...	...	82·50	33·50

Rent Range (England)

Rent Range		% of farms
£ per ha	£ per acre	
less than 20·00	Less than 8·10	2·9
20·00— 39·99	8·00— 16·19	3·7
40·00— 59·99	16·20— 24·24	6·1
60·00— 79·99	24·25— 32·34	9·1
80·00— 99·99	32·35— 40·44	13·5
100·00—124·99	40·45— 50·59	23·8
125·00—149·99	00·00— 00·00	14·9
150·00—199·99	50·60— 80·99	15·3
200·00—499·99	81·00—202·34	7·1
500·00 and over	202·35 and over	3·6

Source of Data

MAFF (Government Statistical Service). Farm Rents in England: Results of 1993 Annual Rent Enquiry. This annual enquiry, carried out by ADAS, covers about 24% of the tenanted agricultural land in England: in 1993, 11,741 farms, 822,743 ha (over 2 million acres).

3. LAND PRICES

Sale Value of Farmland, England and Wales (£ per hectare (acre))

(1) Auction Sales (with Vacant Possession only)

(a) Oxford Institute/Savills series *

Year	Current Prices	Real Values**	Year	Current Prices	Real Values**
1937-9	60 (24)	1328 (537)	1979	4371 (1769)	7562 (3060)
1945	111 (45)	1474 (597)	1980	4265 (1726)	6227 (2520)
1950	198 (80)	2146 (868)	1981	4272 (1729)	5596 (2265)
1955	198 (80)	1732 (701)	1982	4557 (1844)	5468 (2224)
1960	304 (123)	2365 (957)	1983	5145 (2082)	5917 (2395)
1965	581 (235)	3840 (1554)	1984	4888 (1978)	5377 (2176)
1970	605 (245)	3195 (1293)	1985	4781 (1935)	4924 (1993)
1971	647 (262)	3119 (1262)	1986	4193 (1697)	4193 (1697)
1972	1473 (596)	6628 (2682)	1987	4944 (2001)	4746 (1921)
1973	1871 (757)	7727 (3127)	1988	6716 (2718)	6135 (2482)
1974	1572 (636)	5596 (2265)	1989	6558 (2654)	5558 (2249)
1975	1332 (539)	3810 (1542)	1990	6346 (2568)	4913 (1988)
1976	1814 (734)	4462 (1806)	1991	6007 (2431)	4393 (1778)
1977	2449 (991)	5192 (2101)	1992	5441 (2202)	3836 (1552)
1978	3279 (1327)	6427 (2601)	1993***	5456 (2208)	3785 (1532)

* Savills since 1988. ** At 1986 prices.
*** Includes an estimated £270 (109) for the value of milk quota (averaged across *all* farms).

Since 1970, figures based on sales reports in the *Estates Gazette* and the *Farmers Weekly*, plus some unpublished sales, with a minimum size of 10 hectares.

(b) Farmland Market series

Size Group (hectares)	10-20	20-40	40-60	60-80	80-100	100-140	Over 140	All Farms
1973	2530	2080	1815	1805	1885	1735	2100	1975 (799)
1974	2245	1745	1490	1565	1415	1335	1280	1685 (682)
1975	2115	1545	1340	1165	1200	1190	1090	1485 (601)
1976	2560	2015	1855	1830	1670	1610	1730	1965 (795)
1977	2825	2660	2365	2425	2230	2530	2325	2525 (1020)
1978	3970	3425	3125	3265	3180	3480	3595	3380 (1368)
1979	6280	4385	4220	3975	4330	4890	4315	4515 (1828)
1980	5585	4905	4270	4305	4405	4435	4130	4705 (1904)
1981	6135	4680	3880	4315	3760	4710	4355	4500 (1821)
1982	6455	4950	4465	4065	4705	4510	4325	4815 (1949)
1983	6825	5630	5160	5110	5095	5495	5130	5450 (2206)
1984	6565	5815	5300	5520	5435	5360	4625	5480 (2218)
1985	8410	5190	4455	4555	4210	4405	4645	5245 (2123)
1986	7825	5180	3930	3745	N/A	3155	N/A	4185 (1949)
1987	7280	7115	5130	4285	4325	N/A	N/A	5980 (2421)
1988	13255	9035	6225	5825	5320	6220	4275	7205 (2916)
1989	14140	9260	6660	6610	5770	5980	5260	7520 (3044)
1990	8225	6680	7440	6420	5820	N/A	N/A	6505 (2635)
1991	7335	7790	6575	4455	4985	N/A	N/A	6460 (2615)
1992	8920	6255	4280	4890	N/A	4400	N/A	5650 (2285)
1993	8910	7185	5410	5305	4725	N/A	5585	5890 (2385)

Bare land prices (over 2 ha): 1987, £3955 (1600); 1988, £5040 (2040); 1989, £5620 (2275); 1990, £7885 (3190); 1991, £4800 (1945); 1992, £3970 (1605); 1993, £4320 (1750).

(2) Current Agricultural Prices (CALP) series (England)

Cover sales of 5 ha and above but excludes land sold for development or forestry, gifts, inheritances and compulsory purchases. Includes sales of bare land as well as land with dwellings, buildings, etc. (see (iii) (d) below).

Data collected jointly by ADAS (Agricultural Development and Advisory Service), AMC (Agricultural Mortgage Corporation) and CLA (Country Landowners Association); published by the AMC until mid-1993, but figures supplied until the end of that year. It is hoped that the series will be resumed at an early later date.

(i) *Annual Figures* (Vacant Possession Only)

	Average price (A)	Average price (B): in 1993 £	Index (of B) (1978 = 100)
1978	3160 (1280)	8905 (3605)	100
1979	4140 (1675)	10295 (4165)	116
1980	3975 (1610)	8375 (3390)	94
1981	3940 (1595)	7420 (3005)	83
1982	4125 (1670)	7155 (2895)	80
1983	4630 (1875)	7675 (3105)	86
1984	4555 (1845)	7195 (2910)	81
1985	4340 (1755)	6460 (2615)	73
1986	3675 (1485)	5300 (2145)	59
1987	3780 (1530)	5220 (2115)	59
1988	5350 (2165)	7045 (2850)	79
1989	5595 (2265)	6835 (2765)	77
1990	4440 (1795)	4955 (2005)	56
1991	4145 (1676)	4370 (1770)	49
1992	3658 (1480)	3715 (1505)	42
1993	3608 (1460)	3608 (1460)	41

(ii) *Quarterly Figures, 1988-93*

3 months ended	Vacant Possession Average Price (1)	Vacant Possession Weighted Price (2)	Price Index (3)	Real Price Index (3)	Tenanted
1990: March	5286	5191 (2100)	113	86	1622 (655)
June	4850	5395 (2185)	117	88	2376 (960)
September	3681	4184 (1695)	91	67	2108 (855)
December	4344	4901 (1985)	106	77	1749 (710)
1991: March	3777	4112 (1665)	89	64	2098 (850)
June	3952	4360 (1765)	95	67	2786 (1125)
September	4437	4567 (1850)	99	69	3900 (1580)
December	4350	4356 (1765)	95	66	1767 (715)
1992: March	3822	3809 (1540)	83	57	1653 (670)
June	4001	3748 (1515)	81	55	3029 (1225)
September	3427	3516 (1425)	76	51	2143 (865)
December	3544	3517 (1425)	76	51	1986 (805)
1993: March	3414	3578 (1450)	78	53	1841 (745)
June	3435	3213 (1300)	70	47	2356 (955)
September	3978	4130 (1670)	90	60	2256 (915)
December	3497	3727 (1510)	81	54	1346 (545)

(1) Total value of sales divided by total area sold. The most recent figures are provisional.

(2) Average price for each region × size-group category weighted by the area of land sold in that category in the three years 1986-88.

(3) Index based on weighted price: 1985 = 100 (£4,606/ha (£1,865/acre)).

N.B. *Vacant Possession Premium:* The annual average price of all tenanted land sold as a percentage of all vacant possession land in the four years 1990 to 1993 inclusive averaged approximately 55%. It is to be borne in mind that the number of reported sales of tenanted land is small and at least partly for this reason there is a considerable variation in the average premium from month to month.

(iii) *Regional, Size-group, Land Quality and Type of Property Figures, 1988-92.* (Vacant Possession Only). *The figures for 1993 are regretfully unavailable at present.*

(a) *By Regions*

	1992	1991	1990	1989	1988
Northern	4064	4162	3159	2975	3645
Yorks/Humberside	3108	4080	5250	4737	4044
East Midlands	3292	3673	4460	4266	4295
East Anglia	3255	3823	4801	5052	4680
South East	3472	4220	5634	6806	6191
South West	3795	4009	5001	7223	5662
West Midlands	4283	4555	3071	5907	6005
North West	4045	5736	3187	4670	6505
England	3658 (1480)	4145 (1677)	4441 (1797)	5596 (2265)	5349 (2165)

(b) *By Size-Group*

Size Group (ha)	1992	1991	1990	1989	1988
5—9	5399	4456	5206	5703	4982
10—19	4584	4644	5024	6156	4385
20—49	3682	4903	5095	5688	5136
50—99	3604	4412	4724	5566	5425
100 and over	3305	3578	3911	5488	5635

(c) *By Land Classification*

Land quality	(% of total area)	1992	1991	1990	1989	1988
1	(3·3)	4386	4253	5899	4608	5259
2	(16·7)	3626	4822	5036	5683	5765
3	(54·0)	3726	4115	4638	5721*	5164
4	(15·7)	3271	3668	2345	4167	4491
5	(10·3)	3081	769	1132	2109	2391

* Figure distorted by value and volume of milk quota. Most dairy farms are on Grade 3 land and the amount of quota transferred is 10 times higher per hectare than for Grade 2. If the average value of quota is deducted the value of Grade 3 land falls below that of Grade 2.

(d) *By Type of Property*

	1992	1991	1990	1989	1988
Land, Dwelling(s) and Buildings	4197	4713	4782	6698	5948
Land and Dwelling(s) only	3156	4016	3347	5262	7398
Land and Buildings only	3280	3341	4842	3887	4244
Bare Land	3066	3847	3808	3847	3746

(3) **Inland Revenue Returns** (England only)

Year[1]	Vacant Possession		Tenanted	
	Farms[2]	Bare Land	Farms[2]	Bare Land
1980/1	3568 (1444)	3325 (1346)	2334 (945)	2354 (953)
1981/2	3503 (1418)	3281 (1328)	2644 (1070)	1340 (542)
1982/3	3766 (1524)	3525 (1427)	2549 (1032)	2210 (894)
1983/4	3761 (1522)	3835 (1552)	2389 (967)	2511 (1016)
1984/5	4258 (1723)	3466 (1403)	2879 (1165)	2310 (935)
1985/6	4055 (1641)	3477 (1407)	2192 (887)	2217 (897)
1986/7	3703 (1499)	3023 (1223)	2141 (866)	1777 (719)
1987/8	3750 (1518)	3140 (1271)	2252 (911)	2476 (1002)
1988/9	4739 (1918)	3521 (1425)	3178 (1286)[3]	1929 (781)
1989/90	5355 (2167)	4080 (1651)	2143 (867)	2093 (847)
1990/91	5515 (2231)	3750 (1517)	2090 (846)	2505 (1014)
1991/92	5015 (2030)	3370 (1363)	2505 (1015)	1465 (592)
1992/93	4405 (1785)	3120 (1265)	1680 (680)	2045 (830)[3]
1993/94 (1st ½)[5]	3891 (1575)	3230 (1307)	2273 (920)[4]	874 (354)[4]

1. October 1-September 30 years. There is a delay between the dates when a price is agreed and when it is notified to the Inland Revenue and thus included in the above figures; this time-lag is thought to average about 9 months; hence, for example, the 1992/93 figures roughly approximate to 1992 calendar year prices.
2. Farms = Land and Buildings, including the farmhouse.
3. High figure caused by a few untypically high-priced transactions.
4. Few transactions.
5. October 1-March 31.

The above figures relate to all sales of agricultural properties of 5 ha and over except those for development and other non-agricultural purposes. They include any sales at prices below ruling open market value (as between members of a family), sales where the vendor retains certain (e.g. sporting) rights, sales in which the farmhouse represents a substantial part of the total value, and sales of land which may, in the purchaser's view, have an element of development value.

Source: M.A.F.F. Statistics (Government Statistical Service).

Woodland

Average price range of average quality established lowland woodland: £1250-1500/ha (£500-600/acre).

4. BUILDINGS

A. Building Costs

Building costs are notoriously variable. Many factors influence a contractor's price, including distance from his yard, size of contract, site access, site conditions, complexity of work, familiarity with the type of work and his current work load. There will also be differences in efficiency and standard of work between contractors and, as is often the case with farm buildings, the absence of detailed specification by the client may mean that different contractors will not have quoted for identical buildings. The number of extras that are found to be required after a contract has been agreed will also vary.

The costs given below can only be taken as an approximate guide. They refer to new buildings, erected by contractor on a clear level site and exclude VAT and any grants that may be available. Prices are forecasts for mid 1995.

Sources of Further Information

The costs below are based on information gathered by John MacCormack at the SAC's Centre for Rural Building, cross-checked with other sources to ensure general applicability. More detailed information is available in the following publications. The books and journals giving general building cost information generally assume knowledge of how to take off quantities for building work.

Specialised Information on Farm Building Costs

Farm Building Cost Guide published annually by the Centre for Rural Building, Craibstone, Bucksburn, Aberdeen.

Standard Costs Part 1: Specifications; Part 2: Costs. Published by MAFF and the Agricultural Departments in Scotland, Wales and Northern Ireland. Used when claiming government grants on a standard-cost basis.

General Building Cost Information

Books are produced by a number of publishers with annual or more frequent new editions and updates. Examples are *Griffiths Building Price Book, Spon's Architects' and Builders' Price Book,* and *Wessex Building Price Book.* Regularly updated cost information is also given in several professional and trade journals.

I. Constituent Parts

Frame, Roof and Foundations   *per m² floor area*

1. Open-sided timber framed pole barn with round pole uprights on concrete bases, sawn timber rafters and purlins, high-tensile galvanised steel cladding to roof and gable ends above eaves, hardcore floor, eaves height 4·8 m, 9 m span, no side cladding, rainwater drainage to soakaways.   £36

2. Open-sided steel portal-framed building with fibre-cement or plastic coated steel cladding to roof and gables above eaves, hardcore floor, eaves height 4·8 m, no side cladding, rainwater drainage to soakaways.

9 m span	£78
13·2 m span	£67
18 m span	£59

3. Cost breakdown of 2 above

Materials:	portal frame and purlins	26%
	foundations	3%
	roofing	16%
	rainwater and drainage	3%
	hardcore and blinding	2%
	Total Materials	50%
Erection:	portal frame and purlins	19%
	foundations	2%
	roofing	19%
	rainwater and drainage	5%
	hardcore and blinding	5%
	Total Erection	50%

Roof cladding   *per m²*

1. Natural grey fibre-cement, 146 mm corrugations fixed with drive screws

Materials	£7.70	
Fixing	£8.30	
Total		£16.00

2. Extra for coloured sheet   £1.60
3. Extra for translucent sheets   £1.80
4. Deduct for PVC-coated steel   £6.60
5. Deduct for high-tensile corrugated galvanised steel sheeting   £7.80
6. PVC 150 mm half-round gutter on fascia brackets, including stop-ends and outlets   £12.40
7. PVC 100 mm rainwater pipe with fixings, swanneck and shoe   £19.40

	per m run
8. Fibre-cement close-fitting ridge	£19.40
9. Fibre-cement ventilating ridge	£22.60

Walls and Cladding

	per m²
1. Concrete blockwork, fair faced and pointed both sides	
150 mm thick	£23·10
215 mm thick	£33·70
215 mm thick hollow blocks	£33·70
215 mm thick hollow blocks, filled and reinforced	£46·10
2. Extra for rendering or roughcast to blockwork on one side	£10·50
3. Vertical spaced boarding 21 × 145 mm with 19 mm gaps including horizontal rails, all pressure treated	£16·10
4. Fibre-cement vertical cladding, including rails	£21·80
5. Corrugated high-tensile steel side cladding, including rails	£18·70
6. Wall element: 215 mm thick blockwork, including strip foundation (base 750 mm below ground level), 2.5 m height above ground level	£109 per m run

Floors

	per m²
1. Concrete floor 100 mm thick, C20P mix, on 150 mm hardcore, including excavation:	£19·30

Breakdown:	
(a) excavate, level and compact	£1·60
(b) hardcore	£2·40
(c) blinding	£1·30
(d) damp-proof membrane	£1·00
(e) premixed concrete spread and compacted	£11·40
(f) float finish	£1·60

2. Extra to above for	
(a) 150 mm instead of 100 mm	£4·20
(b) laying concrete to falls	£1·20
(c) broom or textured finish	£1·60
(d) Carborundum dust non-slip finish	£3·00
(e) insulating concrete	£3·10

3. Reinforced concrete slatted floors for cattle	
(a) cattle loading	£51
(b) tractor loading	£56
4. Reinforced concrete slats for pigs	£37
5. Insulating floor, including excavation and base	
(a) 27 mm expanded polystyrene, 38 mm screed	£31

(b) insulating concrete with lightweight
aggregate   £22
(c) as (b) with 20 mm screed   £29
6. Form channel in concrete   £2.50 per m run
7. Excavate for cast 1 m^3 in-situ concrete bases
for stanchions   £71 each

Services and Fittings
1. Drainage: 100 mm PVC pipe laid in trench,
including 750 mm deep excavation and backfill £13.50 per m run
Breakdown:
 (a) excavate and backfill   £7·60
 (b) 100 mm PVC pipe laid   £5·90
Extras:
 (c) add to (a) for 1 m deep   £2·40
 (d) add to (b) for 150 mm pipe   £5·00
2. Excavate soakaway and fill with stones   £76 each
3. Trap and grid top, 100 mm PVC   £15·10 each
4. Yard gully with heavy duty road grating 400 ×
300 mm   £180 each
5. Inspection chamber 900 mm deep, 450 × 600
mm opening and medium duty cast iron cover   £260 each
6. Above-ground vitreous enamel slurry tank on
concrete base, 1000 m^3 £22,500 each
7. Reception pit, 20 m^3 £1,350 each
8. Slurry channel beneath (not including)
slats, 1.8 m deep, 3 m wide   £275 per m run
9. Lighting: 1.5 m 60W single flourescent unit,
including wiring and switch   £62 each
Extras:
 (a) PVC conduit   £49
 (b) screwed steel conduit   £100
10. Power: 13A switched outlet   £51 each
11. Diagonal feed fence, fixed, including posts
(painted)   £40 per m run
12. Tombstone feed fence, fixed, including posts
(painted)   £46 per m run
13. Feed bunker   £26 per m run
14. Hay rack, wall fixing   £21 per m run
15. Cubicle division, galvanised, fixed in place   £45 each
16. Fencing: three-rail timber with posts, all
pressure treated   £12·60 per m run
17. Gate, 3 m wide, galvanised steel, including
posts set in concrete
 (a) medium duty   £130 each
 (b) heavy duty   £190 each
Deduct for painted instead of galvanised finish £33

II Complete Buildings

Fully Covered and Enclosed Barn

Portal frame, 18 m span, 6 m bays, 6 m to
eaves, 3 m high blockwork walls with sheet
cladding above, 6 m sliding doors at either
end, 150 mm thick concrete floor

£116 per m² floor area

Cows and Cattle Housing

1. Covered strawed yard, enclosed with ventilated
   cladding, concrete floor, pens only, with 4·0 m²
   per head floor area — £420 per head
2. Extra to 1 for 4·0 m wide double-sided feeding
   passage, barrier and troughs — £180 per head
3. Kennel building — £260 per head
4. Portal framed building with cubicles — £470 per head
5. Extra to 4 for feed stance, feeding passage,
   barriers and troughs — £270 per head
6. Extra to 4 for slatting of cubicle passages — £280 per head
7. Covered collecting yard, 1·1 m² per cow — £130 per head
8. Milking parlour building, example:
   5·5 × 11·5 m for 8/16 parlour — £12,700
9. Parlour equipment, herringbone parlours:
   (a) low level, 1 stall per point — £1,760 per point
   (b) pipeline — £1,590 per point
   (c) extra for meter and auto cluster removal — £1,090 per point
   (d) auto feed dispenser — £410 per stall
10. Dairy building — £150 per m² floor area
11. Bulk tank and washer — £4·80 per litre
12. Loose box, 16 m² floor area laid to falls,
    rendered walls — £240 per m² floor area
13. Bull pen and open run — £6,900
14. Cattle crush and 20 m race — £2,700
15. Slatted floor cattle building for 120 growing
    cattle (1·7 m² pen space per head) with
    drive-through feed passage/troughs — £500 per head

Silage   *per tonne stored*

1. Timber panel clamp on concrete base with
   effluent tank — £42
2. Precast concrete panel clamp with effluent tank — £43
3. Glass-lined forage tower and unloader — £160

Waste Storage   *per m³ stored*

Lined lagoon with safety fence — £18
Glass-lined steel slurry silo
    small (400 m³) — £31
    medium (1,200 m³) — £22
    large (3,600 m³) — £17

GRP below-ground effluent tank, encased in concrete	*per m³ stored*
small (12 m³)	£340
large (36 m³)	£260

Sheep Housing

1. Penning, troughs, feed barriers and drinkers installed in suitable existing building — £20 per ewe

2. Purpose-built sheep shed with 1·35 m² per ewe pen space, concentrate troughs, feed passage and barrier for forage feeding — £81 per ewe

   Extras:
   (a) softwood slatted floor panels, materials only — £3·40 per m²
   (b) slatted panels as (a), made up, plus supports — £13·70 per m²

Pig Housing

per sow and litter

1. Farrowing and rearing
   (a) Prefabricated farrowing pens with crates, side creep areas, part-slatted floors, including foundations, electrical and plumbing work — £1,280
   (b) Steel-framed farrowing house with insulated blockwork walls, part-slatted pens with side creeps in rooms of eight with off main passage — £2,030

   per weaner

   (c) Flat-deck rearing house 3-6 weeks with fully perforated floors to pens, 0·25 m² per pig pen area — £87
   (d) Prefabricated verandah house including foundations, electrical and plumbing work, 0·3 m² per pig internal lying area — £58

2. Fattening

   per baconer

   (a) Prefabricated fattening house with part-slatted floors, trough feeding — £138
   (b) Prefabricated fattening house with part-slatted floors, floor fed — £115
   (c) Steel framed building with insulated blockwork walls, part-slatted floors, trough fed — £190
   (d) Automatic feeding systems for items (a), (b) and (c) above:
   dry-feed system with ad-lib hoppers — £4
   dry on-floor feeding — £9
   wet feeding — £11

3. Dry sows and boars	*per sow*
(a) Yards with floor feeding	£250
(b) Sow cubicle system	£360
(c) Yards with electronic feeders	£370
(d) Yards with individual feeders	£460
(e) Two-yard system with flat-rate feeding	£480
(f) Boar pens as part of sow house	£1,700 each

4. Complete pig unit
Building costs calculated on basis of three-week weaning, 23 pigs per sow per year to bacon, excluding external slurry or dung storage, feed storage and handling/weighing facilities:

(a) Breeding and rearing only	£810 per sow
(b) Breeding with progeny to bacon	£1,520 per sow

Poultry Housing and Equipment   *per bird*

Battery cages with automatic feeding and egg collection, 5 layers per cage (large unit)	£10·00
Battery cages: *average* cost	£11·00
(Cost varies with size of unit and degree of automation; minimum stocking rate 450 cm² per bird)	
Deep litter, 7 layers per m² (0·14 m² per bird)	£11·30-£15·00
Perchery/barn	£11·30-£15·00
Free Range: maximum stocking rate of 1,000/ha.	
(Cost varies with size of unit and degree of automation)	£11.00-£16.00
Broiler breeders, deep litter, 0·167 m² per bird	£16·80
Pullets (cage reared)	£6.80
Broilers, deep litter house, 0·05 m² per bird	£4·10-£4·30
Turkeys, 20,000 pole barn fattening unit	£11·30-£16·60
(Cost varies with size of unit and degree of automation)	

(N.B. Source of Poultry Housing costs: ADAS)

Grain Storage and Drying   *per tonne stored*

1. Intake pit, conveyor, elevator, overhead conveyor and catwalk, storage bins within existing building	£125
extra for low volume ventilation of bins	£30
2. As 1 in new building	£205
3. Portable grain walling for on-floor storage in existing building	£25
4. On floor grain storage in purpose-built building	£63
Extras:	
(a) low volume ventilation	£5
(b) on-floor drying with above-ground main duct and laterals	£86
(c) add to (b) for below-ground laterals	£13
5. Sealed towers for moist grain, including loading and unloading equipment	£112

Potato Storage

	per tonne stored
1. Pallet-box store with recirculation fans	£117
Pallet boxes, 1 tonne	£44
2. Bulk store, building only	£110
Ventilation system: fans, main duct, below-floor lateral ducts	£23

Roads and Fences

	per m length
3.2 m wide hardcore road with drainage ditches	
using locally excavated material	£21
using imported hardcore (£5.60/m³)	£31
extra for bitumen macadam surfacing, two coats	£23
Traditional 7-wire stock fence	£2.60
High tensile 7-wire stock fence	£2.40

Construction Equipment Hire

	hourly rate, with driver
Excavator	£14
Tipping lorry	£17
10-tonne crane	£20

	weekly rate
Concrete mixer, 100 litre (5/3)	£20
Compressor and heavy breaker	£64

B. Standard Costs

Standard costs are published by MAFF and the Scottish Office and Welsh Office Agriculture Departments on the basis of the cost of farm or casual labour and new materials. They do not include an allowance for overheads and profit: in most cases building contractors would add 15-30% to cover them. Standard costs are therefore usually lower, sometimes by a larger percentage than this, particularly where the labour content of the item is high. The following examples are based on standard costs issued in 1992.

	per m² floor area
Open-sided framed building with cladding to roof and gable peaks only, hardcore floor, rainwater drainage to soakaways:	
9 × 18 m	£32
13·2 × 24 m	£29

	per m² wall or roof
Corrugated cladding to roof or walls, *including supports* (purlins or rails):	
fibre cement sheeting	£13·10
extra for coloured sheeting	£0·70
extra for PVC coated steel instead of fibre cement	£0·70
deduct for metallic coated (eg galvanised) steel	£3·75

Spaced boarding	£14·60

Wall element, concrete blockwork 190-324 mm thick with strip foundation (base 750 mm below ground level) and 2·5 mm height above ground level — £72 per m run

Extra for rendering blockwork on one side — £4·85 per m²

Concrete floor, 100 mm thick, including excavation, hardcore and waterproof membrane — £11·10 per m²

Concrete floor, 150 mm thick as above — £13·90 per m²

Reinforced concrete slats for cattle (supports not included) — £38 per m²

Yard gully with heavy grating — £195 each

Drainage pipes, 100 mm, jointed in UPVC, clayware or spun concrete including 900 mm trench and backfill — £8·30 per m run

Drainage pipes 150 mm as above — £14·90 per m run

Tank for water, effluent etc, 20 m³ — £2,330 each

Gate, 3 m wide, steel, including posts concreted in:

light duty — £84 each
cattle yard type — £112 each

Fully covered enclosed building with concrete floor, and rainwater drainage to soakaways

per m² floor area
10 × 18 m — £64
15 × 24 m — £57

C. Storage Requirements

Bulk (cubic metres (feet) per tonne):

Beans	1·2 (43)
Wheat, peas	1·3 (46)
Barley, rye, oilseed rape, linseed, fodder beet	1·4 (50)
Oats	1·9 (68)
Potatoes	1·6 (57)
Dry bulb onions	2·0 (71)
Concentrates: meal	2·0 (71)
cubes	1·6 (57)

Grass silage:	18% DM	1·3 (46)
	30% DM	1·6 (57)
Maize silage		1·3 (46)
Wheat straw		13·0 (464)
Barley straw	small bales	11·5 (411)
Hay		7·0 (247)
Wheat straw		20·0 (714)
Barley straw	big bales	18·0 (643)
Hay		10·0 (353)
Brewers' grains		0·9 (32)

Boxes (floor area in square metres (feet) per tonne):

Potatoes: 0·5 tonne boxes, 5 boxes high	0·52 (5·6)
1·0 tonne boxes, 4 boxes high	0·52 (5·6)
1·0 tonne boxes, 5 boxes high	0·45 (4·8)

Bags (floor area in square metres (feet) per tonne):

Feeding stuffs: 2 bags high	1·6 (17)
Fertilizer: 6 bags high	1·1 (12)
10 bags high	0·7 (8)

V. CAPITAL, TAXATION AND GRANTS

1. CAPITAL

(i) *Tenant's Capital* consists of:

(a) *Machinery.* Costs of new machinery are given on pages 114-118. Written-down values in 1995 are likely to be averaging about £500 per hectare (£200 per acre) taking all farm types together—based on current (*i.e.* replacement) costs (approx. £400/ha based on historic costs).

(b) *Breeding Livestock.* Over all types of farm the 1995 average is estimated to be about £700 per hectare (£280 per acre), but the figure can vary from zero to over £2,000 (£800) for grazing livestock alone. Approximate average market values (£) of various categories of breeding livestock (of mixed ages in the case of adult stock) are as follows (actual value will vary according to average age and weight, quality and breed):

Friesian Dairy Cows (inc. dry cows): 1000.
Channel Island Dairy Cows (inc. dry cows): 575.
Other Dairy Cows (inc. dry cows): 725.
Beef Cows: 675.

Other Cattle:	Friesians	Dairy Followers Ayrshires and C.I. Breeds	Beef Cattle
In-calf heifers	825	500	620
Stores over 2 years	600	370	535
Stores 1-2 years	510	300	460
Stores 6-12 months	385	250	385
Calves under 6 months ...	230	135	260

Ewes: 55. Rams 250.
Sows and In-pig Gilts: 150. Boars 475.

(c) *Working Capital.* This is the capital needed to finance the production cycle, the length of which varies considerably between different crop and livestock enterprises and different combinations of these enterprises. Because of this, no generalizations are possible, but it can include the cost of purchased fattening stock, feed, seed, fertilizers, regular labour, machinery running costs, general overhead costs, rent and living expenses. This capital may be only a few pounds per hectare on an all-dairying farm but £500 or more per hectare on an all-cereals farm where the crop is stored until the spring. The average is likely to be about £300 per hectare (£120 per acre) in 1995.

(ii) *Return on Capital*

(a) *Tenant's Capital.* For all lowland farms (excluding intensive pig and poultry units, fruit and glasshouse production), total tenant's capital will average about £1,500 per hectare (approximately £605 per acre) in 1995, with the (written-down) machinery valuations based on current ('replacement') costs; (for range, see table on page 156). On the same basis, the average U.K.

management and investment per hectare (acre) in the mid-1990's could be in the order of £125 per hectare (£50 per acre), given an average season for crops and grass. The average return on tenant's capital would then be 8·35 per cent. 'Premium' levels (the average of the top 50 per cent of farms) would be likely to be some 50 per cent higher (i.e. 12·5 per cent), with the levels achieved for cash mixed cropping on the very best soils and top dairy farms at least double the average. Note that no charge has been included for management (but that a rental value for owner-occupied land and the value of the unpaid labour of the farmer and wife have been deducted).

(b) *Landlord's Capital* (*i.e.* land, buildings, roads, etc.). With farms averaging, say, £4,000 per hectare (£1,620 per acre), with vacant possession (assuming no special amenity or house value), an average lowland rent of say, £130 per hectare (£52·50 per acre) (see p. 139), and assuming ownership expenses at £50 per hectare (£20 per acre), the (net) return (which is £80 per hectare (£32·50 per acre)) averages 2·0 per cent . If land is taken at its tenanted value, with a vacant possession premium of 50 per cent, the return obviously doubles, to 4·0 per cent. If 'tender' rents were paid, at say one-third per cent above the average level for established tenants (i.e. £172·50/ha (£70/acre)), the return would average about 3·05 per cent with land at the vacant possession price assumed and 6·1 per cent with land at the tenanted value assumed. Full repairing and insurance leases clearly raise the returns above these levels. Above average quality farms acquire higher rents but also obviously command higher prices than the average levels quoted above.

(c) *Total Owner-Occupier's Capital* (*i.e.* land plus 'tenant's' capital). The combined (net) return (£205 per hectare, or £82·50 per acre) on total capital, (£5,500 per hectare, or £2,225 per acre), with land at its vacant possession value, averages 3·75 per cent. This increases to 5·85 per cent if land is taken at its tenanted value and this is half the vacant possession value. If higher rent levels are assumed (given the same farming return), the overall return remains the same, the distribution simply being reallocated in favour of the landownership share at the expense of the farming share. 'Premium' farming returns (as defined above), assuming the same capital requirements, raise the returns to 5·0 per cent with land at the vacant possession price and 7·85 per cent with tenanted land values. (To repeat, the above figures all assume that machinery depreciation and valuation are based on its current cost.)

(iii) *Average Tenant's Capital per hectare* (per acre in brackets) for Different Farm Types, as estimated for 1995, are as follows:

Farm Type Group	Average No. Hectares	Livestock £	Crops, Cultivns., Stores £	Machinery and Equipment* £	Total Tenant's Capital £ £
Mainly Dairying:					
under 50 ha ...	35	1600	225	800	2625 (1060)
50 to 100 ha ...	75	1400	250	700	2350 (950)
Over 100 ha ...	150	1150	250	575	1975 (800)
Mainly Arable:					
under 100 ha ...	65	125	450	475	1050 (425)
100 to 200 ha ...	150	150	450	475	1075 (435)
over 200 ha ...	350	150	450	450	1050 (425)
Dairy and Arable:					
under 100 ha ...	75	1100	375	525	2000 (810)
100 to 200 ha ...	150	875	425	525	1825 (740)
over 200 ha ...	300	675	375	525	1575 (635)
Mainly Sheep/Cattle:					
under 100 ha ...	60	700	175	300	1175 (475)
over 100 ha ...	170	550	175	275	1000 (405)
Sheep/Cattle and Arable:					
under 100 ha ...	65	675	250	350	1275 (515)
100 to 200 ha ...	150	600	225	325	1150 (465)
over 200 ha ...	240	525	200	300	1025 (415)
Dairy, Sheep/Cattle and Arable: ...	225	750	225	400	1375 (555)
Intensive Arable:					
Fruit	75	0	4500	1000	5500 (2225)
Field Vegetables ...	35	0	650	2600	3250 (1315)
Mainly Pigs Poultry: *(per £1000 output)*	—	400	50	150	600 (245)
Glasshouse: *(per £1000 output)*	—	0	50	1000	1050 (425)

* Based on current (*i.e.* replacement) costs.

Note: The above (deliberately rounded) data are based on Farm Business Survey results compiled annually by University/Colleges centres (as listed on page 133), where actual figures for previous years can be found. None includes the value of milk quota on farms with dairying.

(iv) *Return on Capital to Individual Enterprises* on a mixed farm is virtually impossible to ascertain, except perhaps for a full-time pig or poultry enterprise, nor would it be of very much use even if it could be determined. It would require the arbitrary allocation both of costs and capital inputs that are common to several, in some cases all, of the enterprises on the farm.

What is relevant and important is the extra (net) return from an enterprise either to be introduced or expanded, as calculated by a partial budget, related to the extra (net) capital needed. The "net" in brackets relates, as regards return, to the addition to gross margins less any addition to (or plus any reduction in) "fixed" costs, bearing in mind that another enterprise may have to be deleted or reduced in size; and, as regards capital, to the fact that deletion or reduction of another enterprise may release capital.

In most cases of "marginal" substitution, it is differences in the value of breeding livestock and differences in variable costs that are particularly relevant, but the timing of both inputs and sales are also obviously very important.

(v) *"Marginal" Capital Requirements* for small changes in crop areas or livestock numbers can be estimated as follows:

Crops: variable costs till sale.

Dairy Cows and Egg Production: value of the cow (1) (2) or hens, plus one month's food.

Other Breeding Livestock: average value of stock (1) (2), plus variable costs to sale of the progeny (e.g. lambs)—or their transfer to another enterprise (e.g. weaners to the pig fattening enterprise).

Rearing Breeding Livestock (e.g. heifers, tegs, gilts, pullets): cost of the calf, lamb, weaner or chick (2), plus variable costs till they produce their first progeny/eggs.

Fattening Livestock and Production of Stores: cost of stock (2), plus variable costs till sale.

Notes

1. Value of breeding stock, including dairy cows: either the average value over their entire breeding or milk producing life (see table on page 154) or their value when they first produce progeny can be taken. The latter will give the lower return on (marginal) capital and is thus the severer test.

   Home-reared stock: where stock to be used for milk or egg production, breeding or fattening are home-reared, there are two possibilities:

   (i) either they can be valued at variable costs of production when they are transferred from the rearing to the "productive" enterprise; in this case the return on (marginal) capital will be estimated over the combined rearing and "productive" enterprise.

   (ii) or they can be valued at market value at point of transfer. This is the procedure if one wishes to work out a return on (marginal) capital for the rearing and the "productive" enterprises separately.

(vi) *Return on "Marginal" Capital.* This is sometimes expressed as the gross margin less fuel and repair costs of the enterprise expanded as a percentage of the "marginal", or extra, capital. However, two points have to be remembered:

   (i) If another enterprise has had to be reduced in size to enable the enterprise under consideration to be expanded, the capital released and the gross margin forfeited by reducing the size of the first enterprise must be brought into the calculation in estimating the net result of the change.

   (ii) All the above statements on "marginal" capital refer to small changes. If the change is large enough to cause changes in labour, machinery or building requirements the capital changes brought about may be considerably greater.

(vii) *Return on Investments in Medium-Term and Long-Term Capital. Rate of Return and the Discounted Yield.*

Example: If £5,000 investment results in an annual net return of £500 (after deducting depreciation, but ignoring interest payments):

$$Rate\ of\ Return\ on\ Initial\ \text{Capital} = \frac{500}{5,000} \times 100 = 10\%$$

$$Rate\ of\ Return\ on\ Average\ \text{Capital} = \frac{500}{2,500} \times 100 = 20\%$$

It is more accurate to calculate the *"Discounted Yield"*, which is the discount rate that brings the present value of the net cash flows (which means ignoring depreciation) to the value of the investment.

The tables on pages 159 and 160 may be used.

"Short-Cut" Estimates of the Discounted Yield on depreciating assets
The Discounted Yield falls between the simple Rates of Return on Initial and Average Capital. In fact, for investments lasting 5 to 15 years, when the Rate of Return on Initial Capital is 10 per cent and on Average Capital 20 per cent, the Discounted Yield will be almost exactly halfway between, i.e. about 15 per cent. However, this is only so providing the anticipated annual net cash earnings are fairly constant—or fluctuate unpredictably around a fairly constant level.

There are three circumstances when the Discounted Yield will get closer to the Rate of Return on Initial Capital (i.e. the lower per cent return) and further from the Rate of Return on Average Capital:

(a) The longer the life of the investment.
(b) The higher the Rate of Return.
(c) The higher the net cash flow is in the later years of the investment compared with the earlier years.

When the opposite circumstances obtain, the Discounted Yield will be closer to the Rate of Return on Average Capital (i.e. the higher per cent return).

Granted that there are inevitably varying degrees of estimation and uncertainty in calculating future net annual earnings of investments, the following short-cuts might reasonably be used where the annual net cash earnings are expected to be fairly constant—or fluctuate unpredictably (e.g. through weather effects on yields) around a fairly constant level. (W.O. period = write-off period; R.R.I.C. = rate of return on initial capital).

1. Where (i) the W.O. period is 5 years or less,

      (ii) the W.O. period is 6 to 10 years and the R.R.I.C. is 15 per cent or less,

      (iii) the W.O. period is 11 to 20 years and the R.R.I.C. is 10 per cent or less,

calculate the Return on Capital as being approximately midway between the Rates of Return on Initial and Average Capital, i.e. by calculating the Rate of Return on $\frac{2}{3}$ of the original investment.

For example, following the earlier example (page 158):

$$\frac{500}{3,333} \times 100 = 15\%.$$

2. Where (i) the W.O. period is 6 to 10 years and the R.R.I.C. exceeds 15 per cent,

      (ii) the W.O. period is 11 to 20 years and the R.R.I.C. is between 10 per cent and 25 per cent,

      (iii) the W.O. period exceeds 20 years and the R.R.I.C. is 10 per cent or less,

calculate the Return on Capital on 80 per cent of the original investment.

For example, again following the earlier example:

$$\frac{500}{4,000} \times 100 = 12\frac{1}{2}\%.$$

3. Where (i) the W.O. period is 11 to 20 years and the R.R.I.C. exceeds 25 per cent,

      (ii) the W.O. period exceeds 20 years and the R.R.I.C. exceeds 10 per cent,

take the Return on Capital to be the R.R.I.C.

In borderline cases, use method 1 rather than 2, or 2 rather than 3 if there is a tendency for the cash flow to be higher in the earlier years, e.g. because of tax allowances on machinery. Take 2 rather than 1, and 3 rather than 2 if the likelihood is that the cash flow will be lower in earlier years and increase in later years.

However, where the annual cash flow is expected to vary (apart from unpredictable fluctuations) it is safer to make the full D.C.F. calculation. This is particularly so where the variation is both up and down and where further periodic investments are to be made during the life of the project.

Discounting Table A

Discount Factors for Calculating the Present Value of Future (irregular) Cash Flows.

Year	3%	4%	5%	6%	7%	8%	9%	10%	11%	12%	13%	14%	15%	16%	18%	20%	25%
													Percentage				
1	0·971	0·962	0·952	0·943	0·935	0·926	0·917	0·909	0·901	0·893	0·885	0·877	0·870	0·862	0·847	0·833	0·800
2	0·943	0·925	0·907	0·890	0·873	0·857	0·842	0·826	0·812	0·797	0·783	0·769	0·756	0·743	0·718	0·694	0·640
3	0·915	0·889	0·864	0·840	0·816	0·794	0·772	0·751	0·731	0·712	0·693	0·675	0·658	0·641	0·609	0·579	0·512
4	0·888	0·855	0·823	0·792	0·763	0·735	0·708	0·683	0·659	0·636	0·613	0·592	0·572	0·552	0·516	0·482	0·410
5	0·863	0·822	0·784	0·747	0·713	0·681	0·650	0·621	0·593	0·567	0·543	0·519	0·497	0·476	0·437	0·402	0·328
6	0·837	0·790	0·746	0·705	0·666	0·630	0·596	0·564	0·535	0·507	0·480	0·456	0·432	0·410	0·370	0·335	0·262
7	0·813	0·760	0·711	0·665	0·623	0·583	0·547	0·513	0·482	0·452	0·425	0·400	0·376	0·354	0·314	0·279	0·210
8	0·789	0·731	0·677	0·627	0·582	0·540	0·502	0·467	0·434	0·404	0·376	0·351	0·327	0·305	0·266	0·233	0·168
9	0·766	0·703	0·645	0·592	0·544	0·500	0·460	0·424	0·391	0·361	0·333	0·308	0·284	0·263	0·225	0·194	0·134
10	0·744	0·676	0·614	0·558	0·508	0·463	0·422	0·386	0·352	0·322	0·295	0·270	0·247	0·227	0·191	0·162	0·107
11	0·722	0·650	0·585	0·527	0·475	0·429	0·388	0·350	0·317	0·287	0·261	0·237	0·215	0·195	0·162	0·135	0·086
12	0·701	0·625	0·557	0·497	0·444	0·397	0·356	0·319	0·286	0·257	0·231	0·208	0·187	0·168	0·137	0·112	0·069
13	0·681	0·601	0·530	0·469	0·415	0·368	0·326	0·290	0·258	0·229	0·204	0·182	0·163	0·145	0·116	0·093	0·055
14	0·661	0·577	0·505	0·442	0·388	0·340	0·299	0·263	0·232	0·205	0·181	0·160	0·141	0·125	0·098	0·078	0·044
15	0·642	0·555	0·481	0·417	0·362	0·315	0·275	0·239	0·209	0·183	0·160	0·140	0·123	0·108	0·084	0·065	0·035
20	0·554	0·456	0·377	0·312	0·258	0·215	0·178	0·149	0·124	0·104	0·087	0·073	0·061	0·051	0·037	0·026	0·012
25	0·478	0·375	0·295	0·233	0·184	0·146	0·116	0·092	0·074	0·059	0·047	0·038	0·030	0·024	0·016	0·010	0·004
30	0·412	0·308	0·231	0·174	0·131	0·099	0·075	0·057	0·044	0·033	0·026	0·020	0·015	0·012	0·007	0·004	0·001

Example: The Present Value of £500 received 10 years from now, at 12 per cent discount rate of interest = 500 × 0·322 = £161. Conversely, £161 invested now, at 12 per cent compound interest, will be worth £500 in 10 years' time.

Discounting Table B

Discount Factors for Calculating the Present Value of Future Annuity (i.e. Constant Annual Cash Flow) Receivable in Years 1 to n inclusive.

Year	3%	4%	5%	6%	7%	8%	9%	10%	11%	12%	13%	14%	15%	16%	18%	20%	25%
1	0·971	0·962	0·952	0·943	0·935	0·926	0·917	0·909	0·901	0·893	0·885	0·877	0·870	0·862	0·847	0·833	0·800
2	1·913	1·886	1·859	1·833	1·808	1·783	1·759	1·736	1·713	1·690	1·668	1·647	1·626	1·605	1·566	1·528	1·440
3	2·829	2·775	2·723	2·673	2·624	2·577	2·531	2·487	2·444	2·402	2·361	2·322	2·283	2·246	2·174	2·106	1·952
4	3·717	3·630	3·546	3·465	3·387	3·312	3·240	3·170	3·102	3·037	2·974	2·914	2·855	2·798	2·690	2·589	2·362
5	4·580	4·452	4·329	4·212	4·100	3·993	3·890	3·791	3·696	3·605	3·517	3·433	3·352	3·274	3·127	2·991	2·689
6	5·417	5·242	5·076	4·917	4·767	4·623	4·486	4·355	4·231	4·111	3·998	3·889	3·784	3·685	3·498	3·326	2·951
7	6·230	6·002	5·786	5·582	5·389	5·206	5·033	4·868	4·712	4·564	4·423	4·288	4·160	4·039	3·812	3·605	3·161
8	7·020	6·733	6·463	6·210	5·971	5·747	5·535	5·335	5·146	4·968	4·799	4·639	4·487	4·344	4·078	3·837	3·329
9	7·786	7·435	7·108	6·802	6·515	6·247	5·995	5·759	5·537	5·328	5·132	4·946	4·772	4·607	4·303	4·031	3·463
10	8·530	8·111	7·722	7·360	7·024	6·710	6·418	6·145	5·889	5·650	5·426	5·216	5·019	4·833	4·494	4·192	3·570
11	9·253	8·760	8·306	7·887	7·499	7·139	6·805	6·495	6·207	5·938	5·687	5·453	5·234	5·029	4·656	4·327	3·656
12	9·954	9·385	8·863	8·384	7·943	7·536	7·161	6·814	6·492	6·194	5·918	5·660	5·421	5·197	4·793	4·439	3·725
13	10·635	9·986	9·394	8·853	8·358	7·904	7·487	7·103	6·750	6·424	6·122	5·842	5·583	5·342	4·910	4·533	3·780
14	11·296	10·563	9·899	9·295	8·745	8·244	7·786	7·367	6·982	6·628	6·302	6·002	5·724	5·468	5·008	4·611	3·824
15	11·938	11·118	10·380	9·712	9·108	8·559	8·061	7·606	7·191	6·811	6·462	6·142	5·847	5·575	5·092	4·675	3·859
20	14·877	13·590	12·462	11·470	10·594	9·818	9·129	8·514	7·963	7·469	7·025	6·623	6·259	5·929	5·353	4·870	3·954
25	17·413	15·662	14·094	12·783	11·654	10·675	9·823	9·077	8·422	7·843	7·330	6·873	6·464	6·097	5·467	4·948	3·985
30	19·600	17·292	15·372	13·765	12·409	11·258	10·274	9·427	8·694	8·055	7·496	7·003	6·566	6·177	5·517	4·979	3·995

Example: The Present Value of £500 a year for the next 10 years, at 12 per cent discount rate of interest = 500 × 5·650 = £2,825. This is the same answer that would be obtained by multiplying 500 by each discount factor (at 12 per cent) in Table A for each year from 1 to 10, and adding together the ten resulting figures.

To obtain the Discounted Yield of a constant annual net cash flow, divide this into the original investment and look up the resulting figure in the table above, against the number of years. *Example:* an investment of £1,000 is estimated to produce £80 a year additional profit over 10 years (before charging interest). Add £100 depreciation a year = £180 annual net cash flow. 1000 ÷ 180 = 5·56. This equals just over 12 per cent (the 10 years/12 per cent figure being 5·650).

161

Compounding Table A
The Future Money Value of £1 after n Years

Year	Rate of Interest																
	3%	4%	5%	6%	7%	8%	9%	10%	11%	12%	13%	14%	15%	16%	18%	20%	25%
1	1·03	1·04	1·05	1·06	1·07	1·08	1·09	1·10	1·11	1·12	1·13	1·14	1·15	1·16	1·18	1·20	1·25
2	1·06	1·08	1·10	1·12	1·14	1·17	1·19	1·21	1·23	1·25	1·28	1·30	1·32	1·35	1·39	1·44	1·56
3	1·09	1·12	1·16	1·19	1·23	1·26	1·30	1·33	1·37	1·40	1·44	1·48	1·52	1·56	1·64	1·73	1·95
4	1·13	1·17	1·22	1·26	1·31	1·36	1·41	1·46	1·52	1·57	1·63	1·69	1·75	1·81	1·94	2·07	2·44
5	1·16	1·22	1·28	1·34	1·40	1·47	1·54	1·61	1·69	1·76	1·84	1·93	2·01	2·10	2·29	2·49	3·05
6	1·19	1·27	1·34	1·42	1·50	1·59	1·68	1·77	1·87	1·97	2·08	2·19	2·31	2·44	2·70	2·99	3·81
7	1·23	1·32	1·41	1·50	1·61	1·71	1·83	1·95	2·08	2·21	2·35	2·50	2·66	2·83	3·19	3·58	4·77
8	1·27	1·37	1·48	1·59	1·72	1·85	1·99	2·14	2·30	2·48	2·66	2·85	3·06	3·28	3·76	4·30	5·96
9	1·30	1·42	1·55	1·69	1·84	2·00	2·17	2·36	2·56	2·77	3·00	3·25	3·52	3·80	4·44	5·16	7·45
10	1·34	1·48	1·63	1·79	1·97	2·16	2·37	2·59	2·84	3·11	3·39	3·71	4·05	4·41	5·23	6·19	9·31
11	1·38	1·54	1·71	1·90	2·10	2·33	2·58	2·85	3·15	3·48	3·84	4·23	4·65	5·12	6·18	7·43	11·64
12	1·43	1·60	1·80	2·01	2·25	2·52	2·81	3·14	3·50	3·90	4·33	4·82	5·35	5·94	7·29	8·92	14·55
13	1·47	1·67	1·89	2·13	2·41	2·72	3·07	3·45	3·88	4·36	4·90	5·49	6·15	6·89	8·60	10·70	18·19
14	1·51	1·73	1·98	2·26	2·58	2·94	3·34	3·80	4·31	4·89	5·53	6·26	7·08	7·99	10·15	12·84	22·74
15	1·56	1·80	2·08	2·40	2·76	3·17	3·64	4·18	4·78	5·47	6·25	7·14	8·14	9·27	11·97	15·41	28·42
20	1·81	2·19	2·65	3·21	3·87	4·66	5·60	6·73	8·06	9·65	11·52	13·74	16·37	19·46	27·39	38·34	86·74
25	2·09	2·67	3·39	4·29	5·43	6·85	8·62	10·83	13·59	17·00	21·23	26·46	32·92	40·87	62·67	95·40	264·7
30	2·43	3·24	4·32	5·74	7·61	10·06	13·27	17·45	22·89	29·96	39·12	50·95	66·21	85·85	143·4	237·4	807·8

Compounding Table B

The Future Money Value of £1 per annum after n Years *

Year	3%	4%	5%	6%	7%	8%	9%	10%	11%	12%	13%	14%	15%	16%	18%	20%	25%
1	1·03	1·04	1·05	1·06	1·07	1·08	1·09	1·10	1·11	1·12	1·13	1·14	1·15	1·16	1·18	1·20	1·25
2	2·09	2·12	2·15	2·18	2·21	2·25	2·28	2·31	2·34	2·37	2·41	2·44	2·47	2·51	2·57	2·64	2·81
3	3·18	3·25	3·31	3·37	3·44	3·51	3·57	3·64	3·71	3·78	3·85	3·92	3·99	4·07	4·22	4·37	4·77
4	4·31	4·42	4·53	4·64	4·75	4·87	4·98	5·11	5·23	5·35	5·48	5·61	5·74	5·88	6·15	6·44	7·21
5	5·47	5·63	5·80	5·98	6·15	6·34	6·52	6·72	6·91	7·12	7·32	7·54	7·75	7·98	8·44	8·93	10·26
6	6·66	6·90	7·14	7·39	7·65	7·92	8·20	8·49	8·78	9·09	9·40	9·73	10·07	10·41	11·14	11·92	14·07
7	7·89	8·21	8·55	8·90	9·26	9·64	10·03	10·44	10·86	11·30	11·76	12·23	12·73	13·24	14·33	15·50	18·84
8	9·16	9·58	10·03	10·49	10·98	11·49	12·02	12·58	13·16	13·78	14·42	15·09	15·79	16·52	18·09	19·80	24·80
9	10·46	11·01	11·58	12·18	12·82	13·49	14·19	14·94	15·72	16·55	17·42	18·34	19·30	20·32	22·52	24·96	32·25
10	11·81	12·49	13·21	13·97	14·78	15·65	16·56	17·53	18·56	19·65	20·81	22·04	23·35	24·73	27·76	31·15	41·57
11	13·19	14·03	14·92	15·87	16·89	17·98	19·14	20·38	21·71	23·13	24·65	26·27	28·00	29·85	33·93	38·58	53·21
12	14·62	15·63	16·71	17·88	19·14	20·50	21·95	23·52	25·21	27·03	28·98	31·09	33·35	35·79	41·22	47·50	67·76
13	16·09	17·29	18·60	20·02	21·55	23·21	25·02	26·97	29·09	31·39	33·88	36·58	39·50	42·67	49·82	58·20	85·95
14	17·60	19·02	20·58	22·28	24·13	26·15	28·36	30·77	33·41	36·28	39·42	42·84	46·58	50·66	59·97	71·04	108·7
15	19·16	20·82	22·66	24·67	26·89	29·32	32·00	34·95	38·19	41·75	45·67	49·98	54·72	59·93	71·94	86·44	137·1
20	27·68	30·97	34·72	38·99	43·87	49·42	55·76	63·00	71·27	80·70	91·47	103·8	117·8	133·8	173·0	224·0	428·7
25	37·55	43·31	50·11	58·16	67·68	78·95	92·32	108·2	127·0	149·3	175·8	207·3	244·7	289·1	404·3	566·4	1318
30	49·00	58·33	69·76	83·80	101·1	122·3	148·6	180·9	220·9	270·3	331·3	406·7	500·0	615·2	933·3	1418	4034

Rate of Interest

* Payments made at the beginning of each year.

Amortisation Table

Annual Charge to write off £1,000

Write-off Period (Years)	Rate of Interest															
	3	4	5	6	7	8	9	10	11	12	13	14	15	16	18	20
5	218	225	231	237	244	250	257	264	271	277	284	291	298	305	320	334
6	185	191	197	203	210	216	223	230	236	243	250	257	264	271	286	301
7	161	167	173	179	186	192	199	205	212	219	226	233	240	248	262	277
8	142	149	155	161	167	174	181	187	194	201	208	216	223	230	245	261
9	128	134	141	147	153	160	167	174	181	188	195	202	210	217	232	248
10	117	123	130	136	142	149	156	163	170	177	184	192	199	207	223	239
11	108	114	120	127	133	140	147	154	161	168	176	183	191	199	215	231
12	100	107	113	119	125	133	140	147	154	161	169	177	184	192	209	225
13	94	100	106	113	120	127	134	141	148	156	163	171	179	187	204	221
14	89	95	101	108	114	121	128	136	143	151	159	167	175	183	200	217
15	84	90	96	103	110	117	124	131	139	147	155	163	171	179	196	214
16	80	86	92	99	106	113	120	128	136	143	151	160	168	176	194	211
17	76	82	89	95	102	110	117	125	132	140	149	157	165	174	191	209
18	73	79	86	92	99	107	114	122	130	138	146	155	163	172	190	208
19	70	76	83	90	97	104	112	120	128	136	144	153	161	170	188	206
20	67	74	80	87	94	102	110	117	126	134	142	151	160	169	187	205
25	57	64	71	78	86	94	102	110	119	127	136	145	155	164	183	202
30	51	58	65	73	81	89	97	106	115	124	133	143	152	162	181	201
40	43	51	58	66	75	84	93	102	112	122	131	141	151	160	180	200

Example: £3,000 is borrowed to erect a building. The annual charge to service interest and capital repayment on the £3,000, repayable over 10 years at 12%, is 3 × £177 = £531. Where the write-off period of the building (10 years) is equal to the repayment period of the loan, then the average annual depreciation and interest will also equal £531.

The proportion of the total annual charge representing the average amount of capital repaid per annum can be readily determined by dividing the sum borrowed by the number of years of the loan: (in the above example this is £3,000 ÷ 10 = £300/year). The remainder is clearly the average amount of interest paid per annum: (in the above example, £531—£300 = £231/year). The year to year variations between the two items (i.e. capital repaid and interest) are shown in the tables on pages 166 to 167, which demonstrate the way in which the capital repayment part increases and the interest part decreases over time.

Sinking Fund Table

The annual sum required to be set aside at the end of each year to accumulate to £1,000 at the end of the period

No. of Years	Rate of Interest															
	3	4	5	6	7	8	9	10	11	12	13	14	15	16	18	20
5	188	185	181	177	174	170	167	164	161	157	154	151	148	145	140	134
6	155	151	147	143	140	136	133	130	126	123	120	117	114	111	106	101
7	131	127	123	119	116	112	109	105	102	99	96	93	90	88	82	77
8	112	109	105	101	97	94	91	87	84	81	78	76	73	70	65	61
9	98	94	91	87	83	80	77	74	71	68	65	62	60	57	52	48
10	87	83	80	76	72	69	66	63	60	57	54	52	49	47	43	39
11	78	74	70	67	63	60	57	54	51	48	46	43	41	39	35	31
12	70	67	63	59	56	53	50	47	44	41	39	37	34	32	29	25
13	64	60	56	53	50	47	44	41	38	36	33	31	29	27	24	21
14	59	55	51	48	44	41	38	36	33	31	29	27	25	23	20	17
15	54	50	46	43	40	37	34	31	29	27	25	23	21	19	16	14
16	50	46	42	39	36	33	30	28	26	23	21	20	18	16	14	11
17	46	42	39	35	32	30	27	25	22	20	19	17	15	14	11	9
18	43	39	36	32	29	27	24	22	20	18	16	15	13	12	10	8
19	40	36	33	30	27	24	22	20	18	16	14	13	11	10	8	6
20	37	34	30	27	24	22	20	17	16	14	12	11	10	9	7	5
25	27	24	21	18	16	14	12	10	9	7	6	5	5	4	3	2
30	21	18	15	13	11	9	7	6	5	4	3	3	2	2	1	1
40	13	11	8	6	5	4	3	2	2	1	1	1	1	—	—	—

MORTGAGE REPAYMENT DATA

Items per £1,000 invested where I = Interest, P = Principal repaid, L = Loan outstanding

Loan through 5 years	6%			8%			10%			12%			14%			16%		
	I	P	L	I	P	L	I	P	L	I	P	L	I	P	L	I	P	L
1	60	177	823	80	170	830	100	164	836	120	157	834	140	151	849	160	145	855
2	49	188	635	66	184	645	84	180	656	101	175	670	119	172	677	137	169	686
3	38	199	435	52	199	447	66	198	458	80	197	469	92	196	481	110	196	490
4	26	211	224	36	215	232	46	218	240	56	221	248	67	224	257	78	227	263
5	13	224	0	19	232	0	24	240	0	30	248	0	32	257	0	42	263	0

10 years	6%			8%			10%			12%			14%			16%		
	I	P	L	I	P	L	I	P	L	I	P	L	I	P	L	I	P	L
1	60	76	924	80	69	931	100	63	939	120	57	934	140	52	948	160	47	953
2	55	80	844	75	75	856	94	69	868	113	64	879	133	59	889	152	54	899
3	51	85	758	69	81	776	87	76	792	106	71	808	124	68	821	144	63	836
4	46	90	668	62	87	689	79	84	709	97	80	728	115	77	744	134	73	762
5	40	96	572	55	94	595	71	92	617	87	90	638	104	88	656	122	85	677
6	34	102	471	48	101	494	62	101	516	77	100	538	92	100	556	108	99	579
7	28	108	363	39	110	384	52	111	405	65	112	425	78	114	442	93	114	465
8	22	114	249	31	118	266	40	122	282	51	126	299	62	130	312	74	133	332
9	15	121	128	21	128	138	28	134	148	36	141	158	44	148	164	53	154	178
10	8	128	0	11	138	0	15	148	0	19	158	0	23	164	0	29	178	0

MORTGAGE REPAYMENT DATA (continued)

Loan through 20 years	6%			8%			10%			12%			14%			16%		
	I	P	L	I	P	L	I	P	L	I	P	L	I	P	L	I	P	L
1	60	27	973	80	22	978	100	17	983	120	14	986	140	11	989	160	9	991
5	53	34	847	72	30	872	92	26	893	112	22	912	132	19	927	153	16	940
10	41	46	642	58	44	683	76	41	722	95	38	756	115	36	788	136	33	815
15	26	61	367	38	64	407	51	66	445	66	68	483	82	69	518	99	69	552
20	5	82	0	8	94	0	11	107	0	14	120	0	19	132	0	23	145	0
30 years																		
1	60	13	987	80	9	991	100	6	994	120	4	996	140	3	997	160	2	998
5	57	16	929	77	12	948	97	9	963	118	7	974	138	5	986	158	3	987
10	51	21	833	71	18	872	92	14	903	113	11	927	134	9	951	155	7	960
15	44	29	706	63	26	760	83	23	807	104	20	846	126	17	890	147	15	903
20	34	38	535	51	38	596	69	37	652	88	36	701	108	35	751	130	32	782
25	21	51	306	33	56	355	46	60	402	61	63	488	83	60	494	95	66	530
30	4	69	0	7	82	0	10	96	0	13	111	0	16	127	0	22	140	0

MORTGAGE REPAYMENT DATA (continued)

Loan through 40 years	6%			8%			10%			12%			14%			16%		
	I	P	L	I	P	L	I	P	L	I	P	L	I	P	L	I	P	L
1	60	6	994	80	4	996	100	2	998	120	1	999	140	1	999	160	0	1000
5	58	8	964	79	5	977	99	3	986	119	2	992	139	2	995	160	1	997
10	56	11	915	76	8	944	97	5	964	118	4	977	138	3	989	159	2	991
15	52	15	850	73	11	895	94	9	928	115	6	951	136	5	973	157	3	978
20	47	20	762	67	17	823	88	14	871	110	11	906	130	11	942	153	7	951
25	40	26	645	59	24	718	80	22	778	102	20	826	123	18	874	145	15	894
30	31	35	489	48	36	563	66	36	628	86	35	685	109	32	742	129	31	775
35	20	47	280	31	53	335	45	58	388	60	61	437	85	56	487	95	66	525
40	4	63	0	6	78	0	9	93	0	13	108	0	18	123	0	22	138	0

Note—All figures rounded to nearest £.

Rates of Interest: Further Points

(i) *Rate of Interest on Bank Loans.* Typically 2·5% above Base Rate. Main range is 1·5% above to 3·5% above. Extremes are likely to be 1% above (minimum) and 5% above (maximum).

(ii) *Annual Percentage Rate (APR).* This is the effective rate of interest calculated on an annual basis and should be used when seeking to make a true comparison between interest charges on money borrowed from different sources. The *APR* allows for the fact that when interest is applied to accounts at half yearly, quarterly or monthly intervals an element of compounding will arise. For example, £100 borrowed for one year at a quoted annual *nominal* interest rate of 12% (*e.g.* 2% over base rate of 10%) with interest charged quarterly, will lead to an accumulated interest charge of £12·55 (*i.e.*, giving an APR of just under 12·6%). The higher the annual nominal interest rate and the more frequently the interest charges are applied to the account, the more pronounced the compounding element becomes. For example, an annual nominal interest rate of 20% produces an APR of 21% with half yearly charging, 21·6% with quarterly charging and 21·9% with monthly charging.

   In the case of some loans and hire purchase agreements, interest charges may be quoted as a *flat rate* on the original amount borrowed. The APR will be considerably greater than the flat rate if the loan is repaid by equal periodic instalments, comprising part capital and part interest, so that the borrowing is completely repaid by the end of the agreed term. For example, the APR for a loan at a flat rate of interest of 8% repaid by monthly instalments over 5 years will be 15%. The shorter the repayment period, and the more frequent the payments, the higher is the APR compared with the flat rate.

(iii) *The Real Rate of Interest.* When preparing simple profit and loss budgets to estimate the worthwhileness of an investment in a fixed asset (machinery, buildings, land), it is usual to price inputs and outputs at present-day values even when most costs and returns are expected to rise due to inflation over the life of the investment. Where this *real terms* approach is adopted a more realistic estimate of the effect on profitability can be gained by basing charges for capital on the *real rate of interest* rather than the APR. The real rate of interest is the APR adjusted for the annual rate at which prices relevant to the investment are expected to increase. A crude estimate of the real rate of interest can be obtained by simply subtracting the expected rate of price increase from the APR; for example, if the APR were 11% and the expected rate of inflation 6%, the real rate of interest would be $11 - 6 = 5\%$.

Financial Ratios

1. Common Ratios

The following ratios are often quoted as rough guidelines:

		% of Gross Output
Variable Costs		30-35%
Labour	15-17½% ⎫	
Machinery	15-17½% ⎭	35-40%
Sundry Fixed Costs	5%	
Rent & Interest		15%
Margin*		15%

* to cover drawings, tax, capital repayments, reinvestments

It has to be borne in mind, however, that these are indeed only rough guidelines and need to be considered with great care. Values vary, for example, with type of farming and size of farm. Furthermore, it is often unclear how certain items are being measured, especially whether unpaid manual labour of the farmer and family has been included or whether a rental value has been allowed for owner-occupied land.

2. Farm Survey Ratios

The following are rounded averages over three recent years on a large sample of *all types of farm*. It is to be noted that Total Output includes the market value of any production retained for use/consumption on the farm (e.g. cereals for feed or seed), Rent includes the rental value of owner-occupied land and Interest charges are not included in the costs. Casual labour and all contract work are included in fixed costs.

	% Total Output	% Total Gross Margin	% Total Fixed Costs
Variable Costs (excl. casual labour and contract work)	37·5		
Fixed Costs:			
Labour: Paid (inc. casuals)	10 ⎫ 20	16 ⎫ 32	18·5 ⎫ 37
Labour: Unpaid	10 ⎭	16 ⎭	18·5 ⎭
Power & Machinery (inc. contract work)	17·5	28	33
Labour & Machinery	37·5	60	70
Rent/Rental Value	9	14	17
Occupier's Repairs	1·5	3	3
Sundry Fixed Costs	4·5	8	10
Total Fixed Costs	52·5	85	100
Margin	10	15	—

N.B. The higher outputs and gross margins expected from many of the major farm enterprises in 1993 and 1994 (owing to the devaluation of sterling in September 1992) means that the above percentages of total output and gross margin are likely to be ten or so percent lower and the margin substantially higher.

3. *Lending Criteria*

Another set of standards widely used by lending and leasing institutions is as follows:

Finance Charges

(rent, interest, leasing charges, etc.)

% of Gross Output	Lending Criteria
0-10%	Normally very safe
11-15%	Common range, should be safe
16-20%	Care required
20% plus	Potentially dangerous

As lenders will be well aware, however, these ratios too must be regarded with caution and in conjunction with the farm's level of net worth (% equity) and its trend in recent years, recent trends in its profitability and the potential borrower's record of expenditure both on and off the farm, together with his or her character and potential.

2. TAXATION

1. *Income Tax*

Husbands and wives have been taxed independently since April 1990.

(a) *Rates of Tax (1994-95)*

Slice of taxable income £	Rate per cent	Cumulative Tax (at top of slice) £
0-3,000	20	600
3,000-23,700	25	5,775
Over 23,700	40	—

(b) *Allowances and Reliefs (1994-95)*

(i) Personal Allowance: £3,445.

(ii) Married Couple's Allowance: £1,720.

Couples are able to choose to allocate this allowance either all to the husband or all to the wife or to share it equally between them. Action is required before the start of the tax year from which election is to have effect. For the 1994-95 tax year this allowance will be made at the lowest (20%) rate of tax and from 6th April 1995 it will be reduced to 15%.

(iii) Personal Pension Plans. Subject to a maximum income rule of £76,800 a year, full relief is obtainable for premiums which fall within the following limits:

Age at start of tax year	Max. % of earnings
35 or less	17·5
36-45	20·0
46-50	25·0
51-55	30·0
56-60	35·0
61-75	40·0

Different percentages apply for continuing Retirement Annuity Premiums.

2. *Private Company Taxation*

(i) Profits are chargeable to Corporation Tax at 33 per cent (1994-1995) except where profits are less than £300,000 and where there are no associated companies, when the rate is reduced to 25 per cent. There is also marginal relief between £300,000 and £1·5 million: within this band the marginal rate is 35%, the rate on the first £300,000 being 25%.

(ii) Capital Gains of companies are charged at the appropriate rate of Corporation Tax.

(iii) Distributions, e.g. dividends are not deductible in arriving at the amount of Corporation Tax profit. An Advanced Payment of Corporation Tax is required at the rate of $\frac{1}{4}$ of distributions made between April 1994 and April 1995. The recipient of distributions will be credited with a tax payment of one-quarter of distributions received, which will be deemed to discharge the liability of basic rate (25%) taxpayers; however, higher rate taxpayers will have to pay additional tax of 20% of the grossed up value of the dividend; dividends are treated as the top slice of income.

3. Agricultural Businesses: Other Items.

(a) Livestock

Dairy cows or breeding livestock may be treated on the herd basis or on a trading stock basis.

Herd basis: valuation changes are not included in the trading account, nor are additions to the herd, but sales from the herd and replacements are. On the sale of all or a substantial proportion (normally taken as 20% or more) of the herd, no tax is paid on any profit over the original cost price, nor is there any relief for loss.

Trading stock basis: purchases, sales and valuation changes are all included in the trading account.

(b) Allowances for Capital Expenditure

Machinery and Plant (whether new or second hand). For machinery purchased after 30 October 1993 a 25 per cent annual writing down allowance is available on a reducing balance basis. The writing down allowances will normally be calculated on a "pool" basis. However, where it is expected that a machine will be sold within five years of acquisition and realise less than its written-down value for tax it will be possible for the taxpayer to elect to have allowances calculated separately for each machine. Although the annual writing down allowance will still be 25 per cent this system will enable balancing allowances to be claimed when a machine is sold for less than its written-down value. If at the end of five years the machine has not been sold its tax written-down value will be transferred to the main machinery pool. Motor-cars are included in a separate "pool" in the year of purchase, on which a 25 per cent writing down allowance is available. The allowance is restricted to a maximum of £3,000 for motor cars with a written-down value of more than £12,000. Special rules apply where a motor car is only partly used for business purposes.

Machinery Leasing. Tax allowances for rental payments on new financial leases entered into after 11th April 1991 will be spread to reflect the commercial depreciation of the asset. This may mean that full tax relief for rental payments may no longer be gained in the years in which the payments are made.

Buildings. From 1st April, 1986, farm buildings, fencing, drainage and other improvements (including up to one-third of farmhouses) qualify for a writing-down allowance of 4 per cent annually, given equally over 25 years. These annual allowances are normally available to succeeding owners during the 25 year period. Balancing allowances can now be claimed where buildings are demolished and also on the transfer of the land, but only with the new owner's consent.

(c) *Profit Averaging*

This relief is to enable farmers, other than companies, to average their taxable profits over two consecutive years; (but is not available for opening and closing years). Where the difference between the profits of two consecutive years is 30 per cent or more of the higher profits, the total profits for the two years are equally divided between the two years. Marginal relief is available where the difference is less than 30 per cent but more than 25 per cent of the higher profits. Profit for the purposes of tax averaging calculations will be before the deduction of capital allowances. There is a two year limit in which to make the claim.

(d) *Assessing Self Employed Profits*

From 1997-98 self employed people will be assessed for tax in any tax year on the basis of the profits recorded in the annual accounts which end in that tax year, i.e. on a 'current year basis' rather than the existing 'preceding year basis'. For existing businesses 1996-97 will be a transitional year and effectively two years' profits will be summed and tax will be paid on half this amount in one tax year. One effect of this will be to make the leasing of machinery relatively less attractive. For new businesses starting after 6th April 1994 the current year basis comes into effect immediately.

(e) *Losses*

Losses can normally be set off against other income in the year in which they are incurred and in the subsequent year. If other income is insufficient in the year when the loss occurs and in the subsequent year, any unrelieved loses can be carried forward and set off against future profits from farming. Special rules apply to prevent abuse of loss relief provisions by "hobby" farmers who are not running their farms on a commercial basis with a view to producing a profit: normally losses are disallowed against other income after 5 consecutive years of loss.

With effect from 5 April 1991 trading losses may be set against capital gains.

(f) *Stock Valuations: Crops*

The deemed cost method now allows 75% (previously 80%) of market value to be used, but market value must include a proportion of the relevant area aid payment (including set-aside).

4. Capital Gains Tax

Applies to capital gains by an individual. Capital gains accruing to companies are chargeable to Corporation Tax. A capital gain is the difference between the acquisition value and the sale price. In the case of agricultural property, allowance would be made for any capital expenditure undertaken to improve the property, even though the expenditure may have obtained a buildings allowance referred to at 3 (b) above. For assets owned on 31st March, 1982 and disposed of subsequently, providing an appropriate election is made (within two years), only the gain attributable to the period after that date is taxable, i.e. the chargeable gain is the gain from a valuation at 31st March, 1982 to the date of disposal. Capital Gains Tax is designed to tax that part of the gain which exceeds the rise in the Retail Price Index. Capital Gains Tax is chargeable only on the disposal (including gifts) of assets.

The first £5,800 of capital gains realised by an individual in a year are free of tax. Capital gains in excess of £5,800 are chargeable at rates equivalent to the rates of income tax that would apply if the gains were treated as the top slice of income.

Capital Gains Tax is not payable on death. For persons of 55 or over, the first £250,000 of gain and half the gains between £250,000 and £1 million may be exempt (subject to claimants meeting certain conditions) where they accrue from the disposal by sale or gift of a family business or shares or securities in the family trading company; this exemption also applies to individuals who have to retire before reaching 55 because of ill-health; full relief only applies where the business or the interest in the business has been owned at least ten years and the person has been either the proprietor, a partner, or a full-time working director in a family company. C.G. Tax retirement relief is also available in part for those over the age of 55 who have held the assets for more than one year, increasing to full relief after ten years.

Exempt assets include a principal private residence (e.g. farm house, if non-exclusive business occupation applies) if occupied as such, normal life assurance policies, animals and tangible movable property (i.e. chattels) disposed of for £6,000 or less.

Payment of tax may be deferred on gains accruing from the sale of business assets (including land and buildings occupied and used for trade purposes, fixed plant and machinery, milk, ewe, suckler cow and potato quotas, and from the sale of shares in a family business) if part or all of the proceeds are spent on acquiring new assets liable to the tax. The tax is deferred by deducting the gain from the acquisition price of the new asset. Normally it can only be done if the new asset is acquired within 12 months before and 3 years after the disposal of the old assets. Disposal and acquisition dates for Capital Gains purposes are almost always contract, not completion, dates.

Payment of tax may be deferred by investing the gains in unquoted trading companies.

Payments of tax may be deferred where disposal is by gift. This relief only applies to gifts of business assets, land which qualifies for agricultural property relief at either the 100 per cent or 50 per cent rate under Inheritance Tax (see next section) and gifts which lead to an immediate charge to Inheritance Tax (e.g. gifts into a discretionary trust). The amount of the chargeable gain which would normally have accrued to the donor will be held over; the value at which the donee is deemed to acquire the asset will be its market value reduced by the amount of the donor's chargeable gain held over. The held over gain is netted down by any time apportionment, indexation allowance or retirement relief available to the donor. Where deferral is not available payment of tax by interest bearing annual instalments over 10 years will be allowed for gifts of land, controlling share holdings and minority share holdings in unquoted companies.

Should a transaction produce a loss, this may be set against any long term chargeable gains arising in the same year or, if these are insufficient, those accruing in subsequent years. Losses brought forward will be used only to the extent necessary to reduce gains for the year to £5,800. For disposals after 30th November 1993 indexation allowances (for inflation) may not be utilised to create or increase a capital loss. Transitional rules will allow individuals and certain trustees to claim up to £10,000 of indexation losses to 5th April 1995.

After 5th April 1991, where a trading loss can be set off against other income in the same or following year, for income tax purposes, any unused loss can be set against capital gains for those years.

Payment of Capital Gains Tax is due on the 1st December in the tax year following disposal.

5. *Inheritance Tax*

This tax, which has replaced Capital Transfer Tax, is charged on life-time gifts and transfers on death.

Slice of Chargeable Transfer	Rate per cent
£0 - 150,000	0
Over 150,000	40

Outright gifts to individuals, accumulation and maintenance trusts and interest in possession trusts will be exempt from tax at the time of the gift. All other gifts will be taxed at half the above rates at the time of the transfer. Tax will be charged on the value of an individual's estate at death plus the value of all gifts made within seven years of death. Allowance is made for any tax paid on lifetime gifts included in the value of the estate on death. Relief is given for outright gifts made more than three years before death according to the following scale:

Years between gift and death	Percentage of the full charge to tax
0 - 3	100
3 - 4	80
4 - 5	60
5 - 6	40
6 - 7	20

Exemptions include: transfers between husband and wife; the first £3,000 of gift made by a donor in the income tax year and separately up to £250 per year to any number of persons; gifts made out of income which form part of normal expenditure; marriage gifts within limits of £5,000 for a parent, £2,500 for a lineal ancestor and £1,000 for other donors.

Relief may be available for agricultural land. Subject to a general rule that the agricultural land must have been occupied by the transferor (or by his controlled company) for two years, or owned by the transferor for 7 years and occupied for agricultural purposes by someone else before any relief is granted, the relief is at two different rates. If the basis of valuation is vacant possession, the taxable value of the land is reduced by 100%. If the basis of valuation is tenanted value, the taxable value of the land is reduced by 50% of that tenanted value. Ownership and occupation periods normally include prior periods of ownership or occupation by husbands and wives.

Relief is also available in respect to "business property" transferred during lifetime or on death. The relief extends to the business assets of a proprietor and the interest of a partner or controlling shareholder of a company in the business capital. The value of such property, providing certain tests are satisfied (e.g. it has been owned by the transferor for two years preceding transfer), is reduced by 100 per cent. Where a partner or controlling shareholder owns assets (e.g. land) that the business uses the value will be reduced by 50 per cent. Shareholdings of more than 25 per cent of issued share capital in unquoted companies are eligible for a 100 per cent reduction in market value. Minority shareholdings of 25 per cent or less of issued share capital of unquoted companies are eligible for a 50 per cent reduction in value.

Lifetime gifts of property eligible for Agricultural and Business Property Relief have to be retained (or replaced by similar property) until the death of the donor (or earlier death of the donee) if those reliefs are to be available when the tax (or additional tax) becomes payable subsequent to the donor's death.

In the case of the transfer of property eligible for Agricultural Relief and Business Property Relief the tax can be paid by annual instalments over ten years free of interest.

6. *Stamp Duty*

Stamp Duty arises when the title to property changes hands. In the case of land the duty will usually be paid by the purchaser; the rate payable is 1 per cent on the full value where the consideration (purchase price) or value is over £60,000. However, the 1 per cent ad valorem duty does not apply on lifetime voluntary gifts. Such gifts are only liable to a 50p fixed duty. Stamp duty on share purchases and sales is at the rate of 0·5 per cent.

7. *Value Added Tax*

Agricultural businesses with a turnover of taxable goods and services in excess of £45,000 per annum are required to register for VAT. Businesses with a turnover below this limit may apply for voluntary registration. The standard rate of VAT is 17·5 per cent. Most agricultural products are zero rated for VAT purposes. VAT has to be paid on certain inputs. Registered businesses are eligible to reclaim the tax paid where the goods or services purchased have been used in the production of zero-rated supplies.

A flat rate scheme is available to farmers as an alternative to registering for VAT. Farmers under the flat rate scheme do not have to submit tax returns and consequently cannot reclaim tax.

They can, however, charge (and keep) a flat rate addition of 4 per cent when they sell to VAT registered customers goods and services which qualify. This addition is not VAT but acts as compensation for losing input tax on purchases. The local VAT office may refuse to issue a certificate to participate in the flat rate scheme if this would mean the farmer would recover substantially (£3,000) more than through the normal system.

8. *National Insurance Contributions (1994/95)*

Class 1.

Employee's weekly earnings	Employee	Employer
Not contracted out		
£57·00 to £99·99	10%*	3·6%
£100·00 to £144·99	10%*	5·6%
£145·00 to £199·99	10%*	7·6%
£200·00 to £430·00	10%*	10·2%
Over £430·00	no additional liability	10·2%

* 2% on first £57·00

Contracted out	Employee		Employer	
	on first £57·00	on remainder	on first £57·00	on remainder
£57·00 to £99·99	2%	8·2%	3·6%	0·6%
£100·00 to £144·99	2%	8·2%	5·6%	2·6%
£145·00 to £199·99	2%	8·2%	7·6%	4·6%
£200·00 to £430·00	2%	8·2%	10·2%	7·2%
Over £430·00	no additional liability		10·2%	£32·67 plus 10·2% on excess over £430

Class 2.

Self-employed flat rate (no liability if earnings below £3,200 a year)	£5·65 a week

Class 3.

Non-employed (voluntary) flat rate	£5·55 a week

Class 4.

Self-employed. On profits or gains between £6,340 a year and £21,840 a year)	7·3% (max. £1,158·51 a year)

50% of any Class 4 contributions are an allowable expense of the business for Income Tax purposes, and 100% of all employer's contributions are tax deductible from the employer's profits.

3. GRANTS

1. *GRANTS FOR AGRICULTURAL AND HORTICULTURAL BUSINESSES*

FARM AND CONSERVATION GRANT SCHEME

Application can be made either with or without an improvement plan which will determine eligibility to claim grant aid for certain types of expenditure. If an improvement plan is submitted it must be agreed with the Ministry of Agriculture at the outset. Grant aid is only available for some types of expenditure if an improvement plan is submitted. In other cases higher rates of grants are paid under an improvement plan than where no plan is submitted.

Businesses submitting an improvement plan must have an initial income per labour unit (= 2,200 hours of work per year) of less than the reference income of £15,400 for the 1994 calendar year. The improvement plan must show that the proposed investment will bring about an improvement in income per labour unit.

In order to qualify for grant aid under an improvement plan the person who runs the farm on a day-to-day basis must:

(i) earn at least half his/her annual income from the business and a minimum of 25 per cent must derive from the agricultural part of the business.

(ii) spend at least 1,100 hours per year working on the farm business, and

(iii) either have been working in farming for at least five years or hold a suitable training certificate.

For non-plan grants for traditional buildings the person who runs the business on a day-to-day basis must satisfy conditions (i) and (ii) above.

Young farmers under the age of 40 may qualify for increased aid in the form of a supplement of one-quarter on the grant rates available for an improvement plan.

Investment for which grant aid is available will usually be limited to a maximum of £42,500 per labour unit within an overall limit of £85,000 of eligible expenditure.

There are three main types of work for which grant aid is available:

Land improvement and energy saving
Waste handling facilities
Environment and countryside

Special rules apply to investment for pig, dairy, beef and poultry production.

Rates of grant are higher in Less Favoured Areas (LFA's) for some types of expenditure:

	Grant Rates (%)			
	Improvement Plan		Non-Plan	
Expenditure on:	Non-LFA	LFA	Non-LFA	LFA
Hedges, walls and banks constructed of traditional material	25	30	25	30
Effluent and waste handling	25	25	25	25
Poultry manure stores	—	—	25	25

Shelter belts:—				
(i) 50% or more broadleaves	25	30	25	30
(ii) other shelter belts	15	30	15	30
Enclosure of grazed woodland. Burning heather or grass, muirburn, or regenerating heather by cutting. Bracken control. Enclosure of heath or moor to encourage heather regeneration.	25	30	25	30
Repair or reinstatement of traditional buildings	20	25	20	25
Signs and stiles to facilitate public access to set-aside land	—	—	25	30
Supply and installation of:—				
(i) energy saving facilities	15	25	—	—
(ii) thermal insulation, vapour or gas sealing (excluding glasshouses)	15	25	—	—
Fences, walls not constructed of traditional materials, flood protection, replacement drainage, reseeding and regeneration of grassland	15	25	—	—
Preparation of improvement plans	25	25	—	—

2. *GRANTS FOR PROCESSING AND MARKETING AGRICULTURAL PRODUCTS*

A. MARKETING DEVELOPMENT SCHEME

The scheme is administered by MAFF and provides grant aid to individual farmers and growers or groups of producers, food processors or manufacturers and trade associations or industry bodies, towards the non-capital costs of projects designed to improve the efficiency of the food marketing chain. Assistance is given at the rate of 50 per cent of approved expenditure on:—

— Feasibility studies and market research.

— Costs of establishment, expansion and merger of producer groups including legal and accountancy costs, redundancy costs of key staff and the costs of recruiting new members.

—Salaries of key staff of a project including recruitment costs.

—Production and dissemination of suitable promotional material intended to encourage the take-up of industry-wide projects.

- Promotional events to demonstrate marketing innovation on excellence of marketing practice.
- Training of directors and key staff members.
- Expenses of outside directors.

The maximum grant payable for a project is £150,000.

B. PROCESSING AND MARKETING GRANT

Under EU Regulation 866/90 the UK Government and the European Agricultural Guidance Fund jointly fund grant aid towards the cost of investment aimed at the improvement, rationalisation of the treatment, processing and marketing of agricultural produce. It is proposed that grants at the rate of 30% (40% in Merseyside) will be available for projects costing a minimum of £70,000 and not more than £1.2 million. Final approval of the scheme is likely to be issued in the autumn of 1994.

C. EUROPEAN AGRICULTURAL GUIDANCE AND GUARANTEE FUND (EAGGF)

Under EC Regulation 866/90 grant aid is available from the EAGGF towards the cost of investment which aimed to improve and rationalise the treatment, processing and marketing of agricultural produce. The scheme was competitive and EAGGF grant aid was at the rate of 25 per cent of eligible expenditure for successful applicants. It was designed to assist large-scale projects costing at least £7,000 and not more than £6 million. In 1991 the EC made 53 grants to UK companies, worth £15·2 million.

The scheme closed at the end of September 1992 (the last date for applications) and although it is intended that a replacement scheme will be introduced at some future date details have yet to be published.

3. *GRANTS FOR ENVIRONMENTAL IMPROVEMENT*

ENVIRONMENTALLY SENSITIVE AREAS (ESAs)

The first eight ESAs were designated in 1987, six more were set up in 1988 and proposals are in place to establish still more, which would bring the area in England alone to 1,150,000 hectares, some 10% of its agricultural land. Within these areas farmers are offered annual payments if they enter into 10 year agreements to manage their land, buildings, walls and other features in ways which will conserve the traditional environment. The levels of annual payments vary between ESAs and between different tiers within ESAs depending upon the severity of the restrictions imposed upon farming activities and any extra costs associated with additional work which farmers are required to undertake. They can be substantial, e.g. £400 per ha under tier 3 of the Somerset Levels and Moors ESA where the requirement is to create wet winter and spring conditions. Farmers may submit a Conservation Plan which is aimed at enhancing the environment, e.g. by planting new hedgerows, which, if accepted, will entitle them to grant aid towards the cost of undertaking the work. Farmers in ESAs can enter a voluntary public access option and will be paid £274 per mile (£170 per km) of access route plus grants of up to 80% of relevant capital work.

GRANTS FOR LANDSCAPE CONSERVATION
See pages 185-6

COUNTRYSIDE STEWARDSHIP SCHEME

A pilot scheme offering capital and annual payments for conserving, managing and re-creating valued landscapes was announced in June 1991. Seven landscapes have been targeted: chalk and limestone grassland, lowland heath, waterside landscapes, coastal areas, historic landscapes (such as deer parks and old orchards), old meadows and pastures (in Hereford and Worcester, N.W. Devon and N.E. Cornwall) and uplands. Participants must enter a 10 year agreement. Annual payments range from £20 per hectare for conserving salt marshes to £250 per hectare for re-creating lowland heath and are reviewed on a fixed three-year cycle. An additional payment of £50 per hectare is available for allowing public access. The scheme also offers grant aid towards the cost of restoring hedgerows which are either long-established features of the landscape, important wildlife habitats or of high amenity value. The scheme is administered by the Countryside Commission; priority is given to proposals offering the best potential for environmental improvement and public benefit. Originally funded by the DoE, it is to be run and funded in the future by MAFF.

NITRATE SENSITIVE AREAS (NSAs)

In 1990 ten pilot NSAs were set up in England to reduce nitrate levels in water supplies to below the EC-permitted levels of 50 mg/litre. A further 22 new NSAs were established in 1994, adding a further 35,000 ha to the 10,500 ha of the pilot NSAs.

Under the scheme, farmers who change their farming practices to reduce nitrate leaching receive payments of between £65 and £590 per hectare.

Entry into the scheme will be voluntary. Farmers will have to enter whole fields, or, in the case of the arable conversion option, parts of fields of at least 4 hectares in area. Agreements will be for five years' duration. Farmers will have three main options available to them:

(i) Arable conversion—which requires the conversion of arable land to extensive grassland. Four sub-options include:

a.	Grassland with no fertilizer and no grazing	£450-£550/ha
b.	As A but with native grass species	£490-£590/ha
c.	As A but with limited grazing	£420-£520/ha
d.	Reversion to grassland with limited fertilizer and grazing	£340-£440/ha

(ii) Low nitrogen grassland—which requires a change from intensive to extensive grassland management. Payment is £250/ha.

(iii) Low nitrogen arable—where the level of nitrogen applied is restricted. Two sub-options include:

a.	Nitrogen usage restricted to 150 kg/ha for all 5 years of the scheme and no potatoes or vegetable brassicas	£80-£105/ha
b.	Nitrogen usage restricted to 200 kg/ha in 1 out of 5 years and to 150 kg/ha in remaining 4 years. No restrictions on cropping.	£65/ha

HABITAT SCHEME

Introduced in 1994, this scheme is designed to encourage farmers to take land out of production for 20 years to create important wildlife habitats. A number of options are proposed. The annual payments are introduced to reflect the cost of entering land into the scheme.

	Proposed Annual Payment (£ per Ha)	
	Land currently in arable/temporary grass	Land currently in permanent grass
Creation of intertidal habitats, particularly salt marshes for birds	525	195
Establish/enhance water fringe habitats in designated pilot areas by:		
— creating buffer strips with no agricultural production	360	240
— extensive grazing	260	125
Management of valuable habitats established under the Five Year Set-aside Scheme	275	

MOORLAND SCHEME

Proposed for introduction in 1994, this scheme is designed to encourage the conservation and enhancement of heather and other shrubby moorland vegetation in those parts of the Less Favoured Areas which are not part of Environmentally Sensitive Areas. Sheep farmers who adopt a more extensive system of production will receive an annual payment for each ewe eligible for Hill Livestock Compensatory Allowances by which their flock is reduced. £15 per ewe is proposed.

4. *OTHER GRANTS/SCHEMES*

WOODLAND GRANT SCHEME and FARM WOODLAND PREMIUM SCHEME (See pages 40-42)

COUNTRYSIDE PREMIUM SCHEME and COUNTRYSIDE ACCESS SCHEME (See page 45)

ORGANIC AID SCHEME (See page 33)

BEEF and SHEEP (including HILL LIVESTOCK) (See page 72)

V. MISCELLANEOUS DATA

1. CONSERVATION COSTS

(N.B. *Abbreviations.* CC: Countryside Commission; FC: Forestry Commission; EN: English Nature; BTCV: British Trust for Conservation Volunteers; CPRE: Council for Preservation of Rural England; ATB: Agricultural Training Board).

Hedge Trimming (flail). Contract labour, £13 to £15/hour. 3 miles a day (maximum; much less if overgrown or difficult). Aug.-Feb. (*not* April-July). Every 2 or 3 years; (*possibly* annually).

Hedge Laying. Contract labour, £2-£4 a metre, or £5 per hour. Contractor, 15 metres/day; BTCV, 5 metres/day per person. Nov./March. Every 8 to 20 years. Grant aid: CC, MAFF, EN. ATB quote £1·50 a metre plus 60p a metre for stakers and pleachers, 40 metres a day.

Hedge Planting. Transplants av. £25/100; netlon guards av. 25p; canes av. 10p; fencing (labour and materials): stock proof £2/metre, stock and rabbit proof up to £3/metre. Overall, £1·80/metre unguarded and unfenced, £6·50/metre guarded and fenced. Contract labour: planting up to £2/metre, fencing up to £2·50/metre. Contractor 100-150 metres/day; BTCV 20 metres/day. Pref. Oct./March. Above includes repair. Grant aid: CC, MAFF, EN.

Hedge Coppicing. By hand: 2 men and a chain saw, 100 metres/day, £1/metre. Contractor: tractor mounted saw, driver and 2 men, 13 metres/hour, £27/hour. Grant aid: CC, MAFF.

Dry Stone Walling. £8-£15/cubic metre with skilled contract labour. Cornish Hedging: £25-£40/metre length depending upon type of stone. Grant aid: MAFF, CC.

Amenity Tree Planting; (half acre block or less). Transplants av. 75p; shelter plus stake and tie av. £1; stake av. 50p; whip av. 70p. (50p-£1); rabbit spiral guard 30p; netlon guard av. 50p (but 15p in a 50 m roll); cane av. 10p. Trees per man day: farmer 200, contractor 400; (large-scale, 33 man days/ha). Nov.-April. Grant aid: CC, MAFF, CLA, CPRE (occasionally).

Shelter belts. Per 100 metre length: 100 large species (oak, lime, etc.) £35; 66 medium species (cherry, birch, etc.) £25; 100 shrubs, £30; 166 tree stakes, shelters and ties, £250; total £340; (site preparation, weed control, labour and fencing extra). MAFF standard costs £637·50/ha; windbreaks £33·85/ha. Grant aid: CC, MAFF.

Woodland Establishment. Conifers £150/1000. To supply and plant oak or beech transplants in tubes £2 each. Rabbit fencing £2·80/metre. Contract labour: conifers at 2m (inc. trees) £580/ha; broadleaves at 3m (inc. trees) £800/ha; forest transplants (not inc. trees) £70/1000. 12·5 days/ha (contractor). Nov.-April. (Above not inc. maintenance). Grant aid: FC, CC, MAFF.

Forestry: General. Contract labour: chain sawing £8/hr., brush cutting £7·15/hr., extracting timber/pulp £4-£10/tonne, chemical spot weeding 5p-7p/tree, rhodedendron control £600-£800/acre.

Pond Construction. Butyl lining (0·75mm) £5/m^2; other lining £2·5/m^2. Contract labour: Hymac £12·50/hr., 150 Komatsu £16/hr.; bulldozer D6C £16·50/hr. Autumn (dry ground conditions). Grant aid: MAFF, CC (discretionary), EN (possibly).

Pond Maintenance. Hymac £12/hr.; Backhoe £12·50/hr. 5m^2/day (BTCV); 100 m^2/day (contractor). Timing: probably winter; time depends on ground condition and species whose life cycles may be disturbed. Every 5 to 50 years. Grant aid: CC, EN.

Ditch Maintenance. Backhoe excavator £12·50/hr. Preferably in winter. Every 3 to 7 years on rotation. Grant aid: MAFF (improvement plan), EN (conservation interest).

Pollarding and Tree Surgery. Pollard: £40-£60/stool; surgery: £150/tree. Pollarding: 2 or 3 trees/day. Surgery: 2 days/tree. Winter. Pollard every 20-40 years. Grant aid: CC (discretionary).

Grassland Establishment. Grass seed/wild flower mixes: £400-£1800/ha. Grasses only mix, low seed rate, £200-£350/ha. 11 ha/day. Pref. Aug.-Oct. Grant aid: possibly CC for small areas as part of whole farm plan.

Reducing Pesticide Drift. Use of appropriate spray nozzles: tilt jets £22-£25 for 6; lo-drift nozzles £15 for 6.

Permanent Grass Margins at Field Edges. To provide wildlife benefits and help control pernicious weeds, reducing herbicides at the field edge. A sterile strip provides virtually no wildlife benefit and the initial establishment costs may be offset by savings in maintenance costs in future years. Establishment costs (2m wide) per 100m run, approx. £3, with maintenance (mowing) 50p. Subsequent years, mowing only.

Fertilizer Losses at Field Boundaries. For a 12m spread pattern, at 150 kg/ha, loss is approx. 30p per 100m per application, or £3 for a 6 ha field (450 × 150m). Loss avoided by driving further away from the field boundary/using a tilting hopper mechanism/using an appropriate border disc or deflector, costing £90.

GRANT AID. For a summary of "Grants for Landscape Conservation" available from the CC, FC, MAFF and EN: apply for leaflet from Countryside Commission, Publications Despatch Dept., 19/23 Albert Road, Manchester, M19 2EQ. Countryside Commission grants are usually available through local authorities.

Acknowledgement. Above information supplied by Farming and Wildlife Advisory Group (FWAG). Sources: County FWAG personnel, BTCV, Local authorities.

2. FERTILIZER PRICES

A. Compounds

Analysis			Price per tonne
N	P$_2$O$_5$	K$_2$O	£
0	24	24	115
0	18	36	115
0	20	30	115
0	30	15	115
0	30	20	115
5	24	24	120
8	24	24	122
10	24	24	124
10	10	30	125
12	15	20	115
13	13	20	115
15	15	20	119
15	19	19	121
17	17	17	117·50
20	4	14	107·50
20	10	10	111
20	8	12	115
22	11	11	115
24	4	4	103
25	5	5	107·50
25	0	16	110

B. Straights

Type	Price per tonne*
	£
Ammonium Nitrate: UK (34·5% N.)	112·50
Imported (34·5% N.)	90—105
Sulphate of Ammonia (21% N.)	90
Urea (46% N.): granular/coated prills	122·50/110
Liquid Nitrogen	80
Triple Superphosphate (47% P_2O_5)	130
Muriate of Potash (Granular) (60% K_2O)	110

Average price (p) per kg: N : 32·5 (UK AN)
P_2O_5 : 27·5 (triple supers).
K_2O : 18·5 (muriate).

The fertilizer prices are estimates for 1995 harvested crops, rounded, delivered to the farm in bags. Delivery in bulk averages £6/tonne less. Discounts for cash payment approx. £2·50/tonne. Where separate prices are quoted for granular and blended the former average about £5/tonne more. They assume delivery in 20 tonne lots; add approximately £2 for 10 tonne lots, £4 for 6-9 tonne lots, £6 for 4-5 tonne lots.

3. MANURIAL VALUE OF SLURRY AND FARMYARD MANURE

1. **Composition** (% by weight)

	N	P_2O_5	K_2O
Undiluted Slurry (faeces plus urine, or droppings):			
Cow	0·5	0·2	0·5
Pig	0·6	0·2	0·2
Poultry	1·7	1·4	0·7
Farmyard Manure:			
Cattle	0·5	0·4	0·6
Pig	0·6	0·6	0·4
Poultry	1·8	1·8	1·2

2. **Available Nutrients** (kg)

	N	P_2O_5	K_2O
Undiluted Slurry (per 10m³*):			
Cow	35	11	58
Pig	42	11	23
Poultry	118	82	82
(* = 10 tonnes; 10,000 litres)			
Farmyard Manure (per 10 tonnes):			
Cattle	17	20	46
Pig	20	31	31
Poultry	110	92	92

3. **Amount per head**

(faeces plus urine, or droppings)	litres per day	N	kg per year (1) P_2O_5	K_2O
1 dairy cow	40	51	16	84
1 pig (dry meal fed)	4.5	6·8	1·8	3·7
100 laying hens	13	55	39	39

(1) assuming housed all year and no losses.

4. AGROCHEMICAL COSTS (1994)

Only the names of the active ingredients are given below, with their principal use. These materials should only be applied in accordance with the manufacturers' recommendations. Application rates can vary and there are differences between the prices of various proprietary brands. The list is not intended to be exhaustive and there is no implied criticism of materials omitted.

Crop	Function	Material	Approx. Cost £ per ha per application
Cereals	Herbicides: General	MCPA	3·00- 7·50
		Mecoprop	7·00- 8·50
		Dicamba+Mecoprop+MCPA	20·00
		Ioxynil+Bromoxynil	12·00-24·00
		Ioxynil+Bromoxynil+	
		Mecoprop	22·00-32·00
		Metsulfuron-methyl	16·00-18·00
	Undersown	MCPA+MCPB	24·00
	Crops	Benazolin+2, 4-DB+MCPA	37·50
	Blackgrass	Chlortoluron	30·00-38·00
		Isoproturon	20·50-24·50
		Isoproturon+Diflufenican	46·00
		Isoproturon+Ioxynil+	
		Mecoprop	37·00-64·00
		Isoproturon+Trifluralin	26·00-39·00
	Wild Oats	Difenzoquat	35·00-46·00
		Tri-allate	22·00-27·00
	Growth Regulator	Chlormequat	3·00- 6·00
		Chlormequat + Choline Chloride	5·00- 7·00
		2-chloroethylphosphonic acid	
		+ Mepiquat Chloride	19·00-38·00
	Fungicides	Benomyl	11·00
		Carbendazim	2·50- 3·00
		Fenpropimorph	17·00-22·00
		Prochloraz	21·00-27·00
		Propiconazole	21·00
		Triadimefon	21·50
	Seed Dressing	Ethirimol + Flutriafol	
		+ Thiabendazole	11·50-17·00
		Fuberidazole + Triadimenol	10·00-15·00
	Aphicide	Cypermethrin	2·00- 2·50
		Deltamethrin	4·25
		Pirimicarb	11·00-13·00
	Slug Killer	Metaldehyde	13·00-14·00
		Methiocarb	21·00-25·00
Oilseed Rape	Herbicides	Propyzamide	42·00-58·00
		Trifluralin	6·00- 7·00
	Insecticide	Triazophos	15·00
	Fungicide	Iprodione	35·00-37·00
		Prochloraz + Carbendazim +	
		Xylene	34·25

Crop	Function	Material	Approx. Cost £ per ha per application
Potatoes	Herbicides: Pre-emergence	Monolinuron	47·00-71·00
	Pre-and post-	Metribuzin	36·00-73·00
	emergence	Terbutryne + Terbuthylazine	32·00-48·00
	Blight Control	Fentin Acetate + Maneb	15·00
		Metalaxyl + Mancozeb	28·50
	Haulm Dessicant	Diquat	44·00
	Sprouting Suppressant	Chlorpropham	30-40p/tonne
		Tecnazene	£6·00/tonne
Sugar Beet	Herbicides: Pre-emergence	Chloridazon:	
		overall	37·00-108·00
		band spray	12·00-36·00
		Metamitron:	
		low dose	25·00-28·00
		band spray	26·00-33·00
	Post-emergence	Phenmedipham:	
		low dose	24·00
		band spray	16·00-21·00
	Insecticide	Aldicarb	44·00-50·00
Beans	Herbicide	Simazine	6·50- 8·50
Peas	Herbicide	Cyanazine+Bentazone+MCPB	38·00
Beans and Peas	Insecticide	Demeton-S-methyl	6·00
Maize	Herbicide	Atrazine	8·50-11·00
Brassicas	Herbicides	Desmetryne	43·00-67·00
		Propachlor	62·00-89·00
		Trifluralin	6·00- 7·00
Broadleaved Crops	Grass weeds and volunteer cereals	Fluazifop-P-butyl	30·00-90·00
Grassland	Herbicides	MCPA	8·00-10·00
		MCPA + MCPB	24·00
		2,4-D+ Dicamba + Triclopyr	35·00-53·00
General	Weed and Grass Killer General	Paraquat	8·00-22·00
	Prior to Direct Drilling	Paraquat	16·00-38·00
	Couch Grass Control	Glyphosate	24·00-32·00
	Woody Weed Control	Triclopyr	98·00

Note. The above prices are based largely on manufacturers' recommended prices (Spring 1994). In recent years it has been possible to obtain discounts of up to 20 per cent where competing products have been available from several manufacturers.

5. FEEDINGSTUFF PRICES

		£ per tonne
1. *Cattle*	Dairy: Nuts	130-170
	Summer Grazing Nuts	115-130
	Concentrate	215-270
	Beef: Nuts	115-150
	Concentrate	205-235
	Calf: Baby Calf Food	1,150-1,250
	Calf Weaner Pellets	150-165
	Calf Rearer Nuts	140-155
2. *Sheep*	Lamb Pellets	145-155
	Sheep/lamb cake	130-140
	Ewe cake	135-145
3. *Horses*	Horse and Pony Pencils	195-205
4. *Goats*	Goat Nuts	185-195
5. *Pigs*	Creep Feed Pellets	260-280
	Sow Nuts	150-175
	Grower/Finisher Pellets	170-190
	Sow Concentrate	260-275
	Grower Concentrate	265-280
6. *Poultry*	Chick and Rearer Feeds	210-230
	Layers Feeds	190-200
	Broiler Feeds	200-225
	Turkey Feeds	200-220
7. *Rabbits and*	Rabbit Feeds	190-200
Pheasants	Pheasant Feeds	180-260
8. *Straight Feeds*	Fish Meal (English; 66/72%)	290-340
	Soya Bean Meal (45/46%)	150-180
	Rapeseed Meal (35/36%)	115-140
	Palm Kernel Cake (23%)	95-105
	Sunflower Seed Pellets	90-105
	Citrus Pellets/Nuts	90-110
	Rice Bran	85-95
	Grass Nuts/Cubes (15/16%)	90-100
	Wheatfeed	95-115
	Maize Germ Meal	125-145
	Maize Gluten (20-23%)	100-120
	Molasses	85-100
	Sugar Beet Pulp Nuts/Pellets	105-120
	Molassed Sugar Beet Feed	105-120
	Pressed Sugar Beet Pulp	20-30
	Wet Brewers' Grains	17-30
	Citrus pulp	15-20
	Supergrains	25-35
	Fodder Beet	20-25

The straight feed prices are approximate ranges for 1993-94 (including delivery). The other prices are estimated ranges for 1995. They are (mainly) delivered prices on the farm *in bulk*, in 15-20 tonne loads, and exclude any credit charges. The additional cost for *bags* is generally £15 to £20 a tonne. Delivery in bags is assumed for horse and pony pencils, goat nuts, chick and rearer feeds, and pheasant feeds.

ME requirements for Friesian cows (590kg LW) (see page 192)

Liveweight Change (kg/day)	Maintenance	Milk yield (kg/day)			
		20	25	30	35
−0·5		147	172	196	221
0	62	161	186	210	235
+0·5		178	203	227	252

Source: Broster, W.H. and Alderman, G., Livestock Production Science, 4 (1977).

6. FEEDINGSTUFFS: NUTRITIVE VALUES

Type of Feed	Dry Matter Content g/kg	Metab- olizable Energy MJ/k DM	Digestible Crude Protein g/kg DM
Pasture, rotational close grazed (monthly)	200	11·2	130
Ryegrass, perennial post flowering	250	8·4	72
Hay—moderate digestibility grass	850	8·8	39
Silage—moderate digestibility grass	200	8·8	102
Pea Haulm and Pods (Canning) Silage	210	8·7	95
Barley (spring) Straw	860	7·3	9
Oat (spring) Straw	860	6·7	11
Threshed Ryegrass Hay (approximate)	850	7·0	38
Kale (marrow stem)	140	11·0	114
Mangels	100	12·4	80
Swede	105	13·9	64
Turnips	100	12·7	70
Fodder Beet	180	12·5	50
Sugar Beet Tops	160	9·9	88
Rape	140	9·5	144
Potatoes	205	13·3	80
Brewers' Grains (barley)—fresh	280	10·4	154
Barley	860	12·9	82
Oats	860	12·0	84
Maize	860	13·8	69
Wheat	860	13·5	105
Flaked Maize	900	15·0	106
Maize Gluten Feed	900	12·5	195
Maize Gluten Meal	900	17·2	736
Pressed Sugar Beet Pulp	180	12·3	60
Dried Molassed Sugar Beet Pulp	860	12·5	80
Beans, field spring	860	12·8	248
Cassava	880	12·8	18
Dec. Groundnut Cake	900	12·3	449
Dec. Cotton Cake	900	12·3	393

Source: M.A.F.F. (1984) Reference Book 433, Energy Allowances and Feeding Systems for Ruminants (including 1983 revised values).

For relative value of different feeds see page 80.

7. STANDARD OUTPUTS, STANDARD GROSS MARGINS AND STANDARD MAN-DAYS (1)

Crops (per hectare)

	S.O.	S.G.M.	S.M.D.
Winter Wheat	910	680	
Spring Wheat	725	530	
Winter Barley	770	570	1·25/2 (2)
Spring Barley	685	535	
Winter Oats	820	660	
Spring Oats	700	570	
Winter Oilseed Rape	850	650	1·25
Spring Oilseed Rape	710	565	1·25
Field Beans	670	540	1·25
Dried Peas	710	500	1·5
Linseed	690	515	1·25
Vining Peas	875	680	3·0
Potatoes	2850	1200	12/22 (3)
Sugar Beet	1750	1150	3·5
Herbage Seeds	750	450	1·5
Hops	5500	3800	75
Mangolds (carted)	—	—	25
Turnips/Swedes:			
folded	—	—	4
lifted	—	—	10
Kale: cut and carted	—	—	10
Kale: grazed	—	—	1·5
Hay/Silage: 1 cut	—	—	2·5
Hay/Silage: 2 cuts	—	—	4
Grazing only	—	—	0·75
Hay for sale	400	300	2·25
Keep let	175	150	0·75
Bare Fallow	—	—	1·25
Set-aside	—	—	0·25

Livestock (per head) (4, 5)

	S.O.	S.G.M.	S.M.D.
Dairy Cows	1280	900	5
Bulls	—	—	3·5
Beef Cows (S.S. inc. Calf):			
Lowland	375	240	1·5
Upland	450	325	1·75

Livestock (per head) (4, 5)

	S.O.	S.G.M.	S.M.D.
Cereal Beef (0-12 months)	425	110	2·5
18 month Beef (0-18 months)	500	250	2·5
Other Cattle over 2 years	200	105	2·0
Other Cattle 1-2 years	200	105	1·5
Other Cattle ½-1 year	100	55	0·75
Calves, M.S.-to 6 months (add to S.S.)	145	105	0·75
Calves, Others, to 6 months (6):			
steers	210	80	1·5
heifers	180	65	1·5
Ewes (lowland)	60	35	0·5
Rams	—	—	0·5
Other Sheep over 6 months	27	15	0·3
Sows	550	130	3
Boars	—	—	2
Other Pigs over 1 month	140	27	0·3
Laying Birds (Intensive)	9·5	2·5	0·025
Pullets reared (6)	2	0·5	·005
Broilers (6)	1·2	0·23	0·002
Turkeys (6):			
Heavy	13	5	
Lt./Med.: Christmas	8/11	4·2/5·8	
All year	6/9	2·5/3·5	
Capons (6)	8	4·75	
Ducks (6)	5·75	3	
Geese (6)	18	13	

1. Author's estimates for 1995.
2. 1·25 if straw ploughed in; 2 if straw harvested.
3. Automatic planter and mechanical harvester/hand-fed planter and hand harvesting. Including casual labour.
4. In calculating the Standard Outputs and Standard Gross Margins for livestock, herd depreciation or livestock (e.g. calf) purchases or the value of transfers in have been deducted.
5. Note that for grazing livestock, the S.M.D. per head exclude field work, e.g. grass production and silage making, i.e. the labour for these has to be added to give the *total* labour for these enterprises.
6. For these livestock, S.O., S.G.M. and S.M.D. per annum should be based on numbers produced during the year. *For all other livestock, average numbers during the year should be used* (i.e. average of numbers at end of each month).

For number of Standard Man-Days per worker per year, see page 93.

8. FARM RECORDS

The following records should be kept for management purposes:

1. *Basic Whole Farm Financial Position*

   1. Cash Analysis Book, fully detailed.
   2. Petty Cash Book.
   3. Annual Valuation, including physical quantities, with crops in store and livestock at (near) market value, less any variable costs yet to be borne. Fertilizers, seeds, sprays, casual labour or contract work applied to growing crops should be recorded, but "cultivations" and manurial residues can be ignored for management purposes.
   4. Debtors and creditors at the end of the financial year.

2. *Other Financial and Physical Records*

   1. Output (quantities and value) of each Crop and Livestock Enterprise for the "Harvest Year" (or Production Cycle). It may be possible to get information of Sales from a fully detailed cash analysis book (although, for crops, the financial year figures will then have to be allocated between crops from the current harvest and those from the harvest in the previous financial year, in order to check on the accuracy of the opening valuation of crops in store; this is particularly a problem with Michaelmas ending accounts). The following records of Internal Transfers and Consumption will also be required:

      (a) Numbers and Market Value of livestock transferred from one livestock category to another, e.g. dairy calves to Dairy Followers or Beef Enterprise, or dairy heifers to Dairy Enterprise.

      (b) Quantity and Market Value of Cereals fed on farm and used for seed.

      (c) Quantity and Market Value of Milk and other produce consumed by the farmer or his employees, used on the farm (e.g. milk fed to calves), or sold direct.

   2. A Monthly record of Livestock Numbers; preferably reconciled with the previous month according to births, purchases, deaths, sales and transfers.

   3. Costs and Quantities of Concentrate Feed to each category of livestock, including Home-Grown Cereals fed on the farm.

4. Allocation of costs of seed, fertilizer, sprays, casual labour and contract work specific to an enterprise. This is in order to calculate gross margins, where required. It is less essential than the other records listed.

5. Breeding record for cows, including bulling dates, date(s) served, type of bull used, pregnancy testing, estimated calving date, actual calving date, and date when dried off.

6. For each crop, total output and yield per hectare, in both quantity and value. Include each field where the crop has been grown and its approximate yield, where this can be satisfactorily obtained.

7. For each field, keep one page to cover a period of say, ten years. Record on this, each year, crop grown, variety sown, fertilizer used, sprays used, date sown, date(s) harvested, approximate yield (if obtainable), and any other special notes that you feel may have significance for the future.

8. A rotation record. On a single page, if possible, list each field down the side and say, ten years along the top. Colour each field-year space according to the crop grown, e.g. barley yellow, potatoes red, etc.

9. DEFINITIONS OF FARM MANAGEMENT TERMS

Mainly abstracted from "Terms and Definitions used in Farm and Horticulture Management", M.A.F.F., 1970.

1. Valuations and Capital

Valuations. Valuation is essentially a process of estimation. Thus alternative bases are sometimes possible, according to the purpose intended. The basis should be consistent throughout the period of any series of figures.

(i) *Saleable crops in store.* At estimated market value (including deficiency payments when based on quantity produced) less costs still to be incurred, e.g. for storage and marketing. Both may be estimated either at the expected date of sale or at the date of valuation.

(ii) *Growing crops.* Preferably at variable costs to the date of valuation, although estimated total cost can alternatively be used.

(iii) *Saleable crops ready for harvesting* but still in the ground. Preferably valued as (i), less estimated harvesting costs, although they can alternatively be treated as (ii).

(iv) *Fodder stocks (home-grown).* Preferably at variable costs when calculating gross margins. Alternatively at estimated market value (based on hay-equivalent value according to quality). Fodder crops still in the ground, e.g. kale, treated as (ii).

(v) *Stocks of purchased materials (including fodder).* At cost net of discounts (where known) and subsidies.

(vi) *Machinery and equipment.* Original cost net of investment grants, less accumulated depreciation to date of valuation.

(vii) *Livestock.* At current market value, including deficiency payments less cost of marketing. Fluctuations in market value expected to be temporary should be ignored.

Tenant's Capital. The estimated total value of capital on the farm, other than land and fixed equipment. There is no easy way of determining this sum precisely and estimates are made in several ways depending on the information available and the purpose for which the estimate is required. One method is to take the average of the opening and closing valuations (at either market value or cost) of livestock, crops, machinery and stores (feed, seed, fertilizers). See also pages 154-7.

Landlord's Capital. Value of the land and fixed equipment (including buildings).

2. Output Terms

Revenue (or Income). Receipts adjusted for debtors at the beginning and end of the accounting period. Items such as subsidies, grants, contract receipts and wayleaves are included.

Returns. Revenue adjusted for valuation changes (add closing, deduct opening, valuation).

Gross Output. Returns plus the value of produce consumed in the farmhouse or supplied to workers for which no payment is made, less purchases of livestock, livestock products and other produce bought for resale.

Enterprise Output. The total value of an enterprise, whether sold or retained on the farm. It therefore equals Gross Output of the enterprise plus the market value of any of the products kept on the farm (transfers out). Products transferred from another enterprise to be used in the production of the enterprise whose output is being calculated are deducted at market value (transfers in). Instead of the accounting year the "harvest year" can be used for crops; valuations are then not relevant.

(Enterprise) Output from Forage. Primarily the sum of the enterprise outputs of grazing livestock, but includes keep let and occasional sales, e.g. of surplus hay, together with an adjustment for changes in the valuation of stocks of home-grown fodder. However, fortuitous changes in stocks caused by yield variations due to the weather, the severity or length of the winter, or minor changes in livestock numbers or forage area can be either ignored (if small in relation to total annual usage) or included in miscellaneous output.

Adjusted Forage (Enterprise) Output is Output from Forage less rented keep and purchases of bulk fodder.

Net Output. Gross Output less the cost of purchased feed, livestock keep, seed, bulbs and plants.

Standard Output. The average enterprise output per hectare of a crop or per head of livestock calculated from either national or local average price and average yield data.

3. Input Terms

Expenditure. Payments adjusted for creditors at the beginning and end of the accounting period. Capital expenditure is not included.

Costs. Expenditure adjusted for valuation changes (add opening, deduct closing, valuation), with the following adjustments. Add:

depreciation on capital expenditure including machinery, any loss made on machinery sales (add to depreciation) and the value of payments in kind to workers if not already included in their earnings. Deduct: purchases of livestock, livestock products and other produce bought for resale, any profit made on machinery (deduct from depreciation), allowance for private use of farm vehicles (deduct from machinery costs), the value of purchased stores used in the farmhouse (e.g. electricity) or sold off the farm (deduct from the relevant item), and fertilizer and lime subsidies.

Inputs. Costs with the following adjustments, made in order to put all farms on a similar basis for comparative purposes. Add: the value of unpaid family labour, including the manual labour of the farmer and his wife, and, in the case of owner-occupiers, an estimated rental value (based on average rents of similar farms in the area), less any cottage rents received. Deduct: any mortgage payments and other expenses of owner-occupation, interest payments and the cost of paid management. A proportion of the rental value of the farmhouse may also be deducted.

Fixed Costs. See pages 1-2, 133.

Variable Costs. See page 1.

4. Margin Terms

Management and Investment Income. Gross Output less Inputs. It represents the reward to management and the return on tenant's capital invested in the farm, whether borrowed or not. It is mainly used for comparative purposes, all farms having been put on a similar financial basis by the adjustments made to costs in calculating Inputs.

Net Farm Income. Management and Investment Income, less paid management, plus the value of the manual labour of the farmer and his wife.

Profit (or Loss). Gross Output less Costs. This represents the surplus or deficit before imputing any notional charges such as rental value or unpaid labour. In the accounts of owner-occupiers it includes any profit accruing from the ownership of land.

Gross Margin. See page 1.

Net Margin. A term sometimes used to denote Gross Margin less direct labour and machinery costs charged to an individual enterprise. This is not, however, nationally accepted terminology.

5. Area Terms

Total Hectares. All hectares comprising the farm.

Hectares. Total hectares less the area of woods, waste land, roads, buildings, etc.

Adjusted Hectares. Hectares reduced by the conversion of rough grazings into the equivalent hectares of average quality grassland. This is the figure often used for lowland farms when calculating "per hectare" results.

Forage Hectares. Total hectares of forage crops grown, less any hectares exclusively used by pigs or poultry and the area equivalent of any home-grown fodder fed to barley beef. Usually, too, the area of rough grazings is converted to its grassland equivalent (see Adjusted Hectares). Forage crops are all crops, grass and rough grazings grown specifically for grazing livestock, other than catch crops and crops harvested as grain and pulses.

Adjusted Forage Hectares. Forage hectares adjusted as follows. Add area equivalent of keep rented, deduct area equivalent of keep let; deduct the area equivalent of occasional sales of fodder, e.g. surplus hay, and seed cuts (note: hay and seed grown regularly for sale should be regarded as cash crops, not forage crops); add or deduct the area equivalent of planned changes in the valuation of stocks of home-grown fodder (fortuitous changes in stocks resulting from weather conditions may be ignored); convert rough grazings into their grassland equivalent if not already done. The following adjustments also may be made: add the area equivalent of catch crops and of grazing from cash crops of hay or seed: add the area equivalent of purchased fodder.

In calculations such as *Gross Margins per Forage Hectare,* Adjusted Forage Hectares are usually used. If the area equivalent of purchased fodder has been added the cost of purchased fodder must not be charged as a variable cost: this is probably the best calculation for comparative purposes. Alternatively, when considering all the grazing enterprises taken together, purchased fodder can be deducted as a variable cost and no addition made for its area equivalent.

10. AGRISTATS

Some basic agricultural statistics relating to U.K. agriculture. (All figures are for the U.K. in 1993 unless otherwise stated. Figures marked with an asterisk are provisional.)

A. Structure

1. **Agriculture's contribution to Gross Domestic Product:** £7,599 million
1·4%

2. (a) **Agriculture's proportion of total workforce in employment:** 2·2%

(b) **Numbers of Persons Engaged in Agriculture** (June):

	1988	1993
A. Employed:		
(i) Regular Whole-time:		
Hired: male	91,100	74,300
female	10,150	10,500
Family: male	29,300	22,000
female	4,380	3,100
Total male	(120,400)	(96,300)
Total female	(14,530)	(13,600)
Total	134,930	109,900
(ii) Regular Part-time:		
Hired: male	18,500	18,600
female	21,900	18,600
Family: male	13,000	13,200
female	7,330	7,000
Total male	(31,500)	(31,800)
Total female	(29,230)	(25,600)
Total	60,730	57,400
(iii) Seasonal or Casual:		
Total male	57,700	58,100
Total female	37,200	30,400
Total	94,900	88,500
(iv) Salaried managers*	7,890	7,600
Total Employed	298,450	263,400
B. Employers (farmers, partners, directors):**		
Whole-time	191,500	***176,100
Part-time	97,300	***107,800
Total employers**	288,800	283,900
Wives/husbands of farmers, partners and directors doing farm work	77,800	77,800
Overall Total	665,050	625,100

* Great Britain only.

** Doing farm work. Excludes wives/husbands of farmers, partners and directors, even if themselves partners or directors.

*** 139,100 whole-time and 82,900 part-time are principal farmers and partners. Other partners and directors are for Great Britain only, those for Northern Ireland being included with principal partners and directors.

3. Crop Areas (in June)

	Area ('000 ha) 1988	Area ('000 ha) 1993	% Total Area 1993	% Crops and Grass (excl. R.G.) 1993
Wheat	1,886	1,759	9·5	15·5
Barley	1,878	1,164	6·3	10·3
Oats	120	92	0·5	0·8
Other Grain	12	16	0·1	0·1
Total Cereals	3,896	3,031	16·4	26·7
Potatoes	180	170	0·9	1·5
Sugar Beet	201	197	1·1	1·7
Oilseed Rape	347	377	2·0	3·3
Field Beans & Peas harvested dry...	260	244	1·3	2·2
Linseed	N/A	150	0·8	1·3
Horticulture	209	187	1·0	1·6
Other Crops and Fallow	218	210	1·1	1·9
Total Tillage	5,311	4,566	24·6	40·3
Temporary Grass (under 5 years old)	1,613	1,561	8·4	13·8
Total Arable	6,924	6,127	33·1	54·1
Permanent Grass (5 years old and over)	5,161	5,209	28·1	45·9
(Total Grass (excluding R.G.)) ...	(6,774)	(6,780)	(36·6)	(59·8)
Total Crops and Grass (excl. R.G.)	12,085	11,335	61·2	100·0
Rough Grazing (R.G.)	5,928	5,840*	31·5	
Other Land (inc. Set-Aside) ...	562	1,355**	7·3	
Total Agricultural Area***	18,575	18,530	100·0	

* Including an estimated 1,229,000 ha of common grazing
** All other land on agric. holdings, inc. woodland (289,000 ha in 1983) and set-aside.
*** Urban land and forest each approx. 2·0 million ha; other non-agricultural land approx. 1·5 million ha; total U.K. land area including inland waters: 24·1 million.

4. Livestock Numbers (in June; '000 head):

		1988	1993
Total Cattle and Calves		11,872	11,751
of which:	Dairy cows (inc. heifers in milk)	2,911	2,667
	Beef cows (inc. heifers in milk)	1,373	1,751
	Heifers in calf (first calf)	834	797
Total Sheep and Lambs		40,942	43,901
of which:	Breeding ewes	15,461	17,092
	Shearlings/gimmers	3,557	3,471
Total Pigs		7,176	7,756
of which:	Breeding sows	703	802
	Gilts in pig	101	115
Total Fowls (excl. ducks and geese)		130,809	130,175
of which:	Table fowls (incl. broilers, excl. turkeys)	73,305	79,504
	Laying flock	37,389	32,824
	Growing pullets	11,236	10,653

5. Size Structure

Number ('000) and Size distribution of holdings, 1993

Area (ha)	Total land area			Tillage and grass area		
	No.	%	% area	No.	%	% area
0·1 to 19·9	101·9	41·7	4·9	100·8	43·6	7·2
20 to 49·9	59·5	24·4	11·5	59·9	25·9	17·5
50 to 99·9	42·4	17·4	17·5	41·0	17·7	25·6
100 and over	40·4	16·5	66·1	29·6	12·8	49·7
Total	244·2	100·0	100·0	231·4	100·0	100·0

Average area (ha/(acres)) per holding: 70·2 (173); tillage and grass 48·9 (121).

Size of business (ESU)	No. of holdings ('000)	% of holdings	% of total ESU
Under 8	106·8	43·7	2·8
8 to under 40	72·2	29·6	17·1
40 to under 100	43·9	18·0	31·9
100 to under 200	15·6	6·4	24·1
200 and over	5·7	2·3	24·2
Total	244·2	100·0	100·0

Average size of holdings over 8 ESU (which is judged to be the minimum for full-time holdings) = 62·0 ESU, 108·5 ha (268 acres). ESU = European Size Unit (the number provides a measure of the financial potential of the holding, based on standardised gross margins).

Number and Size distribution of holdings in England and Wales, 1993

Size Groups (ha)	By Total Area				By Crops and Grass Area			
	Holdings		Hectares		Holdings		Hectares	
	'000	%	'000,000	%	'000	%	'000,000	%
1- 10	52·0	28·4	0·24	2·2	59·8(1)	32·6	0·22	2·5
10- 30	44·4	24·3	0·82	7·6	43·4	23·7	0·81	9·2
30- 50	25·4	13·8	0·99	9·1	25·8	14·1	1·01	11·5
50-100	31·9	17·4	2·27	20·9	31·0	16·9	2·19	25·0
100-200	19·4	10·6	2·67	24·6	16·6	9·1	2·26	25·7
200-300	5·3	2·9	1·29	11·8	3·9	2·1	0·93	10·6
300-500	3·3	1·8	1·25	11·5	2·1	1·1	0·77	8·8
500-700	0·9	0·5	0·52	4·8	0·5	0·3	0·28	3·2
700 and over	0·8	0·4	0·81	7·5	0·3	0·2	0·30	3·4
Total	183·3	100·0	10·86	100·0	183·3	100·0	8·77	100·0

1. Including 9·5 with nil crops and grass.

6. Average Size of Enterprises

	1988	1993		1988	1993
	hectares			no.	
Tillage and Grass	50·8	48·9	Dairy cows	60	64
Cereals	44·2	40·1	Beef cows	19	24
Oilseed Rape	23·4	24·6	Breeding sheep	211	227
Potatoes	5·5	7·6	Breeding pigs	54	68
Sugar Beet	18·2	19·6	Fattening pigs	326	398
			Laying fowls	884	1,031
			Broilers	33,966	30,468

7. Tenure

The following figures are for England and Wales, 1992; the areas are '000 hectares (percentages in brackets).

	No. of holdings	Area owned	Area rented
Wholly owned	115,841 (63·8)	4,956 (45·8)	—
Mainly owned	22,113 (12·2)	1,719 (15·9)	432 (4·0)
Wholly rented	28,446 (15·7)	—	2,225 (20·6)
Mainly rented	15,221 (8·4)	339 (3·1)	1,154 (10·7)
Total	181,621 (100)	7,014 (64·8)	3,811 (35·2)*

N.B. Mixed tenure holdings: mainly owned = over 50% owned;
mainly rented = over 50% rented.
Wholly or mainly owned, 76·0% of holdings; wholly or mainly rented, 24·0%

*N.B. As the above figures for rented land include family arrangements (e.g. farmers, or family farming companies, renting from other members of the family, or family shareholders) the percentage of "truly" rented land is almost certainly a few percentage points less than the figures given above.

B. Finance

1. Inputs and Outputs (1993 provisional, £ million).

Inputs		Outputs		%
Feedingstuffs	3105	Wheat	1688	(10·9)
Seeds	294	Barley	636	(4·1)
Fertilizers and lime	576	Oats and other cereals ...	60	(0·4)
Pesticides	467	Oilseed rape	322	(2·1)
Livestock (imptd. & inter-fm.)	190	Linseed	183	(1·2)
Vet. and med.	182	Potatoes	406	(2·6)
Labour:		Sugar beet	286	(1·8)
Hired 1723		Peas/Beans for stockfeed ...	159	(1·0)
Fam., partns., direcs. 969		Vegetables	1076	(7·0)
	2692	Fruit	292	(1·9)
Power and Machinery:		Ornamentals	538	(3·5)
Depreciation ... 1028		Finished cattle and calves ...	2320	(15·0)
Repairs 708		Finished sheep and lambs ...	1258	(8·1)
Fuel, oil, electricity 500		Finished pigs	994	(6·4)
Other 168		Poultry	985	(6·4)
	2404	Milk and milk products ...	3193	(20·6)
Farm maintenance	308	Eggs	465	(3·0)
Deprec. on buildings		Miscellaneous	458	(2·9)
and works	582	Set-aside	165	(1·1)
Net rent	152	TOTAL GROSS OUTPUT	15484	(100)
Interest	506			
Miscellaneous	1042	Total Crops	3833	(24·8)
		Total Horticulture ...	1913	(12·4)
TOTAL INPUTS	12500	Total Livestock ...	5697	(36·8)
FARMING INCOME	2984	Total Livestock Products ...	3716	(24·0)
	15484	Other	325	(2·0)
		TOTAL GROSS OUTPUT	15484	(100)

2. U.K. Farming Income

Index of UK Farming Income* in Real Terms (average 1940-69 = 100)

Year	Index	Year	Index
1940-49	101	1980	56
1950-59	100	1981	66
1960-69	99	1982	77
1970	95	1983	57
1971	96	1984	86
1972	110	1985	37
1973	138	1986	46
1974	103	1987	50
1975	98	1988	34
1976	113	1989	45
1977	98	1990	41
1978	89	1991	36
1979	73	1992	50
		1993 (forecast)	79

* The return to farmers and spouses for their labour, management, own land and own capital, after providing for depreciation.

Indices of UK Farming Income and Total Income from Farming* in Real Terms (1975 = 100)

Year	FI	TIFF	Year	FI	TIFF
1975	100	100	1984	88	89
1976	115	112	1985	38	51
1977	100	98	1986	47	59
1978	91	90	1987	51	62
1979	74	77	1988	35	50
1980	57	65	1989	46	57
1981	67	73	1990	42	53
1982	79	82	1991	37	50
1983	58	67	1992	51	60
			1993 (forecast)	81	83

* Farming income with the estimated value of the labour of family workers, non-principal partners and directors (and their spouses) added back.

3. Indices of Net Farm Income per Farm in Real Terms by main Types of Farming, UK: 6-year average 1977/8-1982/3 = 100.

	Dairy	LFA Cattle and Sheep	Lowland Cattle and Sheep	Specialist Cereals	Other Cropping	Pigs and Poultry
6-year average 1977/8-1982/3* ...	100	100	100	100	100	100
1983/84	69	94	63	134	137	50
1984/85	64	99	41	160	108	119
1985/86	70	80	18	16	23	82
1986/87	72	61	10	62	104	65
1987/88	94	105	22	10	43	47
1988/89	116	121	22	12	27	21
1989/90	102	85	11	25	125	91
1990/91	71	64	7	30	98	71
1991/92	75	72	9	29	80	43
1992/93	94	91	12	40	85	49
1993/94 (forecast)	120	125	18	35	71	24

* i.e. 1980 is the centre year.

4. *Balance Sheet of UK Agriculture* (estimated, 1992*, £ mills.), and Ratios

Assets			£	£
Fixed:	Land and buildings		34,000	
	Plant, machinery and vehicles		5,050	
	Breeding livestock		5,600	
	Total Fixed Assets			44,650
Current:	Trading livestock		2,900	
	Crops and stores		2,300	
	Debtors, cash deposits		3,850	
	Total Current Assets			9,050
	Total Assets			53,700

Liabilities			£	£
Long and medium-term:				
	Bank loans		1,900	
	Other		1,900	
	Total long & medium-term assets			3,800
Short-term:	Bank Overdraft		4,350	
	Other		2,450	
	Total short-term assets			6,800
	Total Liabilities			10,600
	Net Worth			£43,100

% Equity (Net Worth as % of Total Assets):
  1980: 90·2   1986: 82·7   1992: 80·3

Total Assets, Liabilities & Net Worth: 1992 as % of 1981-83 in real terms:
  total assets 60%   total liabilities 97%   net worth 55%

Net Worth as % of Total Assets, England, 1989/90, owner-occupied and tenanted land:
  owned: 89·5   tenanted: 73·4

Farming Income and Total Income from Farming as % of Net Worth and Total Assets:

	% Net Worth		% Total Assets	
	1979-81	1990-92	1979-81	1990-92
Farming Income	2·81	3·33	2·53	2·70
Total Income from Farming	3·76	5·38	3·39	4·36

5. *Bank Lending, Interest Payments and Investment*

Bank Lending to Agriculture (£ mills. approx.):
  1980: 2,900   1986: 6,000   1992: 6,925   1994: c. 6,500

	1979-81	1984-86	1990	1993 forecast
Interest payments per annum (£ mills.):				
Actual	417	658	1052	506
At 1993 prices (approx.)	895	990	1175	506
Interest as % of Farming Income before interest deducted:				
	25%	30%	43%	14·5%
Gross capital formation per annum (£ mills.):				1992
Actual	1217	1202	1167	1099
At 1993 prices (approx.)	2615	1805	1300	1117
As % 1979-81 (in real terms) ...	100	69	50	43

C. Miscellaneous

1. Crop Yields and Prices, 1989-93

Estimated Average Yields (tonnes/ha) (harvest years)

	1989	1990	1991	1992	1993*	Aver. 1989/93
Wheat	6.74	6.97	7.25	6·82	7·31	7·02
Barley (all)	4·88	5·22	5·47	5·68	5·30	5·31
Winter	5·47	5·63	5·75	6·08	5·70	5·73
Spring	3·77	4·14	4·65	4·58	4·75	4·38
Oats	4·46	4·96	5·04	5·01	5·31	4·96
Oilseed Rape	2·94	3·23	2·90	2·76	2·68	2·90
Linseed	1·84	1·85	1·76	1·56	1·23	1·65
Field Beans (for stockfeed)	3·49	3·50	3·23	3·45	3·50	3·43
Dried Peas (for stockfeed)	3·25	4·23	3·59	3·30	3·50	3·57
Potatoes (all)	35·8	36·4	35·4	43·3	41·8	38·5
Early	20·9	27·4	21·9	27·0	27·0	24·8
Maincrop	37·5	37·4	36·8	44·8	43·3	40·0
Sugar Beet	41·3	40·7	39·1	47·2	43·4	42·3

Average Realised Prices per tonne (calendar years)

	1989	1990	1991	1992	1993
Wheat	104.9	109.8	116.5	120.5	122·2
Barley	106·7	108·8	107·8	113·9	113·9
Oats	98·5	106·4	105·8	115·1	128·2
Oilseed Rape	286	273	248	133	149
Linseed	177	110	106	91	111
Field Beans (for stockfeed)	168	164	169	184	114
Dried Peas (for stockfeed)	173	165	171	193	105
Potatoes (all)	83	88	87	69	62
Early	133	83	143	83	94
Maincrop	80	89	86	73	61
Sugar Beet (less transport)	30·8	34·4	36·0	35·4	33·4

2. Self-Sufficiency

(a) Total Food and Feed:

all food and feed	58·0
indigenous type food and feed	73·4

(b) Individual Products:

(Production as % of total new supply for use in the UK)

	1988	1993*		1988	1993*
Wheat	103	120	Beef and veal	87	102
Barley	140	117	Mutton and lamb	89	115
Oats	99	114	Pork	103	103
Rye/Mixed Corn/Trit.	77	91	Bacon and ham	44	43
Total Cereals	107	109	Poultry meat	98	91
Oilseed rape	107	88	Butter	94	65
Linseed	N/A	139	Cheese	64	67
Potatoes	89	91	Cream	102	250
Sugar	56	62			
Hops	80	102	Eggs	98	98
Apples	33	43	Wool	52	74
Pears	32	24			
Cauliflowers	83	91			
Tomatoes	32	35			

3. Food Consumption and Trends

Expenditure on food and drink as % of total consumers' expenditure (excluding meals out) (1993): household food, 11·4%; alcoholic drinks, 6·5%. (Meals out approx. 5·5%).

Estimated Average Household Food Consumption (ounces per person per week):

	1983	1988	1993
Milk and cream (equivalent pints) ...	4·30	4·01	3·83
Cheese	4·01	4·13	3·85
Fats	10·69	9·86	8·11
Eggs (number)	3·53	2·67	1·92
Meat and meat products	38·13	36·59	33·71
Fish	5·14	5·06	5·10
Fresh potatoes	39·88	36·43	30·88
Fresh green vegetables	10·78	10·42	8·46
Other fresh vegetables	15·71	16·81	16·83
Processed vegetables	17·37	19·43	19·81
Fresh fruit	19·64	21·02	21·75
Processed fruit and nuts	9·05	10·90	11·37
Sugar and preserves	11·88	8·79	6·82
Bread	30·74	30·28	26·70
Cakes and biscuits	9·07	8·95	9·19
Flour and other cereals or cereal products	14·88	14·89	15·64
Beverages	3·02	2·66	2·23
Total expenditure (£ per person per week)	£8·64	£10·77	£13·21

4. Percentage of Total Household Expenditure on Food and Drink, 1992:

Meat/meat products (inc. bacon)	23·4	Cheese	3·2
Cereals (inc. bread, cakes, etc.)	15·6	Beverages	3·0
Vegetables (inc. potatoes)	12·7	Soft drinks	3·0
Milk and cream	10·0	Fats and oils (inc. butter, marg.)	2·6
Fruit	7·2	Confectionery	1·6
Alcoholic drinks	6·3	Eggs	1·3
Fish	4·7	Sugar and preserves	1·3
		Other	4·4

Sources: Agriculture in the UK: 1993 (MAFF). All items except for the following:
A5 (part), A7: Other MAFF Statistics.
B4, Bank Lending: Bank of England, Financial Statistics Division.
C3 and C4: National Food Survey, 1992, MAFF.

11. RATE OF INFLATION; PRICE AND COST INDICES

1. *Retail Price Index* (all items)

	% increase on year earlier	Index* (1970 = 100)	Index (1980 = 100)
1970	—	100	
1971	9·5	109·5	
1972	7	117	
1973	9	128	
1974	16	148·5	
1975	24	184·5	
1976	16·5	215	
1977	16	249	
1978**	8·3	270	
1979	13·4	306	
1980	18	361	100
1981	11·9	404	112
1982	8·6	439	122
1983	4·6	459	127
1984	5·0	482	133
1985	6·1	511	142
1986	3·4	528	146
1987	4·2	551	153
1988	4·9	578	160
1989	7·8	623	173
1990	9·5	682	189
1991	5·9	722	200
1992	3·7	749	207
1993	1·6	761	210
1994 (estimated)	2·5	780	215
1995 (forecast)	3·25	805	222

*Index in 1965: 80.
„ „ 1962: 70.
** N.B. The official indices for 1978 onwards are based on 1975 = 100.
Source: Economic Trends.

2. *Price and Cost Indices 1993* (1985 = 100)

(N.B. Retail Price Index: 149; RPI for Food only: 149)

(a) *Producer Prices*

Breadmaking Wheat	114	Dessert Apples	97
Other Milling Wheat	108	All Fresh Fruit	118
Feed Wheat	108	*All Crop Products*	109
Malting Barley	109	Calves	180
Feed Barley	108	Cattle	135
Milling Oats	127	Cows and Bulls	136
Feed Oats	131	Sheep	126
All Cereals	110	Wool	57
Early Potatoes	112	Pigs	101
Maincrop Potatoes	134	Poultry	111
Sugar Beet	125	Milk	140
Seeds	109	Eggs	105
Fresh Vegetables	109	*All Animals/Animal Products*	127
Flowers and Plants	107	*All Products*	120

(b) *Input Prices*

General Expenses	158	Animal Feedingstuffs	124
Seeds	126	Energy and Lubricants	100
Fertilizers	84	Maintce./Repair of Plant	173
Plant Protection Products	152	Machinery & Other Equipt.	148
Animals for Rearing/Prodn.	146	Farm Buildings	145

Source: MAFF Statistics.

12. METRIC CONVERSION FACTORS

(approximate figures, with accurate figures in brackets)

Metric to Imperial		*Imperial to Metric*	
1 hectare (ha) = 2½ acres	(2·471)	1 acre = ⅖ hectare	(0·405)
(1 hectare = 10,000 sq.m)			
1 gram (g) = 0·035 ounce	(0·0353)	1 ounce = 28 grams	(28·35)
1 kilogram (kg) = 2¼ lb.	(2·205)	1 lb. = ½ kilogram	(0·454)
1 kilogram = ·11 score	(0·110)	1 score = 9 kg	(9·07)
50 kilograms = 1 cwt.	(0·984)	1 cwt. = 50 kilograms	(50·80)
1 tonne (1000 kg) = 1 ton	(0·984)	1 ton = 1 tonne	(1·016)
	(2205 lb.)		
1 kilogram (fert.) = 2 units	(1·969)	1 unit (fert.) = ½ kilogram	(0·508)
£/cwt. = ½ × p/kg	(0·508)	pence/kg = 2 × £/cwt.	(1·967)
£/score = ·09 × p/kg	(0·091)	pence/kg = 11 × £/score	(11·02)
1 kg/ha = 0·9 lb./acre	(0·892)	1 lb./acre = 1 kg/ha	(1·121)
100kg (1 quintal) ha = ⅘ cwt./acre		1 cwt./acre = 125 kg (1¼ quintals)/ha	
	(0·797)		(125·5)
1 tonne/ha = 8 cwt./acre	(7·95)	1 cwt./acre = ⅛ tonne/ha	(0·126)
1 tonne/ha = ⅖ ton/acre	(0·398)	1 ton/acre = 2½ tonne/ha	(2·511)
1 kg (fert.)/ha = ⅘ unit/acre	(0·797)	1 unit (fert.)/acre = 1¼ kg/ha	(1·255)
1 litre/ha = 0·1 gal./acre	(0·089)	1 gal./acre = 11 litres/ha	(11·24)
1 litre = ⅖ gal.	(0·220)	1 gal. = 4½ litres (cu. decimetres)	
			(4·546)
1 litre = 1¾ pints	(1·760)	1 pint = ⅗ litre	(0·568)
1 kg milk = ⅕ gal.	(0·214)	1 gal. milk = 4¾ kg	(4·681)
1 kg milk = 1¾ pints	(1·712)		
1 litre milk = 1 kg	(1·030)		
1 millimetre (mm) = ¹⁄₂₅ inch	(0·039)	1 inch = 25 mm	(25·4)
1 centimetre (cm) = ⅖ inch	(0·394)	1 inch = 2½ cm	(2·54)
1 metre (m) = 3¼ feet	(3·279)	1 foot = ⅓ metre	(0·305)
1 metre = 1·1 yard	(1·094)	1 yard = 0·9 metre	(0·914)
1 kilometre (km) = ⅝ mile	(0·621)	1 mile = 1·6 kilometres	(1·609)
1 sq. metre (m²) = 1¼ sq. yards.			
	(1·196)	1 sq. yd. = 0·85 sq. metre	(0·836)
1 sq. metre = 11 sq feet	(10·764)	1 sq. ft. = ¹⁄₁₀ sq. metre	(0·093)
1 cu. metre (m³) = 1¼ cu. yards	(1·31)	1 cu. yd.= ¾ cu. metre	(0·765)
1cu. metre = 35 cu. ft.	(35·31)	1 cu. ft. = 0·028 cu. metre	(0·028)
		(28 cu. decimetres)	(28·32)
1 kW = 1⅓ h.p.	(1·341)	1 h.p. = ¾ kW	(0·746)

13. USEFUL ADDRESSES AND TELEPHONE NUMBERS *

1. GENERAL

ADAS (Agricultural Development and Advisory Service)
Headquarters: Oxford Spires Business Park, The Boulevard, Langford Lane,
Kidlington, Oxford OX5 1NZ   01865 842742

Agricultural Central Trading Ltd.
90 The Broadway, Chesham, Bucks. HP5 1EG   01494 784931

Agricultural Economics Unit
Queen Elizabeth House, 21 St. Giles, Oxford OX1 3LA   01865 273600

Agricultural Engineers' Association
Samuelson House, Paxton Road, Orton Centre, Peterborough,
Cambs. PE2 5LT   01733 371381

Agricultural Mortgage Corporation PLC
AMC House, Chantry Street, Andover, Hants. SP10 1DD   01264 334344

ATB—Landbase
National Agricultural Centre, Kenilworth Coventry CV8 2LG   01203 696996

Agricultural Wages Board
Nobel House, Room 320D, 17 Smith Square, London SW1P 3JR   0171-238 6540

Association of Independent Crop Consultants
Church Farmhouse, Ingoldsby, Grantham, Lincs NG33 4EJ   01476 585790

British Agricultural and Garden Machinery Association Limited
14-16 Church Street, Rickmansworth, Herts WD3 1RQ   01923 720241

British Agrochemicals Association Ltd.
4 Lincoln Court, Lincoln Road, Peterborough PE1 2RP   01733 349225

British Grassland Society
c/o The Animal and Grassland Research Institute, Hurley, Maidenhead,
Berks. SL6 5LR   01628 823626

British Institute of Agricultural Consultants
Wrest Park, Silsoe, Bedford MK45 4HS   01525 860000

British MilkSheep Association
The Row, Roweltown, Carlisle, Cumbria CA6 6LY   01697 748217

British Pig Association
7 Rickmansworth Road, Watford WD1 7HE   01923 34377

British Poultry Meat Federation
High Holborn House, 52/54 High Holborn, London WC1V 6SX   0171-242 4683

British Sheep Dairying Association
Wield Wood, Upper Wield, Alresford, Hampshire SO24 9RU   01420 563151

British Sugar plc
PO Box 26, Oundle Road, Peterborough PE2 9QU   01733 63171

British Veterinary Association
7 Mansfield Street, London W1M 0AT   0171-636 6544

British Wool Marketing Board
Oak Mills, Station Road, Clayton, Bradford,
West Yorkshire BD14 6JD   01274 882091

---

*For a 500-page current directory of names, addresses and telephone
numbers of agricultural firms and associations, with 75,000 listings
covering 70 categories and in 11 regions, see* **Green Pages,** *5th edition,
1994, available from 192 Acton Lane, London W4 5DL (tel. 0181-747
8028); price £13·50 plus £1·50 p & p.*

CAB International
Wallingford, Oxon OX10 8DE   01491 832111

Central Association of Agricultural Valuers
Estate Office, New College, Oxford OX1 3BN   01865 724015

Centre for Agricultural Strategy
University of Reading, 1 Earley Gate, Reading RG6 2AT   01734 318152

Centre of Management in Agriculture
PO Box 236, Farm Management Unit, University of Reading, Reading
RG6 2AT   01734 351458

Commission of the European Communities
8 Storey's Gate, London SW1P 3AT   0171 973 1992

Council for the Protection of Rural England
Warwick House, 25 Buckingham Palace Road, London SW1 0PP   0171-976 6433

Country Landowners Association
16 Belgrave Square, London SW1X 8PQ   0171-235 0511

Countryside Commission
John Dower House, Crescent Place, Cheltenham,
Gloucestershire, GL50 3RA   01242 521381

Dairy Trade Federation
19 Cornwall Terrace, London NW1 4QP   0171-486 7244

Department of Agriculture, N. Ireland
Dundonald House, Upper Newtownards Road, Belfast BT4 3SB   01232 52000

English Heritage
Fortress House, 23 Saville Row, London W1X 1AB   0171-973 3000

English Nature
Northminster House, Northminster Road, Peterborough
PE1 1UA   01733 340345

English Tourist Board
Thames Tower, Blacks Road, London NE6 9EL   0181 846 9000

Farmers Club
3 Whitehall Court, London SW1A 2EL   0171-930 3751

Farmers Union of Wales
Llys Amaeth, Queens Square, Aberystwyth, Dyfed SY23 2EA   01970 612755

Farming and Wildlife Advisory Group
National Agricultural Centre, Stoneleigh, Coventry CV8 2RX   01203 696699

Federation of Agricultural Co-operatives
17 Waterloo Place, Leamington Spa CV32 5LA   01926 450445

The Fertilizer Manufacturers' Association Ltd.
Greenhill House, Thorpe Road, Peterborough PE3 6GF   01733 331303

Food and Farming Information Service
National Agricultural Centre, Stoneleigh, Kenilworth,
Coventry CV8 2LZ   01203 535707

Food from Britain
301-304 Market Towers, New Covent Garden Market,
1 Nine Elms Lane, London SW8 5NQ   0171-720 2144

Food Manufacturers' Federation
6 Catherine Street, London WC2B 5JJ   0171-836 2460

Forestry Commission
231 Corstorphine Road, Edinburgh EH12 7AT   0131-334 0303

Grain and Feed Trade Association Ltd.
GAFTA House, 6 Chapel Court, Chapel Place, Rivington Street,
London EC2A 3DQ   0171-814 9666

Health and Safety Executive
Baynards House, 1 Chepstow Place, Westbourne Grove, London
W2 4TF   0171-243 6000

Her Majesty's Stationery Office
Publications Centre, PO Box 276, London SW8 5DT   0171-873 0011

Home Grown Cereals Authority
Hamlyn House, Highgate Hill, London N19 5PR   0171-263 3391
Price Information Service   0171-263 3494

Horticultural Development Council
18 Lavant Street, Petersfield, Hants. GU32 3EW   01730 263736

Institute of Agricultural Secretaries and Administrators
National Agricultural Centre, Stoneleigh, Coventry CV8 2LZ   01203 696592

Institute of Chartered Foresters
22 Walker Street, Edinburgh EH3 7HR   0131 225 2705

Institution of Agricultural Engineers
West End Road, Silsoe, Bedford MK45 4DU   01525 861096

International Wheat Council
Haymarket House, 28 Haymarket, London SW1Y 4SS   0171-930 4128

Intervention Board Executive Agency
PO Box 69, Queen's Walk, Reading RG1 7QW   01734 583626

Land Drainage Contractors Association
National Agricultural Centre, Stoneleigh, Coventry CV8 2RX   01203 696683

Lands Improvement Company
1 Buckingham Gate, London SW1E 6HR   0171-222 5331

London Commodity Exchange
1 Commodity Quay, St. Katherine Dock, London E1 9AX   0171-481 2080

Meat and Livestock Commission
PO Box 44, Winterhill House, Snowdon Drive, Milton Keynes
MK6 1AX   01908 677577

Ministry of Agriculture, Fisheries and Food
3 Whitehall Place, London SW1A 2HH   0171-270 3000

National Agricultural Centre
Stoneleigh, Kenilworth, Coventry CV8 2LZ   01203 696969

National Association of Agricultural Contractors
Huts Corner, Tilford Road, Hindhead, Surrey GU26 6SF   01428 605360

National Association of British & Irish Millers
21 Arlington Street, London SW1A 1RN   0171-493 2521

National Cattle Breeders Association
Lawford Grange, Lawford Heath, Rugby, Warwick CV23 9HG   01788 565264

National Dairy Council
National Dairy Centre, 5-7 John Princes Street, London W1M 0AP   0171-499 7822

National Farmers' Union
22 Long Acre, London WC2E 9LY   0171-235 5077

National Farmers Union of Scotland
Rural Centre, West Mains, Ingliston, Newbridge, Midlothian
EH28 2LT   0131-335 3111

National Federation of Young Farmers Clubs
YFC Centre, National Agricultural Centre, Stoneleigh, Coventry
CV8 2LG   01203 696544

National Rivers Authority
30-34 Albert Embankment, London SE1 7TL   0171-820 0101

National Sheep Association
The Sheep Centre, Malvern, Worcs. WR13 6PH   01684 892661

Potato Marketing Board
Broadfield House, 4 Between Towns Road, Cowley, Oxford OX4 3NA   01865 714455

Royal Agricultural Benevolent Institution
Shaw House, 27 West Way, Oxford OX2 0QH   01865 724931

Royal Agricultural Society of England
National Agricultural Centre, Stoneleigh, Warwicks CV8 2LZ   01203 696 969
London Office (35 Belgrave Square SW1)   0171-235 5323

Royal Association of British Dairy Farmers
Dairy House, 60 Kenilworth Road, Leamington Spa, Warwicks
CV32 6JX   01926 887477

Royal Forestry Society 102 High Street, Tring, Herts. HP23 4AF	01442 822028
Royal Highland and Agricultural Society of Scotland Ingliston, Newbridge, Midlothian EH28 8NF	0131-333 2444
Royal Horticultural Society 80 Vincent Square, London SW1P 2PE	0171-834 4333
Royal Institution of Chartered Surveyors 12 Great George Street, Parliament Square, London SW1P 3AD	0171-222 7000
Royal Welsh Agricultural Society Ltd. Llanelwedd, Builth Wells, Powys LD2 3SY	01982 553683
Rural, Agricultural and Allied Workers Trade Group (TGWU) Transport House, Smith Square, Westminster, London SW1P 3JB	0171-828 7788
Rural Development Commission 141 Castle Street, Salisbury, Wiltshire SP1 3TP	01722 336255
Scottish Office: Agriculture and Fisheries Department Pentland House, Robb's Loan, Edinburgh EH14 1SQ	0131-556 8400
Small Farmers' Association PO Box 6, Ludlow, Shropshire SY8 1ZZ	01584 873612
Tenant Farmers' Association 7 Brewery Court, Theale, Reading, Berks. RG7 5AJ	01734 306130
Ulster Farmers Union 475 Antrim Road, Belfast BT15 3DA	01232 370222
United Agricultural Merchants Ltd. Springbank House, Basing View, Basingstoke, Hants. RG21 2 EQ	01256 67171
UK Agricultural Supply Trade Association Ltd. 3 Whitehall Court, London SW1A 2EQ	0171-930 3611
UK Register of Organic Food Standards Nobel House, Room 320c, 17 Smith Square, London SW1P 3JR	0171-238 5915
Welsh Office Agriculture Department Crown Buildings, Cathays Park, Cardiff CF1 3NQ	01222 825111
Women's Farming Union Crundalls, Matfield, Tonbridge, Kent TN12 7EA	01892 722803

2. UNIVERSITY AGRICULTURAL ECONOMISTS
(Farm Business Survey Work)

ENGLAND AND WALES

Northern: Department of Agricultural Economics and Food Marketing,
University of Newcastle-upon-Tyne,
Newcastle-upon-Tyne NE1 7RU   0191 222 6903

North Eastern: Rural Business Research Survey Unit, Askham Bryan College of
Agriculture and Horticulture, Askham Bryan, York YO2 3PR
01904 702121

North Western: Department of Agricultural Economics,
The University of Manchester, Dover Street Building, Manchester
M13 9PL   0161 275 4793

East Midland: Rural Business Research Unit, Department of Agriculture and
Horticulture, University of Nottingham, Sutton Bonington Campus,
Loughborough LE12 5RD   01602 516057

Eastern: Agricultural Economics Unit, Department of
Land Economy, University of Cambridge,
19 Silver Street, Cambridge CB3 9EP   01223 337147

South Eastern: Farm Business Unit,
Department of Agricultural Economics,
Wye College (University of London),
Ashford, Kent TN25 5AH   01233 812401

Southern:	Department of Agricultural Economics and Management, University of Reading, 4 Earley Gate, Whiteknights Road, PO Box 237, Reading RG6 2AR	01734 318966
South Western:	Agricultural Economics Unit, University of Exeter, Lafrowda House, St. German's Road, Exeter EX4 6TL	01392 263839
Wales:	Department of Agricultural Science, The University of Wales, Sir George Stapledon Building, Penglais, Aberystwyth SY23 3DD	01970 623111

SCOTLAND (Advisory Services also)

Scottish Agricultural College
West Mains Road, Edinurgh EH9 3JG   0131-622 4395
Regional Offices:
North: SAC Aberdeen, 581 King Street, Aberdeen AB9 1UD   01224 480291
East: SAC Edinburgh, West Mains Road, Edinburgh EH9 3JG   0131-667 1041
West: SAC Auchincruive, Ayr KA6 5HW   01292 520331

NORTHERN IRELAND (Advisory Services also)

Economics & Statistics Division, Department of Agriculture, Dundonald House, Upper Newtownards Road, Belfast BT4 3SB   01232 520000

3. ADAS

Headquarters: see page 210. Consultancy Centres are located at:

Bury St Edmunds	Lincoln	Ruthin
Cardiff	Maidstone	Starcross
Guildford	Newcastle	Taunton
Huntingdon	Oxford	Wolverhampton
Leeds	Preston	Worcester

4. COMMERCIAL BANKS: AGRICULTURAL DEPARTMENTS

Barclays Bank PLC
Agricultural Services Dept., St. Swithin's House, 11/12 St. Swithin's
Lane, London EC4N 8AS   0171-929 4080
Lloyds Bank PLC
Agricultural Finance, UK Retail Banking, PO Box 112, Canons Way, Bristol BS99 7LB
                                                                       01272 433433
Midland Bank PLC
Midland Agriculture, 70 Pall Mall, London SW1Y 5EZ   0171-599 3040
National Westminster Bank PLC
Agricultural Office, 3rd Floor, 24 Broadgate, Coventry CV1 1NB   01203 553721
The Royal Bank of Scotland PLC
Agricultural Services, PO Box 31, 42 St. Andrew Square, Edinburgh EH2
2YE   0131-556 8555
TSB Bank plc
5 St. Helen's Square, Agricultural Office, York YO1 2QW   01904 671180

5. RESEARCH ORGANISATIONS

Biotechnology and Biological Sciences Research Council
Polaris House, North Star Avenue, London SN2 1UH   01793 413200
AFRC Institute of Grassland and Environmental Research
Plas Gogerddan, Aberystwyth, Dyfed SY23 3EB   01970 828255
Arable Research Centres
Royal Agricultural College, Cirencester, Glos. GL7 6JS   01285 652184

CEDAR (Centre for Dairy Research)
Arborfield Hall Farm, Church Lane, Arborfield, Reading, RG2 9HX   01734 760964

Hannah Research Institute
Ayr, Scotland KA6 5HL   01292 476013

Institute for Animal Health
Compton, Newbury, Berks. RG16 0NN   01635 578411

Institute of Animal Physiology (The Babraham Institute)
Babraham, Cambridge CB2 4AT   01223 832312

Institute of Food Research
Colney Lane, Norwich NR4 7UA   01603 56122

Kingshay Farming Trust
Henley Manor, Crewkerne, Somerset TA18 8PH   01460 72977

Long Ashton Research Station
Long Ashton, Bristol BS18 9AF   01272 392181

Macauley Land Use Research Institute
Cragiebuckler, Aberdeen AB9 2QY   01232 661166

Meat Research Institute
Langford, Bristol BS18 7DY   0117 985 2661

National Institute of Agricultural Botany
Huntingdon Road, Cambridge CB3 0LE   01223 227638

Poultry Research Centre
Roslin, Midlothian EH25 9PS   0131-440 2726

Rothamsted Experimental Station
Harpenden, Hertfordshire AL5 2JQ   01582 763133

Rowett Research Institute
Bucksburn, Aberdeen AB2 9SB   01224 712751

Silsoe Research Institute
Wrest Park, Silsoe, Bedford MK45 4HS   01525 60000

6. NATIONAL AGRICULTURAL COLLEGES

Harper Adams Agricultural College
Newport, Shropshire TF10 8NB   01952 811280

Royal Agricultural College
Cirencester, Glos. GL7 6JS   01285 652531

Seale-Hayne (University of Plymouth)
Newton Abbot, Devon TQ12 6NQ   01626 325800

Shuttleworth Agricultural College
Old Warden Park, Biggleswade, Beds. SG18 9DX   01767 627441

Silsoe College
Silsoe, Bedford MK45 4DT   01525 860428

Welsh Agricultural College
Llanbadarn Fawr, Aberystwyth SY23 3AL   01970 624471

Writtle Agricultural College
Chelmsford, Essex CM1 3RR   01245 420705

N.B. The Scottish Agricultural College and its regional offices are listed on page 214.

INDEX

OTHER PUBLICATIONS

Other Department of Agricultural Economics publications include:

Farm Management Pocket Book, 24th edition (1993). John Nix. £6.50

Farm Business Statistics for South East England, supplement for 1994. £5.00

The Effects of the Reform of the Common Agricultural Policy on Arable Farms in South East England. FBU Occasional Paper No. 23. A. Donaldson, P. Hutley-Bull, J. P. G. Webster. 1994. £10.00

Socio-Economic Evaluation of the Capital Grant Element of the Farm Diversification Scheme. FBU Occasional Paper No. 22. A. M. Edwards, R. M. Gasson, J. E. Haynes and G. P. Hill. 1994. £10.00

Changes in Cropping & Stocking, Kent & England, 1939 to 1992. (With special reference to 1982-92). FBU Occasional Paper No. 21. Angela Edwards and John Nix. 1994. £6.00

Should Farmers Market Direct to Consumers? America Says Yes. Food Industry Perspectives: Discussion Paper No. 6. Harriet Festing. 1994. £6.00

The Milk Price Question. Food Industry Perspectives: Discussion Paper Series No. 5. Derek Ray and Andrew Fearne. 1994. £6.00

An Economic Approach to the Evaluation of Advertising. Food Industry Perspectives: Discussion Paper Series No. 4. Kirby Moulton. 1994. £6.00

Coping with Competition. Food Industry Perspectives: Discussion Paper Series No. 3. Kirby Moulton. 1994. £6.00

Who is Driving The Food Industry? Food Industry Perspectives: Discussion Paper Series No. 2. Derek Ray. 1994. £6.00

A Comparative Study of Agricultural Marketing in the Netherlands and the United Kingdom. Food Industry Perspectives: Discussion Paper Series No. 1. D. R. Hughes, H. M. Martin and M. van Nieuwkerk. 1993. £12.00

Agricultural Business Management in a Changing World
Inaugural Lecture. J. P. G. Webster. 1993. £0.50

The Socio-Economic Effects of Bovine Somatropin (bST)—
A European Review. FBU Occasional Paper No. 20.
M. J. M. Bent and A. E. Buckwell.1993. £10.00

A Socio-Economic Evaluation of the One Year Set-aside Scheme
in England. FBU Occasional Paper No. 19.
N. Young and N. T. Williams. 1993. £15.00

An Evaluation of the Beef and Sheep Pilot Extensification Schemes
in the UK. FBU Occasional Paper No. 18.
N. Young and N. T. Williams. 1993. £15.00

An Economic Evaluation of the Farm Woodland Scheme.
FBU Occasional Paper No. 17. Ruth Gasson and Paul Hill. 1990. £15.00

LP-WYE2: A Linear Programming Package for Microcomputers.
FBU Occasional Paper No. 16. J. P. G. Webster. 1990. £135

Farm Work by Farmers' Wives
FBU Occasional Paper No. 15. Ruth Gasson. 1989. £4.00

The Romney Marsh Story: A Study in Agricultural Change.
FBU Occasional Paper No. 14. Angela Edwards. 1987. £3.00

Knowledge—based Microcomputer Systems for Disease Control
in Winter Wheat.
FBU Occasional Paper No. 13. J. P. G. Webster and R. J. Cook. 1986. £8.50

Agriculture and Countryside Conservation.
FBU Occasional Paper No. 10. Pam Bury. 1985. £6.00

Alternative Support Systems for Rural Areas (2 vols.)
B. Hill, N. Young and G. Brookes. 1989. £15.00

Farm Tenure and Performance. Ruth Gasson and Berkeley Hill. 1985. £5.00

The CAP and Britain's European Involvement (The John Medland Lecture).
M. Tracy. 1991 £4.00

Available from Publications, Department of Agricultural Economics, Wye College, Ashford, Kent, TN25 5AH. (From which a full list of the Department's publications is available). (Telephone: 01233 812 401, ext. 285; Fax: 01233 813320).

Please send cheque or postal order (made out to Wye College) with order. All prices post free UK.